THE LIVING WORLD OF ACHIEVEMENT

Uniform with this volume:

The Living World
OF
ACHIEVEMENT

London   COLLINS   *Glasgow*

This Impression 1970

ISBN 0 00 100102 7

CONTENTS

CONTENTS

CONTENTS

THE CONQUEST OF THE NORTH POLE

The huge ice-cap that lies over the north polar regions is one of the most inhospitable areas of the earth. Bitterly cold and lashed by blizzards, devoid of natural vegetation and with little in the way of animal life, it offers no encouragement even to the modern explorer with all his scientific equipment.

Despite this, men of courage have been probing farther and farther north into the polar regions for many centuries past. In the time of Alexander the Great, a Greek merchant called Pytheas left Marseilles and sailed through the Straits of Gibraltar (then called the Pillars of Hercules), and steered his ship towards the north. Like so many of the great explorers that were to follow him, Pytheas was setting out primarily in search of trade. He was one of the first of the world's " Merchant Adventurers "

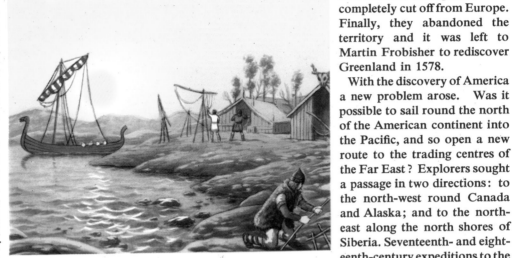

In the tenth century the Vikings settled in Greenland, but a change in climate in the fifteenth century forced them to leave.

in a remote, inhospitable land completely cut off from Europe. Finally, they abandoned the territory and it was left to Martin Frobisher to rediscover Greenland in 1578.

With the discovery of America a new problem arose. Was it possible to sail round the north of the American continent into the Pacific, and so open a new route to the trading centres of the Far East? Explorers sought a passage in two directions: to the north-west round Canada and Alaska; and to the north-east along the north shores of Siberia. Seventeenth- and eighteenth-century expeditions to the polar seas were made with this aim and purpose in mind.

ULTIMA THULE

As Pytheas travelled northwards, he found the sea becoming rougher, the mists thicker, the sky greyer and the rains more frequent than in the Mediterranean. He recorded how the sun remained low on the horizon for all but a few hours a day. This suggests that he reached the coast of Norway, then a legendary country in the most northerly regions of the inhabited world: the *Ultima Thule* which Agricola's Roman fleet was to sight later when sailing off the east of Scotland in A.D. 84. Beyond these latitudes lay the " Stagnant Sea ", a vast expanse of cold grey water carrying masses of floating ice.

A thousand years were to pass before anyone ventured again into these frozen waters. Then, in 870, Othar of Helgeland rounded the North Cape at the extreme tip of Norway and sailed on as far as the White Sea. Later, he told the story of his discoveries to Alfred the Great, and it was this English king who first recorded the existence of the midnight sun. Adventurers then began to explore far beyond the Arctic circle, and it is not difficult to imagine what dangers and hardships these tough sailors had to face and overcome.

THE WORLD'S LARGEST ISLAND

Meanwhile, Iceland had been colonised from Norway and North Britain towards the end of the ninth century. A hundred years later, Eric the Red set sail in the wake of Gunnbjorn Ulfsson who had earlier discovered Greenland, the world's largest island. Taking with him a group of pioneers, he found that Greenland was an excellent fishing centre and formed a settlement on its south-west coast. The descendants of these colonists survived for four centuries

Many of these voyages were undertaken by the Merchant Adventurers of England, an organisation operating under royal charter which owned some of the best ocean-going vessels of the day. Its sea captains were among the boldest and most skilful that England had ever seen.

SOME EARLY SEA CAPTAINS

Since 1500, the Merchant Adventurers had been trying, in the interests of commerce, to find a way to Russia and the East through the Arctic seas. The names of such great Elizabethan sailors as Sir Hugh Willoughby, Stephen Burrough, Arthur Pet and Charles Jackman are linked with those early voyages to Novaya Zemlya and the Kara Sea. Dutch sailors were seeking the same goal. In the 1590s the famous Willem Barents made several expeditions into Arctic waters, exploring the seas around Bear Island and Svalbard at latitude 80°N. If the Arctic winter of 1596-7 had not been so hard this courageous explorer might have been able to penetrate even farther. But the pack-ice closed in, forcing him to spend the winter there, and he was ill-equipped to withstand the bitter cold. Spring came and the party turned south towards Lapland, but Barents died on the way. He is remembered to-day in the name, Barents Sea.

HENRY HUDSON'S TRAGIC FATE

The Dutch now abandoned their search for a north-east passage around Russia. But the efforts of the English navigators were renewed. In 1607, a bold attempt to penetrate deep in the polar regions was made by Henry Hudson, who sailed north up the east coast of Greenland until blocked by ice in about latitude 80°N. Meanwhile, hope of finding a north-east passage was increasing. The vast region to the west of Greenland was known to be a labyrinth of lakes, islands, narrow straits and rocky peninsulas.

Hudson, acting on behalf of the Dutch East India Company, ranged the seas between Spitsbergen and Novaya

William Edward Parry made several expeditions into the Arctic in an effort to find the North-West Passage.

Zemlya making observations that led to the opening-up of whale fishing in that area. Then he set a course for North America and discovered the strait between Baffin Island and Labrador. Was this the long-sought passage which would lead to the Pacific? At first, Hudson thought it was and believed that the great sea which stretched before him was the ocean he was striving to reach. But he was mistaken. The ship and its crew were trapped in a vast bay where they had to spend a severe winter. Half-crazy with hardship and suffering, the sailors mutinied on their way home, casting Hudson and his son adrift to perish in waters that now bear his name.

TOWARDS THE NORTH-WEST PASSAGE

For more than a century, the exploration of these regions was abandoned. British and Dutch whalers set up their stations in northern seas, and some of their vessels must have reached the 80th parallel of latitude at intervals during the seventeenth century. But it was not until 1789 that any real effort was made to continue Hudson's explorations in these treacherous waters. In that year, the Scottish explorer, Alexander Mackenzie, followed the river which now bears his name, from the Great Slave Lake to its mouth in the Arctic Ocean. These were exciting times in world exploration; Captain Cook had just explored the Pacific coast of North America, pushing up through the Bering Strait and into Arctic waters.

Cook had known the right moment to turn back. Others were less skilled in their judgment, and many ventures into polar seas ended in tragedy. It became apparent that even if a north-west passage existed it could be of little use to trading vessels. For many months of the year these waters were frozen solid. And when the thaw began, they were obstructed by huge blocks of ice capable of crushing the wooden hulls of the ships then in use. Interest in the Arctic as a possible trade route diminished. From now on, the motives that moved men to explore in polar regions were largely geographical and scientific. They were inspired by a desire to reach the remotest parts of the earth.

REWARD OF £20,000

In the early summer of 1817, the whale fishers noticed that the weather was exceptionally mild; the ice was thawing more than usual. Taking advantage of these favourable conditions, William Edward Parry sailed westwards from Greenland through Lancaster Sound, Barrow Strait and Melville Sound until he came within sight of Banks Island. Without realising it, he had travelled about two-thirds of the way to the Bering Strait and the Pacific. The north-west passage had not yet been discovered, but interest was revived by the British Government which offered £20,000 to the first explorer to prove that it existed. A further £5,000 was to go to the first explorer to reach 89°N., and Sir William Parry started off from Spitsbergen in 1827 with high hopes of winning it. Travelling on sledge boats over endless ice-fields, he reached as far as 82°45′N. Observations then showed that the ice was drifting southwards faster than he and his men were moving northwards. They had to turn back.

KNIGHTED FOR EXPLORATION

Though the search for the north-west passage continued, success was not achieved until the early 1850s. An expedition led by Robert McClure in the ship *Investigator*, reached Banks Island via the Bering Strait. Changing to sledges, the explorers pressed on to Melville Sound which Parry had reached thirty years previously. In the spring of 1853, McClure was on the point of returning to the Canadian coast, when help arrived from Captain Kellet's schooner *Resolute* which had been wintering nearby. The two parties joined up on 17th June, 1853 and, after an absence of four years, McClure returned to England to be knighted as the first man to traverse the long route from Bering Strait to Davis Strait in the North Atlantic. For two centuries, European and American explorers had struggled to find this famous sea-route, and, at last, the search was over. But this was only a beginning to the real exploration of the polar regions. As yet, no explorer had been within 400 miles of the North Pole itself.

DRIFTING TO FRANZ JOSEF LAND

Arctic exploration now attracted expeditions from many European countries. The seas to the east of Spitsbergen had been neglected, while explorers were sailing in the waters to the north of Canada. When E. Carlsen reached Ice Haven in Novaya Zemlya in 1872, for example, he found a hut that Barents had built 274 years before; he was the first to visit the hut in all that time. The relics that Carlsen brought home are now on show in the Naval Museum at The Hague.

In July, 1872, an Austro-Hungarian expedition led by Julius Payer and Karl Weyprecht sailed from Tromsö in the *Tegethoff* to seek the north-east passage to the Bering Strait.

After reaching a point to the north of Novaya Zemlya, the *Tegethoff* ran into bitter weather and was locked in the ice for a year. The ship drifted helplessly for months, its largely Italian crew suffering terrible privation. Frost-bite, famine and exhaustion were the lot of officers and crew, who survived by eating smoked herrings and occasional seabirds. For water, they depended on ice melted over little fires made by burning wood from the ship's superstructure. Polar currents dragged the ship along until at length the crew sighted a mountainous mass of land at about 80°N. This region, previously unmapped, they named Franz Josef Land after the Austrian Emperor. Two summers after leaving Tromsö, the ship-wrecked party was picked up by a Russian whaler and brought back to civilisation.

The fate of the American ship, Jeanette, *trapped in the drifting ice off the New Siberian islands, and the appearance of driftwood on the shores of Greenland and Spitsbergen, prompted Dr. Fridtjof Nansen to test his theory of Polar currents.*

FORCING THE NORTH-EAST PASSAGE

At about this time, an eminent Swedish-Finnish explorer, named Nils Nordenskjöld, was making expeditions to the Arctic, mainly to carry out geological research. He believed that it should be possible, at certain seasons, to sail along the coast of Siberia and to establish a north-east passage to the Pacific. With this in mind, he set out in the steamship *Vega* on 21st July, 1878. Another ship accompanied him as far as the mouth of the Lena River beyond Cape Chelyuskin, the most northerly point of Russia. Some weeks after the ships had parted, the ice closed in on the *Vega* and the Swedish expedition was marooned for nine months off north-east Siberia. This is the country of the Mongoloid Chuckchi people, who live in skin tents, and Nordenskjöld described them in his story of *The Voyage of the Vega*. When the ice melted, the ship sailed on, passing through the Bering Strait on 20th July, 1879. Yokohama was reached a few weeks later and, in the following April, the *Vega* was back in Stockholm. Nils Nordenskjöld was made a baron in recognition of his voyage through the north-east passage which sailors had been seeking for more than 300 years.

THREE YEARS IN AN ICE-BOUND SHIP

The North Pole itself remained unconquered. At the turn of the last century, many brave men struggled in vain to cross the snowy wastes in the hope of hoisting their flag " on top of the world ". One of them was Dr. Fridtjof Nansen, the great Norwegian explorer who had made a thorough study of the winds and currents of the Arctic.

Believing that a marine current flowing from Siberian waters to the Greenland coast actually passed close to the Pole, Nansen decided to put his theory to the test. In September, 1893 he allowed his ship, the *Fram*, to be trapped in the ice floes off the New Siberian Islands. The vessel drifted for two years, in a north-westerly direction, maintaining an even keel. At latitude 85°55′N., the farthest

Returning to Spitsbergen after a winter spent on Franz Josef Land, Nansen and his companion, Johansen, by chance met a party from the Jackson-Harmsworth expedition. They returned to Norway on the British ship, Windward, *and arrived there about the same time as the* Fram *and its crew were breaking out of the ice north of Spitsbergen.*

The honour of being the first man to reach the North Pole goes to the American, Robert E. Peary.

north a ship had ever reached, the *Fram* stopped moving. Nansen and Lieutenant Johansen set off across the ice with dog sledges and Eskimo kayaks. They were within 200 miles of the Pole before abandoning the attempt on 8th April, 1895, and turning southwards. After spending the next winter in Franz Josef Land, living on bear and walrus meat, they returned to Vardö in Norway on 13th August, 1896. By an amazing stroke of luck, the *Fram* broke out of the ice to the north of Spitsbergen in that same week; the entire party reached Oslo together to celebrate one of the most famous expeditions in the history of polar exploration.

Franz Josef Land was now regarded as the most suitable base from which to reach the North Pole. In fact, it was there that members of the British Jackson-Harmsworth expeditions had met Nansen by chance and helped him return to Norway. Another party, led by the Duke of Abruzzi, spent New Year's Day, 1900, aboard the *Stella Polare* off Rudolf Island. In the spring, a party of ten Italians with Umberto Cagni as leader, harnessed one hundred dogs to their sledges and set off towards the north. They reached a point twenty miles nearer the Pole than Nansen had done, and confirmed that in those high latitudes there was no land, only an infinite expanse of snow and bottomless ice.

PEARY REACHES THE POLE

Finally, the goal that had cost the lives of so many was reached in 1909, by an American, Commander R. E. Peary, who, ten years previously, had lost eight toes from frostbite. Peary had then been using the *Windward*, Jackson's ship presented to him by Lord Northcliffe. Now, in a new ship called the *Roosevelt*, the explorers and their supplies were taken to Cape Sheridan in Canada's northernmost territory of Grant Land. The party, with Peary in charge, numbered twenty-three men, seventeen of whom were Eskimo; they had 133 Greenland dogs and nineteen sledges. The plan was for small groups to break off at intervals, the bulk of the remaining supplies to be carried by the main party which grew smaller as it approached the Pole.

During the journey, the cold became even more intense, disabling some of the men and killing many dogs. Peary pressed on until he was left, as planned, with four Eskimos and one compatriot, Henson, to complete the final 140-mile

stage. On 6th April, 1909, observations showed that the party had reached a latitude 89°57'N.; the North Pole was only three miles distant. Next day, Peary and his companions reached the Pole, so completing another chapter in the story of man's exploration of the earth. After making soundings which showed that the polar ice was over 1,500 fathoms thick, Peary hoisted the American flag. The party then set off on the return journey to the waiting ship *Roosevelt*.

BY AEROPLANE AND DIRIGIBLE

A new phase of polar exploration now began. Having made the long journey over the ice, man was determined to show that the North Pole could also be conquered from the air. In 1925, Roald Amundsen made an unsuccessful attempt to fly to the pole in a seaplane. Then, on 11th May, 1926, Amundsen made a second attempt, this time using a small airship. With his companions, Colonel Nobile and Lincoln Ellsworth, Amundsen took off in the Italian dirigible *Norge*, from the base in Spitsbergen. A three-day flight took them directly over the Pole, and they flew on to Teller in Alaska. On landing, they learned that Commander R. E. Byrd, with his co-pilot Floyd Bennett, had circled the Pole in an aeroplane and returned just sixteen hours before them.

Two years later, General Nobile, as he then was, planned another flight in the airship *Italia*, following a new route over Franz Josef Land. Unfortunately, the dirigible was caught in a violent storm on its way back, and was wrecked on the ice to the east of Spitsbergen. A number of lives were lost, but the survivors, including Nobile, were rescued after camping out for six weeks in bitter weather. Among those who took part in the search was Roald Amundsen; he left Bergen in an aeroplane on 17th June, 1928, never to be heard of again. So the North Pole claimed its victims right up to the hours of its final defeat and conquest.

It is only in the last thirty years that we have learned to live in the frozen wastes of the Arctic. Meteorological stations and scientific research centres are now established in the polar regions. The polar route, the shortest between Europe and the Far East, is now flown regularly by the the world's airlines. These polar flights began during World War II, when the American bombers flew from Canada to Europe over the North Pole.

On 6th October, 1946, an American aeroplane, *Pancusan Dreamboat*, established a long-distance record by flying from Honolulu to Cairo, passing over the magnetic Pole.

On 15th November, 1954, the polar route was opened to passenger flights; a landmark in the history of commercial aviation. On that date, two Scandinavian Airlines planes flew the "great circle" route between Los Angeles and Copenhagen. They passed each other, flying in opposite directions, over the North Pole.

In August, 1958, the journey to the North Pole was made by the only remaining unexplored route—under the ice. The American nuclear submarine, *Nautilus*, sailed on her historic voyage from Honolulu, passing under the polar ice cap to emerge on the other side!

TRANSARCTIC CROSSING

In 1969, the British Transarctic Expedition, under the leadership of Wally Herbert, completed the first surface crossing of the frozen Arctic Ocean. This was possible only with the aid of modern radio equipment, homing devices and air-support and with the skills of sledge travel evolved through generations of polar exploration.

LEAD AND ITS USES

Lead is a bluish-grey metal which, when exposed to the air, develops a fine, dark sheen that obscures its true brightness. Hence the term " leaden ", which we use, for example, in describing a dull, grey sky.

Two of the most striking characteristics of lead are its weight and softness. With a specific gravity of 11·3 it is the heaviest of the common base metals. At the same time, lead is so soft that you can scratch it with your fingernail.

Lead melts at 334°C., a temperature that is quite frequently reached in the oven of a kitchen stove. It is malleable, which means that it can be easily shaped by hammering or beating; but it is not very ductile: you cannot draw it out in fine wires like copper, but it can be rolled into sheets.

ITS ORES AND MAIN SOURCES

Metallic lead is found in nature only in very small quantities. It exists mainly as a constituent of mineral ores from which it is extracted by various methods. The most common ores are galena, cerussite and anglesite. The latter is named after Anglesey where it was first found. Galena, which is the chief source of lead, is also associated with the development of radio. Before the invention of valves, the old wireless sets of the early 1920s were fitted with galena crystal, at that time the only known means of detecting electromagnetic waves.

Lead is obtained from galena ore by washing and crushing the raw material and then roasting it with added silica in reverberatory furnaces. During its second heating a thick dross, or scum, forms on the surface and the molten lead is drawn off from beneath. There are other methods of extraction that depend on chemical reaction and the use of special furnaces.

A less important source of lead is cerussite, or carbonate of lead, with the chemical formula $PbCO_3$. This is a geological derivative of galena and exists as a white, yellow or dark grey substance often called leadspar. From it we get the mixture of carbonate and oxide we call white lead; this is the powder that is used as a pigment in white paint. In combination with other ingredients, white lead is also used for making plaster and putty. The lead compound in such mixtures is poisonous and must be used with care; people have been known to suffer harmful effects after living in rooms decorated with white lead paint.

The countries with the richest reserves of lead are America, Australia, Canada, Mexico, Peru and Russia. America has the largest output (excluding Russia, for which statistics are not available) amounting to one-quarter of the total world production. Australia, Mexico, Canada, Western Germany, Belgium and Britain follow in that order. Small deposits of galena are found in Sardinia.

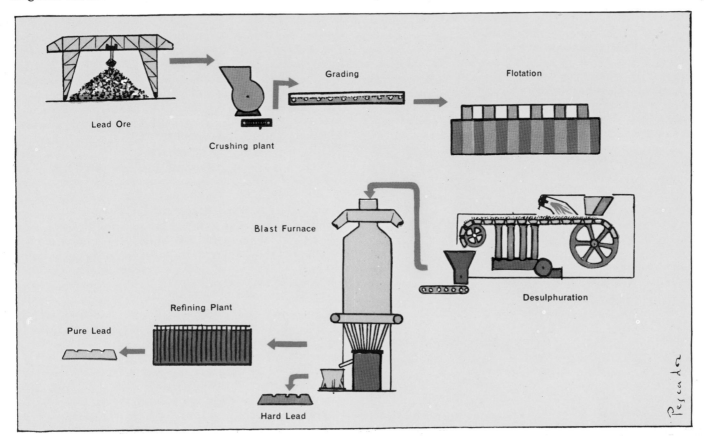

A simplified diagram showing the processing of lead ore. After crushing, the ore is roasted to remove sulphur, and the resultant lumps are taken to the blast furnace where lead is obtained. This is then taken to the refinery for casting.

Despite its weight and lack of strength, lead is a valuable metal. It has specialised properties which have brought it a wide variety of industrial uses.

Lead mining goes back at least to the period 3000-2000 B.C. when it was being extracted from galena in Egypt, Babylon and other parts of the Near East. Even before that date, lead was being used by the Chinese. In classical times it provided the raw material for many articles of general use: ointment pots, writing tablets, toys, weights and so on. Builders used it as a form of cement in the crevices between stones, and for fixing marble and bronze statues to their pedestals. The role of lead seems always to have been that of a most useful yet humble metal. Poor people who could not afford to offer statuettes of gold, silver or bronze to the gods brought votive gifts of lead. In those days lead was also used by forgers for coining false money.

Under the Roman Empire, great progress was made in the use of metals and there was rapid growth in the technique of extraction and separation. Huge quantities of ore were mined in Britain and Spain, for lead was now needed for building aqueducts. The Romans attached great importance to supplying their towns with water. To avoid leakage at vital points the ducts were lined with lead sheeting, which was bent to the shape of the channel and soldered at the edges. Lead sheets were also used for roofing important buildings in ancient Rome.

WINDOWS—BULLETS—PRINTING TYPE

During the Middle Ages, houses began to be fitted with latticed windows. The panes were held in place by *cames*, which are the thin strips of lead you can see in any church with stained-glass windows. To make these strips the lead beaters used a primitive rolling mill and cutter, which was much improved in the 1700s to meet a growing demand for lead sheeting, used in making church organ pipes.

" His bullets were made of lead-lead-lead ", says the old nursery rhyme. But bullets were not the first missiles in which lead made its appearance. Long before guns were invented, lead was used in catapults and slings. And because of the ease with which it melted and the terrible wounds it inflicted, our forefathers poured molten lead on their attackers when besieged behind town walls and castle ramparts. The

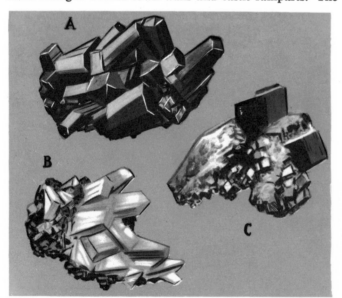

A. Galena, or sulphide of lead, is greyish with a metallic sheen; B. Cerussite is a carbonate; C. Anglesite.

violent death of Edward II at Berkeley Castle is said to have been caused by this same metal. Since then, lead has brought death to millions of men and animals with bullets that have been fired at one time or another in every part of the world.

At a time when the discovery of gunpowder was opening the way to the use of lead bullets, another much happier event gave this metal great importance in the field of culture and learning. This was the invention of printing. In very early days letters for the printing press were made of wood, but by 1500 lead type was already quite common. Modern typesetters still depend on it: not in its pure form, but as an alloy consisting of 75 per cent. lead and 25 per cent. antimony, a mixture which is hard, yet can quickly be melted down to reappear as new slugs of type.

LEAD IN MODERN INDUSTRY

Mixed with tin, lead forms that most useful of alloys which every " do-it-yourself " enthusiast knows as solder. Mixed in varying proportions with copper, tin and antimony, lead is used for making a series of special alloys called white antifriction metals. The function of these alloys is to decrease the wear and tear on certain parts of engines, such as ball bearings. Lead is also used by the petrol industry for making the anti-knock additive that reduces pinking in car engines. Glassmakers produce the well-known lead or flint-glass—not to be confused with the leaded panes of a latticed window. This is used for optical lenses and luxury articles in which a greater clarity and brilliance of glass is needed. Waterford glass, for example, is a lead glass, made by using lead and potassium silicates as ingredients in the glass mix.

The chemical industry uses lead in the construction of laboratory equipment and as a raw material in many processes. Sulphuric acid, for example, is made in lead chambers. The electrical industry uses lead for the electrodes in batteries and accumulators and, much more important, for the protection of high tension power cables. The plaited copper wire of these cables is insulated and then sheathed in lead. Steel ribbon encases the lead and an outside layer of rubber and bitumen makes a final seal.

In nuclear engineering, lead is the metal used as a screen to protect human beings from the deadly effects of atomic radiation. So lead is playing its part in one of the most modern of our scientific industries.

At the beginning of this century a high proportion of the world's lead production was being used by the paint industry. For the manufacture of white and red lead paint and certain pigments the chemical compounds of lead had become vital. Unfortunately, lead compounds are poisonous to man.

Until a few decades ago the poisonous nature of lead was a cause of great concern to the food canning industry. Ordinary soldered tins and even silver paper, or tinfoil wrappings of tea, tobacco and chocolate have, in the past, caused food poisoning. This was due to a chemical reaction which released small quantities of lead to contaminate the product. Nowadays, this problem has been overcome by improved methods of canning and by the substitution of aluminium foil for tinfoil.

Another danger that has not been completely eliminated is the sickness called *saturnism*. For a long time it has been recognised that people working in factories where lead is used may lose weight and suffer a form of wasting sickness. This is caused by lead-poisoning or saturnism, so-called because Saturn was the symbol for lead used by medieval alchemists.

AFRICA AWAKES

In 1866, a small African boy picked up a shiny stone which was to change the future of a continent. The stone was a diamond—the first to be discovered in Africa. It was sold for £500, and its discovery marked the beginning of the vast diamond industry that is now so important to the South African economy.

DIAMOND FEVER

Thousands of prospectors made their way to the diamond fields in the region where the town of Kimberley now stands. Within five years, a " shanty " town of shacks and tents had grown up as the diamond-seekers struggled feverishly to find the stones that could bring them fame and fortune.

Plenty of diamonds were found, but many of the prospectors who endured the heat and thirst were doomed to disappointment. Most of the diamonds were deep in the earth, and getting them out was to become a large-scale industrial undertaking. What was needed was a man of organising ability; a man capable of handling other men, and with the commercial flair that could establish diamond-production on a profitable basis.

Such a man was Cecil John Rhodes, the millionaire who gave his name to the territories we now know as the Rhodesias. Rhodes was to become the outstanding political figure in Africa.

Rhodes was the first man to put money into the pockets of the Bantu natives; the first man to pay them wages. " The Big Hole " at Kimberley became an organised diamond mine, with white men doing the skilled work and natives from surrounding villages doing the actual mining. Fortunes were made by the diamond men, and the native Africans had their first taste of industrial life.

The search for diamonds still goes on in Africa, and there are many rich new mines. The methods used for extracting the diamonds are basically the same as of old. To-day, the soil is hauled out of the earth at a rate of many tons a minute, and every particle must be examined. Thousands of men turn over millions of pounds of earth to find just one pocketful of diamonds; but that trouser-pocketful is worth many fortunes, with each stone worth thousands of pounds.

Natives now do much of the skilled work, handling modern machinery 1600 feet below the ground, digging out the blue clay and piling it into trucks so that it can be lifted to the surface. The clay is then crushed and washed before being carried by a jet of water over a surface coated with petroleum jelly. The diamonds stick to the jelly, in which they are embedded like currants in a cake. The tables are scraped clean, and the mixture—which looks like a large dumpling—is put into an iron pot and heated in boiling water. The jelly melts, and the diamonds are strained off, ready for cleaning and selling to the merchants, who have their head-quarters in Amsterdam.

Africa was not really important to the white man until diamonds and gold were found in apparently unlimited quantity. But wealth is politics, and this vast land—which is three times the size of the United States of America—became a desirable prize. A hundred years ago, the powerful nations of Europe began to interest themselves in this continent with its vast potential wealth.

LIVINGSTONE—MISSIONARY AND EXPLORER

Why had Britain, France, Germany, Portugal and Belgium been so slow to explore Africa, which lay so close to Europe? The answer is to be found in the formidable natural obstacles which were presented by this great continent. Africa has a difficult coast, with even more difficult rivers. Explorers could find no easy way into the interior; the Congo, for example, is barred by cataracts at its mouth; the Niger

An African diamond miner at work, drilling holes for dynamite, preparatory to blasting the diamond-bearing rock.

delta is too shallow; the Zambezi has a natural barrier in the Victoria Falls, while the Orange River loses itself in desert. This land of steamy swamps, unhealthy forests and hostile tribes was waiting for its men of destiny. One of the first and best-remembered of them all was the Scottish missionary, David Livingstone. An account of his life and activities illustrates many important aspects of the European exploration of Africa.

Livingstone was one of the most remarkable men who ever lived. Born of poor parents, he went to work in a cotton mill at the age of ten, beginning at six in the morning and finishing at eight at night. Livingstone worked in this way for fourteen years; but he had made his mind up that his life would be devoted to serving his fellow men, and he was determined to become a missionary.

Somehow, Livingstone found time to study Greek and Divinity in his spare time; he passed medical examinations and became a doctor. Accepted by the London Missionary Society, he went to Africa in 1840 to spread the Christian gospel and bring medical help to the coloured people who needed it.

ACROSS THE KALAHARI

Just as his hard work in the cotton mill had fostered his ambition to become a missionary, so did his first few years in Africa fire him with an enthusiasm to become an explorer. And he was to become one of the hardest and toughest explorers who has ever lived. To extend his mission work, Livingstone determined to cross the Kalahari Desert and make contact with the tribes in the region of Lake Ngami, which had never been seen by any white man.

The Kalahari is not a sandy desert like the Sahara farther north. It has grass and bushes, but contains no running water and few wells. Herds of antelope live on its enormous expanse of sandy soil; water melons grow in abundance in rainy years. The Bushmen living here are among the smallest people in Africa; they are nomads who have learned how to live on the game and on the meagre fruits of this arid land.

Livingstone and another explorer, William Cotton Oswell, began their journey in June, 1849, travelling hard, morning and evening, to avoid the midday heat. Day followed day,

Cecil John Rhodes, after whom the Rhodesias were named, left his fortune for the foundation of the Rhodes Scholarships.

but the landscape never seemed to change. The explorers depended on their guide Ramotobi, but even he was baffled by mirages; suddenly the party would see what they thought were waves dancing and trees reflected in water. But the lake they believed to be so near was still 300 miles away.

Livingstone and his companions found a river, and followed it for nearly a hundred miles. It led them at last to the lake, the fabled Lake Ngami, a shallow saucer of water about seventy miles round. Livingstone, the first white man to cross the Kalahari desert, had made his first great discovery. But to him the most important find was the tribesmen who lived here. He became their friend, and it was with some of these Makololo people that he was to make his amazing trans-African journey; a walk from the Atlantic to the Indian Ocean.

Livingstone was now 40 years of age and had been twelve years in Africa. As he set out from Cape Town in his ox-drawn wagons he was going to put his great experience to the test, forcing a way north and then west and east.

The country enchanted him. He broke new territory, entering a region of giant grasses, and rivers where elephants waded. Wagon poles broke in difficult swamps, and flooded rivers barred the way; but this was all part of the joy of travel to Livingstone. He mapped the land with his survey instruments and wrote up his immensely detailed notes each night. In the jungle he had to climb trees to see the way ahead. In the swamps the heat was stifling and mosquitoes plagued them continually.

PLAGUED BY ILL-HEALTH

In this unhealthy country, where water-snakes and hippopotami were their constant travelling companions, Livingstone had his first attack of fever. His skin was hot, but his body felt cold. He could not cure it, but he wrote in his diary " He who is low spirited and apt to despond will die sooner than the man who is not of such a melancholic nature." How true this is. Livingstone never gave in to the sufferings he endured, or wavered in his resolution to see this journey through.

His equipment was of the simplest: a little food, including tea, sugar, coffee or biscuits, and a few animals which could be killed or given away as gifts. Tent, blankets, survey instruments and books were his main luggage. But he also had his magic lantern and slides which the tribesmen loved. His bearers could not have enough of it, and after a day of hard work manhandling canoes in and out of the water they would plead for one of his lectures.

Livingstone always noted the details of the surroundings; he described how the flowers bloomed after the rains, and enjoyed the bird songs which reminded him of his home in Scotland; he observed that buffalo and rhinoceros are more dangerous than the lion, and that crocodiles return to their nests in time to help the young ones break out of the egg and reach the water. As they left the glare of the open country, the party moved into woodlands where huge mushrooms the size of a hat provided them with food. Soon they were deep in the dense tropical forest, depressing and gloomy.

"A path however narrow is a great convenience to all who travel in Africa," wrote Livingstone in his diary. And he had reason to know this in a country without roads, where even the grass was so rough that it cut the men's bare feet. Progress was possible only by taking on local guides from place to place. Livingstone was now on the great swampy plateau that forms the watershed between the Zambezi and the Congo river systems.

This was hostile territory, where the natives demanded his men as slaves in payment for allowing the explorers to pass through. The fierce warriors, with filed teeth increasing their savage appearance, threatened the party with swords and guns, demanding a gun, a slave or an ox as tribute. But Livingstone calmly sat on his camp stool, his gun across his knees, and invited the aggressive chief to be seated. He agreed to give an ox, but not before he had thrust his gun into the face of a tribesman who had dared to threaten him.

This was Livingstone's strength. He knew when to be tough, even when violent attacks of fever had reduced him almost to a skeleton. His own men, when they tried to mutiny in the face of desperate food shortage, found themselves looking down the end of his revolver. But they were only 300 miles from the coast now, and the sight of the valley of the Quange filled the explorers with enthusiasm and hope.

Livingstone looked down upon a scene that reminded him of Scotland, the valley stretching for a hundred miles, " clothed with dark forest, except where the light green grass covers meadowlands." The party made its way into the valley, following dells and spurs, until at last they met Portuguese traders who had established posts all the way down to the coast. Their troubles were over!

The deliverance was timely for Livingstone, who was now so fever-stricken and mentally sick that he had forgotten the names of his companions, and even the days of the week. He had been marching for two years, entirely cut off from news of the outside world. On the 31st May, 1854, he reached Loanda on the Atlantic coast, where a British Navy ship offered him a passage back to England.

But Livingstone refused it. He had promised his men that he would take them back to their Makololo tribesfolk in the interior. After a rest to regain his strength, he set off back the way he had come, carrying fig, coffee, areca and pawpaw plants with which the natives could develop their agriculture and enrich their monotonous diet of maize and millet.

In this way, Livingstone was extending work already done by the Portuguese in the Congo basin, who introduced crops which are so widespread to-day, including maize, groundnuts, sweet potatoes and cassava—crops which came originally from South America. On the east coast of Africa, Arabs of the north had earlier introduced other crops, including bananas, rice, sugar cane and wheat.

Livingstone saw in Africa a great continent full of wonderful opportunities for civilised development, but dogged by tribal war and a slave trade which threatened the lives of millions. Children and grown-ups were sacrificed to placate tribal gods if the crops failed, and witch doctors held the power of life and death over superstitious tribesmen. Yet Livingstone loved these primitive peoples, and sought to convert them to Christianity.

He had a great belief in their wisdom and wrote: " The acts of a stranger are carefully scrutinised by young and old, and seldom is judgment pronounced, even by the heathen, unfair or uncharitable." Livingstone was allowed to pass through hostile country where any other white man would have been murdered. Boldly he walked among hundreds of sullen natives armed with bows and poisoned arrows.

In due course, Livingstone completed his great return trek, and delivered his men back to their tribe. Here, he was received as a chief, and spent some time writing up notes which were to be the first geological survey of Central Africa. Then he was ready for the second part of his journey; a trip to the Indian Ocean which would complete his crossing of Africa.

On this second stage of the journey, Livingstone saw a strange smoke hanging in the air, as if a fire was raging. It was the Mosi-oi-tunya—the smoke that thunders, the spray of the mighty Victoria Falls. Livingstone was the first white man to see this wonder of the world, the waterfall of the Zambezi which is two-and-a-half times the size of Niagara. Imagine his feelings when he looked over the drop and saw the tremendous gorge where the Zambezi falls through a vertical canyon. Here are Livingstone's words:

" Creeping in awe to the verge, I peered down into a great rent which had been made from bank to bank, and saw a stream a thousand yards broad that leaped down a hundred feet, and then became suddenly compressed into a space of fifteen to twenty yards. The entire falls are simply a crack made in a hard basaltic rock from the right to the left bank, and then prolonged from the left bank away through thirty or forty miles of hills."

To-day this gorge is spanned by the highest railway bridge in the world, and you can travel by modern train to stay at a first-class hotel 900 miles from the sea. Behind it lies the Kalahari Desert over which Livingstone pioneered the way. A statue of the great explorer and a copy of the map he made stand by the Falls.

ABUNDANCE OF WILD LIFE

Modern travellers marvel at the elephants, the lions, the leopards and other animals which still roam wild here, but in Livingstone's time this upland region was a paradise of wild life, with vast undisturbed herds of eland, hartebeest, gnu, elephant, buffalo, zebra and beasts of prey. This land, which we know to-day as Southern Rhodesia, appealed to Livingstone as being most suitable for European colonisation. Africans swarmed round him wherever he went. Food was given free to the explorers, and the people gave every sign of wishing to be friendly. Livingstone was determined to set up a mission here.

Alas, his efforts were not appreciated by the Mission Society, who were lukewarm in their praise of his epic journey. They accused him of spending too much time exploring and not enough on his mission work. They did him an injustice, because it was Livingstone who focused attention on the slave trade which was bringing misery and death to thousands of Africans each year.

The establishment of British rule eliminated this trade in the buying and selling of human bodies. Colonisation created a stability which the natives had never known. It made possible the raising of much of Africa from witchcraft to independence in a matter of a generation or two.

Africa is now thirsting for education, and in the new Universities of Rhodesia and Malawi, African students study on equal terms with Europeans. The old hand-to-mouth agriculture has given way to modern techniques. The mighty Zambezi, which Livingstone knew as a wild, untameable river, is now spanned by a wall of concrete 420 feet high, holding back one of the biggest man-made lakes in the world at the Kariba Gorge.

The Kariba dam connects Rhodesia with Zambia; it has a 40-foot road running along the top of it. The water behind the dam should provide all the electrical power for these two countries and Malawi over the next twenty years. The power is carried by overhead wires to mines and other industries, and it will become cheaper as full output is reached. Italian and British firms carried out the project at a cost estimated at £120,000,000. Two underground power stations contain the turbines for the 150-mile-long lake.

Livingstone would be amazed if he were to return from the dead and see this part of Africa, which was virgin land such a short time ago. He would be even more amazed to find so much of Africa governed by Africans. He would see them driving cars, administering the law, acting as school teachers, journalists, civil servants, prosperous farmers, businessmen and trade union organisers. All this has been made possible by education, and the will of politically-minded Africans to manage their own affairs.

Kenya is an excellent example of the far-reaching effects of these rapid changes. Here, the Masai tribe, a tall, noble-looking people, warred with each other so much that Britain created a Reserve where they could herd their cattle in peace.

IMPORTANCE OF CATTLE

To the Masai, cattle are the most important possessions in life, and each man wants to have as many as possible. In Livingstone's time, warfare kept down the numbers of the tribe and the number of cattle on the land. Fifty years ago, the Masai had approximately 130,000 cattle on the Reserve. But, by 1960, the number of cattle had risen to 973,000 and the human population more than doubled in the same time.

The problem now is that there are too many cattle on insufficient land, and the Masai are burning the forest cover to provide more pasture. Unfortunately, this is a disastrous policy which allows top soil to be blown away and encourages erosion. Already the situation is serious, and the answer will be found only if the people can be persuaded to follow a scientifically planned agricultural policy.

The Masai have exerted a wonderful influence on the natural life of their region, as they alone of the African peoples have allowed wild animals to live free from molestation. Now the position is changing, as the Masai believe that they will have more grazing and more water for their animals if they kill off the wild life. If this is allowed to continue, it could result in disaster.

Unfortunately, it is not simply a question of substituting the meat of wild animals for the meat of domestic cattle. The Masai tap their domestic cattle for blood and milk and do not normally kill them for their meat supply.

ARUSHA CONFERENCE

The biggest achievement in the field of conservation occurred in 1961 at the Arusha Conference, when black men and white men sat round the table to work out a plan for conserving wild life in Tanganyika (Tanzan). In the past, Africa has suffered from the effects of uncontrolled destruction of big game. Africa's wild life can be preserved only if poaching can be controlled, as in the Luangwa Valley where Livingstone saw a plain moving with more animals than any other place he had seen in all his travels. This valley is now one of twelve Game Reserves in Central Africa. Here, the animals are protected from senseless destruction, and the herds are able to flourish. Even so, they are only a fraction of the size of the huge herds that roamed the plains seventy years ago. The fact that tourists are willing to pay to see these animals may help to prevent the total destruction of the herds.

The most accessible of these game parks is at Nairobi, where many films of African wild life have been made. Here, the animals are accustomed to motor-cars and show no fear of people in them. Antelopes, giraffes and zebras are to be seen in great number, but it is, of course, the lions which are the main attraction. It is strange to think that jet aircraft can carry us into this world of wild animals in a matter of

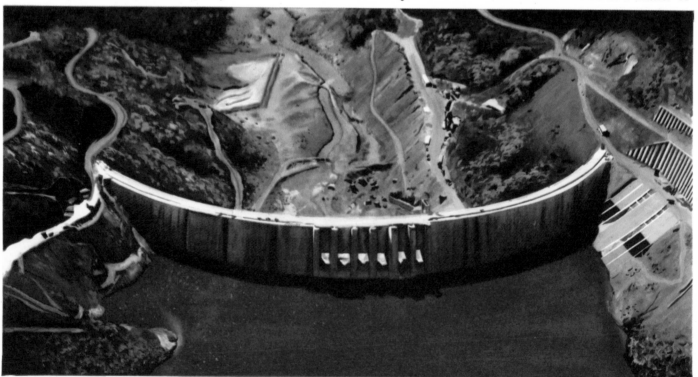

Dr. Livingstone was the first white man to visit the gorge where the Kariba dam is now built. The building of this dam entailed the transfer of thousands of primitive people to new regions and the preservation of the area's wild game from the scheduled flooded area. Built on the Zambezi river between Rhodesia and Zambia, the dam should provide sufficient electrical power for these two countries and Malawi for the next twenty years.

Many of the African national parks and reserves, where the wild life of the country is safe-guarded from wanton slaughter, are easily accessible to the public. The animals are used to their human visitors and ignore both cars and visitors.

hours. Anyone can go on safari under the guidance of professional hunters who supply Land Rovers, bearers, and even aeroplanes for those who can afford to pay.

The size of Africa is its strength and its weakness. Hundreds of languages are spoken, and tribal feuds are still bitter in many regions. This makes self-government difficult, especially when most of the people are uneducated. The strength of Africa lies in its abundance of potential wealth for its 200 million inhabitants. Its weakness is its lack of unity; over 700 different languages are spoken, and a fairly large proportion of the people can neither read nor write.

The harnessing of water can bring greater riches to Africa than all the diamonds and gold, uranium, copper, aluminium and iron. Water could bring fertility to vast areas of desert. By diverting rivers such as the Niger, the annual flooding of the Nile could be copied in many parts of Africa, to produce not only food and crops but electricity as well.

The Blue Nile below Lake Tana has been dammed to provide power for the Ethiopian Highlands. On the other side of the country, another gigantic dam has been built on the River Volta, flooding the valley and making a 200-mile-long lake held by a 260-foot-high wall of concrete. Electricity from this great hydro-electric scheme will enable the vast deposits of bauxite in Ghana to be developed.

It was during the Ashanti War on the Gold Coast, as Ghana was then known, that Baden-Powell had the idea of starting the great youth movement which we know to-day as the Boy Scouts. The Chief Scout was then commanding troops in one of the unhealthiest parts of Africa.

Here, in the Gulf of Guinea, was the terrible slave coast. Farther north up the coast, in 1787, Britain freed Negro slaves captured from the trading ships and settled them in what we know to-day as Sierra Leone. They became neighbours of the Liberians, also former slaves who were brought from America and resettled here as free men. Liberia has been an independent state since 1847.

NIGERIAN INDEPENDENCE

On the 1st October, 1960, Nigeria became independent after nearly 100 years of British rule. It is of great credit to both countries that they parted friends. The Federal Prime Minister said on the first day of the new administration: "We are grateful to the British officers we have known, first as masters and then as leaders and finally as partners, but always as friends."

Nigeria remains in the Commonwealth, a country four times the size of Britain, with about the same number of people. A mixture of many races, they range from pale skinned to black, and speak over 250 different languages. Periods of inter-racial strife between the Ibo and the Hausa, led, in 1967, to the secession of the Eastern Region from the Federation of Nigeria as the Ibo republic of Biafra, culminating in a Civil War which broke out in July, 1967, and ended in victory for the federal forces in January, 1970.

Tribes from the Sahara and from the Libyan deserts came with their cattle and colonised Nigeria, dominating the southerners. The Fulani, who are related to the Masai, were the fiercest of the tribes. It was largely to control these warlike people that the British extended their influence in Nigeria during the early colonial days.

The Portuguese had been running slaves out of Nigeria from as long ago as 1441. Africans made a living by selling other African men, women and children to European and Arab slavers. The British, ashamed at their own part in this traffic, put an end to the slave trade, developing the palm-oil industry to provide an alternative source of income. Palm-oil has been one of Nigeria's most important industries ever since.

The basis of the economy is agriculture, but oil is also being exported, as well as ground-nuts, cocoa, cotton-lint and seed. There are large tin and coal mining industries and Nigeria is the main supplier to the world of columbite for steel alloys. Development of the rivers Niger and Benue will make a tremendous difference to Nigeria's future.

The Niger is badly silted at its mouth, and needs to be made navigable for large vessels. The inauguration in February, 1969, of the Kainji Dam, three hundred miles from Lagos, has already helped the development of navigation on the Niger, as well as improving agriculture and fishing around and on the newly-created lake.

Vast road-building schemes are in progress in Nigeria, and already an efficient communications network is opening up the rich hinterland of this young country.

H.R.H. Princess Alexandra attended the Independence celebrations in Nigeria.

SNOW IN THE TROPICS

Among the many natural wonders of Africa are the vast herds of animals roaming the plains below Kilimanjaro, the monstrous peak thrown up when the earth cracked, lava boiled and pot-holes like Lake Tanganyika, 4,708 feet deep were formed. The snow peaks of the equator, Mount Kenya (17,000 feet) and Kilimanjaro (19,000 feet), are the highest mountains in Africa. The first explorers wondered if the white on the peaks came from a covering of rock salt; they doubted if snow could exist in the tropics.

The Nile rises to the west of these peaks in Lake Victoria. Livingstone died searching for the source of this great river, refusing to give up even when Stanley found him. In the famous meeting, Stanley spoke the words, " Dr. Livingstone, I presume ? " And Stanley continues: " So I found myself gazing at him, conning the wonderful man at whose side I now sat in Central Africa . . ."

DEATH OF LIVINGSTONE

Livingstone died in 1873, on his knees, praying by the side of his camp-bed in Chitambo's village. His men so loved him that they carried his embalmed body through 1,500 miles of hostile country, to hand it over to his countrymen. He was buried in Westminster Abbey with all the honour that he so much deserved.

Livingstone failed to find the source of the Nile, but he discovered and explored Lake Nyasa, reached Lake Tanganyika and discovered the lakes Mweru and Bangweulu. He had explored Africa for thirty-three years, enduring more than any other man had done before him.

SOURCE OF THE NILE

In fact, John Speke, another British explorer, had already found the source of the Nile, though his claim was disputed. Exploring Lake Victoria, Speke found a river flowing from the lake, and followed it far enough to establish that it was indeed the Nile. The river which Livingstone had thought was the Nile was the Congo. In this complicated region of the Great Rift Valley, four of Africa's greatest rivers rise; the Congo, the Niger, the Volta and the Nile. Looking back, it is astonishing how quickly the early explorers, Livingstone,

Emin Pasha, Stanley, Speke, Burton, Du Chaillu and Bruce, sorted out this maze of African rivers.

" MOUNTAINS OF THE MOON "

Stanley, in 1888, solved another geographical problem which had puzzled explorers, by finding the " Mountains of the Moon," known as the Ruwenzori. Ptolemy, the second-century astronomer had named them, but no one else had been able to find these amazing snow peaks which are usually hidden by rain clouds. They lie to the west of Lake Victoria, reaching a height of over 16,000 feet, in a dank, steamy country where heather grows to the size of trees.

The lower slopes of these peaks are the home of the Watutsi, the tallest men in Africa, who stand over six feet high. The country they live in is known as Rwanda. Stanley met the Watutsi in 1876, and found them natural aristocrats; they were easy to get on with and to understand. Living as they do in one of the remotest regions of the world until recently, they had not been spoiled by contact with modern civilisation.

The Belgians colonised a vast territory of the Congo, where over 200 different languages are spoken. They did much to develop this region of Africa, and handed over a rich country to the Congolese when they withdrew from Africa in 1960. The copper mines of Katanga alone produce 8 per cent. of the world's copper. The withdrawal of the Belgians from the Congo was followed by disaster. Tribal war broke out and United Nations troops had to be called in to restore an uneasy peace. The Belgians had not prepared the native population for self-government. The Congolese were helpless in the grip of politicians who often were little more than tribal leaders.

In many parts of Africa, the transformation from a primitive culture to a western type of civilisation is being carried through at breakneck speed. Changes which took place in Europe over a thousand years are occurring in Africa in little more than a generation or two. Inevitably, immense political and economic difficulties must be faced in a social upheaval of this sort. While so much is being achieved in so very short a time, it is to be hoped that no more blood will be shed in the process.

WHEELS MAKE PROGRESS

It would not be true to say that the wheel was known to all the civilisations of the past. When the Spaniards overthrew the Aztecs of South and Central America, they found no indication that the Aztecs had learned to use the wheel. But, generally speaking, the wheel has played its part in most of the civilisations which have flourished and died away since the time of the ancient Egyptians and Assyrians.

What was it that gave man the idea of using the wheel for transport purposes? Maybe he arrived at the axle and wheels as a development of the tree trunk used as a roller to ease the movement of heavy loads. As the centre of the trunk was worn away, two smooth discs would be left; these might then have been sawn off and attached with wooden pins to a new cross-bar.

Later, it may have occurred to someone that wheels like the "wooden cheeses" in the illustration could be lightened by hollowing out the centre, leaving four or five rough spokes. Certainly, spoked wheels began to come into use with the discovery of metals. The next step was perhaps to make a floor and set it over the axle. But this type of simple framework could have had very little stability; it would have tipped like a see-saw. Something was needed to steady it, and the obvious way of doing this was to add another axle with a second pair of wheels. Nobody knows if this was, in fact, the pattern of man's progress in developing the wheel. But one thing we do know is that carts with wheels were being used in Asia Minor at least 5,000 years ago, while in other parts of the world the idea of the wheel had not yet been born.

MODERN WHEELS

Let us see how the wheel has come to be used by us in modern times.

Modern wheels are usually made of metal. They are constructed around a hub whose purpose is to hold the spokes which radiate from the centre to the outer rim.

The discovery of the wheel was followed by the construction of primitive carts.

Though sometimes made in segments, the rim is normally a single piece, which may be "shod" with a circular "tyre" to give solidity to the whole. Wooden wheels are still widely used in countries where primitive horse-drawn carts and carriages are used. Even in highly developed countries, we still find wooden wheels being used in the wheelbarrow and the royal state coach.

The wheels of railway locomotives are made in many types and sizes, depending on the job they have to do. Large wheels, of which there may be as many as sixteen, support and carry the engine; smaller bogie wheels guide it. Iron wheels may look as if they had been cast in a single piece, but this is rarely so, as it would make for great difficulty in changing rims. Usually the hub and central parts are in one piece, consisting of a disc wheel or spoked wheel to which the outer rim is attached. Locomotive wheels are commonly built with spokes so that the rim can easily be changed when worn out; this also makes it easier to get at the engine by reaching between the spokes. They are almost invariably made of cast metal.

Bicycle and motor-cycle wheels, front and rear, are held in place by a fork which forms part of the machine's framework. They are secured by ordinary nuts, or sometimes by wing nuts which can be screwed on and off by hand. Beneath the outer and inner tyres the groove of the rim is pierced by small holes which take the spoke heads. In a bicycle the spokes radiate at a tangent to the hub, but in motor-cycles they are often crossed at the centre to give greater strength.

When cars were first manufactured, wood was used for the spokes, though the hub and outer rim were made of metal. Car wheels are now made from metal stampings welded either to the shape of a disc or to resemble a spoked wheel. The latter, with its spokes radiating at a tangent from the hub, is used only for cars. The wheels of heavy trucks and lorries are made of steel or cast steel sheeting; aircraft wheels are also manufactured in this way. The wheels on modern vehicles are fitted in such a way that they are detachable.

WHEEL MARKS THROUGHOUT HISTORY

At first, the wheeled cart or carriage was used almost exclusively for warlike purposes. The Greeks used it for religious and military functions, and it was only later adapted for industrial and agricultural use. The greatest stimulus to the practical use of the wheel came from the restlessness of nomad tribes, in particular the Celts, who used a primitive type of wagon for hauling their goods and chattels. It has been suggested that the Latin *carrus* comes from an earlier Celtic word for cart. Necessity was the mother of this invention, and nomadic peoples like the Phrygians and the Scythians were among the first to build carts with four and, perhaps, six wheels.

Meanwhile, the ancient world was using only the two-wheeled vehicles already known to the Greeks and the Egyptians: chariots for racing in the arena; the two-horse *biga*, (see illustration) and the *triga* and *quadriga* the

Biga, triga *and* quadriga *were Roman racing chariots. The names refer to the number of horses drawing the vehicle.*

first with three and the second with four horses. These curricles were mainly for officials and army officers. Later in the history of Rome all kinds of conveyances were built for the transport of judges, magistrates, women and invalids: the *cisium, pilentum, arcera* and *benna,* which we might describe as buggies, rickshaws, litters and tumbrils.

The Latin *vehiculum,* familiar to our language, was reserved for more splendid coaches intended for important persons. Another magnificent equipage was the *carpentum,* which has given us the word carpenter. *Carpentiere* in modern Italian still means a maker of carriage wheels. So extravagant did this vehicle become in the days of Rome's greatness that laws were necessary to limit its use to special occasions.

The power of the Roman Empire depended on military supremacy, and the success of the legions was promoted by the quality of their armour. Boadicea's chariot could not have had much of a chance against armoured vehicles bristling with scythes like the one in our illustration. Nor did primitive communities have the skill or means to build

This Roman assault vehicle consisted of a half-circle of armour-plating, the undercarriage bristling with blades.

the mobile crossbow, also shown on these pages. It could be adapted to hurl larger missiles as well as arrows to greater distances than any previous weapon.

MOBILE JUGGERNAUTS

After the fall of the Roman Empire, roads fell into disrepair and wheeled traffic disappeared in the confusion of the Dark Ages. But something of the old tradition was kept up, especially in Italy, whose medieval city states constructed strange vehicles of military and religious significance. Huge carts resembling mobile altars were dragged around the countryside by twelve pairs of young bulls. Christ and the cross, figured large beneath an immense banner and a smaller flag for sending signals. Priests, armed warriors and trumpeters rode the cart which served as a rallying centre in medieval battles, just as the eagles had done on the standards of the Roman legionaries. A distant relative of the *carroccio,* as this juggernaut was called, may be seen in the festival car decked with flowers which carry beauty queens in springtime on the Riviera.

With the advance of the Middle Ages, wheeled traffic

With the aid of the mobile crossbow, arrows and other missiles could be hurled from comparatively great distances.

began to appear again in the streets of Europe's larger cities. The town of Kotze in Hungary claims the honour of having invented the coach in 1457, giving its name to the French *Coche,* which later entered into the English language. By the end of the fifteenth century, rich patrician families like the Sforzas of Milan had as many as ten or twelve coaches. These coaches ran on four wheels, with the body resting square on two axles: clumsy, uncomfortable contraptions, whose passengers were lucky to escape unbruised after driving over the cobbled streets and rutted roads of that period.

CINDERELLA COACHES

Real coaches appeared in England in the reign of Queen Elizabeth I, who was perhaps the first sovereign to drive down Whitehall in a wheeled state vehicle. The coaches were slung on stout leather straps and supports which softened the bumps and jolts, though much less effectively than metal springs do. As the sixteenth century progressed, the great families of Europe rivalled each other in the luxury and elegance of their turn-out. Their carriages were adorned so lavishly that any one of them would have served to carry

Cinderella to her ball. Once again, as in ancient Rome, laws were made to limit the extravagance of this display. The earliest models of these coaches—a type that is now used only on state occasions by the royal family—were made in 1534 in the Italian town of Ferrara.

The coach now developed into a more practical and efficient vehicle, reaching its peak with the splendid carriages made for the kings of England and France during the eighteenth century. It was in one of these—a rather less conspicuous one—that Marie Antoinette made a dramatic flight from Paris when the French Revolution threatened. A handsome closed four-wheeled coupé also became popular, and it was fashionable for owners to take the reins themselves. Women, too, tried their hand at driving in those countries which allowed them such privileges; but not always, we are told, with great success. Roads, which until about 1700 had been mere tracks, were improving. Ordinary people were travelling more frequently, and, since they could not take elaborate protective measures, they offered a tempting prize for highwaymen.

STAGE COACH AND HORSE BUS

In the early days, wheeled transport was reserved almost exclusively for the rich. But as time went on, it developed gradually into a public service. This change took place first in the large cities and towns. In Paris, carriages were made available to the public as long ago as 1600. They had six seats and operated from the old Hôtel de St. Fiacre, from which we get the word *fiacre*, meaning a hackney carriage. In 1662, horse-drawn buses were introduced in the same city, but for various reasons failed to pay and were soon dropped.

Horse buses did not reappear until after the Napoleonic Wars. The truth was that most towns were so small that people could reach everywhere by walking. For longer journeys the stage coach had now come into its own. Regular services plied between all big towns, whether in Britain or on the Continent. The *diligence* in France and the stage coach in England were divided into compartments with seats and racks on the top—which was often called the imperial—for passengers and their luggage. The coachman was a man of some importance, and the place beside him

At each coaching stage, the passengers would alight, the horses would be changed and the mail delivered.

Horse trams appeared in the streets of the larger cities of the world in the first half of the 19th century.

was usually given to the most distinguished passenger. The postilion, who was in charge of the horses and luggage, also considered himself an official to be reckoned with.

In order to run to schedule it was necessary to change horses at intervals on the journey. These were stabled and held in readiness at each stage, or section, of a journey. Fresh, well-fed animals would be waiting at the pull-in to be harnessed to the coach. In many parts of the Continent, armed guards would be picked up at these "stops" to escort the coach through brigand-infested country. One such coach, which suffered attack on its journey to and fro over the St. Gotthard Pass, may be seen in Zurich Museum.

"THE GONDOLA OF LONDON"

The time was coming when the train was to drive the stage coach from the road, leaving it to ply only in remote country places. But the private carriage had a longer lease of life; it was not replaced entirely by the motor car until some eighty years after the invention of the railway locomotive.

During this period horse-drawn vehicles became lighter and more elegant. The hooded Berlin, with its closed windows and ample accommodation, was a truly royal carriage. First built for the German Elector of Brandenburg, it became a favourite at the Court of the Hapsburgs. The Victoria, named after the Queen who made frequent use of it, was introduced in or near 1870. With its collapsible half-hood and low, open sides, it was the ideal vehicle to see from and to be seen in. Another much larger coach was the landau which originated in Germany. It was built for six persons, who sat facing each other beneath two folding tops which could be pulled out to meet in the centre.

The old hansom-cab was once a familiar creature of the London streets. Unlike the vehicles described above, it had only two wheels, with the driver sitting high above them in a "dickey seat". The reins passed over the roof of the cab, whose two occupants sat comfortably inside what Disraeli called "the gondola of London". The hansom-cab has now gone, and the streets where it used to ply are thronged with fast-moving traffic. Millions of motor cars are now running on wheels that have developed from the log wheels invented by primitive man.

PAPER
From Papyrus to Wood Pulp

Thousands of years have passed since our forebears began to seek a really suitable material on which to record their thoughts. Primitive peoples are known to have written in signs and symbols on the dried skins of sheep, goats, antelopes and snakes. But roughly-tanned skin was a clumsy medium on which to record human memories. The inventive brain of man sought better media for the written word, and the answer was found by the ancient Egyptians. They discovered papyrus, a vegetable parchment made from the stems of a plant called *Cyperus papyrus*.

PAPYRUS AND PARCHMENT

Papyrus is an aquatic plant that grows to a height of about fifteen feet. Its stem is as smooth as a reed, triangular in shape and ends in a plume of feathery foliage. It flourishes on swampy ground in hot, moist climates.

Once they had found out how to use papyrus, the ancient Egyptians had at hand an inexhaustible supply of material on which to write. It is said that they made their discovery at Memphis in the Nile Valley where papyrus grew wild in great abundance.

The process of preparing papyrus, which via Greek and Latin has given us the word "paper", is a very simple one. The stems of the plant are dried in the sun, cut into strips and woven in a criss-cross pattern. A layer of strips is placed above the mesh, after which the sheet is soaked in muddy water and thoroughly dried. It is astonishing that pieces of this fragile material, bearing the hieroglyphics of four thousand years ago, have survived to this day. Preserved in tombs beneath the dry sands of the desert, these fragments of papyrus tell the story of ancient civilisations to experts who have learned to read them.

The Egyptians themselves made great use of papyri, but they also exported it to countries of the eastern Medi-

terranean. The story is told that on hearing of the wonderful library of manuscripts collected by the King of Pergamum in Asia Minor, the Pharaoh of that day, a Ptolemy, prohibited the export of papyrus from his kingdom. Unable to obtain further supplies, the ancient Greek colony reverted to the use of sheep and goat skins. Their tanners acquired great skill, and by improving the quality of the skin made it possible for writers to use both sides. This material took the name of the city of Pergamum: *pergamena* in Latin; *parchemin* in French; and *parchment* in our own tongue.

Parchment was not, however, favoured by the Romans. Nor were wax blocks, which were used in some countries at that time. They preferred papyrus, some of their earliest manuscripts being written on old documents obtained from Egypt, washed clean of hieroglyphics and used again for Latin texts. Later, when the Romans conquered Egypt, they made sure of plentiful supplies of papyrus, the finer qualities being reserved for writing on, the coarser material being used for wrapping perishable goods. The rough variety of papyrus was called *papyrus emporeticus*—"emporos" is Greek for merchant—and it is worth noting that the English term "emporetic paper" means parcel paper to this day.

AN ORIENTAL SECRET LEAKS OUT

Long after the fall of the Roman Empire "Egyptian paper", as it was then called, continued to be made in factories on the Italian mainland. But when the Arabs siezed Egypt in the seventh century A.D., communications with the eastern Mediterranean were cut, and Rome could no longer buy papyrus reeds from the Nile. For some time, parchment was the only available material. And so it might have remained had not the Arabs learned the secret of a new process from the Persians, who, in their turn, had acquired it from the Chinese: this was the secret of making paper, which had been known behind the Great Wall of China for a thousand years or more.

This Chinese invention was based on a process quite different from any that had previously been used. In the preparation of papyrus, parchment, and wax tablets, the raw materials were treated in various ways but substantially they remained the same: vegetable fibre, skin and wax. This new form of writing paper made by the Arabs bore no resemblance to the materials which went into its manufacture. They were just as different from the finished product as newspapers are from the wood that is used for making ordinary paper to-day. This was the secret that had been kept for so long by the Chinese.

In Europe and many parts of Asia, men had been racking their brains to find some way of improving on the old methods of weaving dried papyrus and preparing skin for parchment; but the Chinese, maintaining their traditional isolation, had quietly got on with the job. For hundreds of years they had been making paper from old rags, silk waste, hemp, rice leaves and the bark of mulberry trees. This was a way of making good use of material that would otherwise have been thrown away. All that was needed was boiling water and

In the swampy Nile delta, the Ancient Egyptians cultivated papyrus. They used the stems for paper-making, and manuscripts made from papyrus grown over four thousand years ago have survived to this day.

plenty of patience; the waste material was pulped into a fine thick paste, spread thinly on hot slabs of chalk or felt, and left to dry. As the bottom surfaces of these sheets were rough and uneven, the Chinese glued the sheets together, two at a time, to produce strong paper which could be used for writing on both sides.

PAPER FROM OLD CLOTHES

The method adopted by the Arabs was very similar to the one used by the Chinese. With a primitive machine of their own invention, the Arabs pulped all the cast-off clothing they could find and turned it into good writing paper. In order to safeguard the industry, their government declared it a state monopoly. A big factory was set up at Fez in Morocco in about the year 1200. Camel caravans laden with bundles of old linen and cotton fabrics made their way there from many parts of North Africa. But the old clothes they carried had to be white or near white, for there was no known process for bleaching coloured garments. This is one reason, according to legend, why white has remained so popular in Arab dress to this day.

PAPER-MAKING FACTORIES

In Fez the Arabs produced a vast amount of white paper comparable in quality to some papers now being made. But this was not their only centre of paper-making. Other factories were set up in countries such as Spain, which was then dominated by Islam. Sicily, too, was held by the Arabs for several centuries, and at Fabriano they were able to obtain better materials and to improve on their old production methods. When the Normans conquered Sicily— at the time of William the Conqueror's landing in England— Fabriano was making the best quality of white paper that the world had yet seen.

Little by little, Arab techniques spread to other countries. The Fabriano paper-makers carried their knowledge far and wide, teaching the craft which they had learned in a remote Mediterranean town to the people of central and northern Europe. But production remained tedious and slow; every sheet of paper had to be made laboriously by hand, and the cost of writing materials was far too high to meet the growing need. This is one reason why, in the Middle Ages, education

Parchment, another ancient writing material, takes its name from the Greek town of Pergamum in Asia Minor.

At a time when paper had never been seen in Europe, the Chinese had been making it for more than a thousand years.

and culture were restricted to the aristocracy and professional classes.

WOOD PULP

As time went on, machinery for paper-making was steadily improved and the demand for paper increased with the growth of book publishing. But the manufacturers still depended on the old-clothes trade for their raw material. Worn-out cotton and linen fabrics turned up as paper pulp, and this situation remained unchanged until little more than one hundred years ago. No wonder daily newspapers cost more at that time than they do even to-day!

In 1799, a French workman named Louis Robert perfected a machine for the cheap and rapid production of broad rolls of paper of almost limitless length. Only one thing restricted the output of this machine—lack of suitable material from which to make the paper.

The problem was solved by a German, Frederick Keller, who had long been studying the paper-making process; he found that ordinary wood could be reduced to a perfectly satisfactory paper-pulp. Keller made this discovery in 1845, a year famous in the history of the paper-making industry. Louis Robert's machine could now draw upon unlimited supplies of raw material, which could be turned into rolls of paper of unlimited length. With wood pulp easily available, acres of paper now streamed from the mills of Europe and America: newsprint, writing paper of every quality and grade, thick brown paper, tissue paper and coloured paper for decorative use.

PAPER—A CHEAP COMMODITY

The immediate result of this discovery was that paper became a cheap material. The cost of books and newspapers fell, and the spread of learning increased at an extraordinary rate. It is no coincidence that education began to touch the mass of the population at this time. Wood-pulp paper and new printing techniques have done much to make this possible during the last century or so. To-day paper reaches us in such abundance that familiarity tends to breed contempt. Few of us bother to think about the wonderful industry that provides us with the vast amount of paper that we need to sustain our modern civilisation.

AUSTRALIA
The Transformation of a Continent

Civilisation arrived late in the huge island continent of Australia. Less than 200 years ago, only primitive men and, in the main, marsupial animals unknown elsewhere, lived on its tired soil. Giant tree-ferns grew in this isolated land, matching the animals in their antiquity; strange trees were to be seen, like the "blackboys" which resembled woolly heads bristling with spears.

FIRST SETTLEMENT

In 1770, Captain Cook took possession of 150 miles of the east coast in the name of Great Britain. Eighteen years later, Captain Phillip brought 1,500 soldiers, sailors and convicts to raise the British flag on what was later to become the site of Sydney. Beyond this tiny settlement lay a vast, unknown continent; 2,967,909 square miles of land—an area twenty-five times the size of the United Kingdom and Ireland.

To the north were tropical regions, with monsoonal rains and intense heat; in the centre lay deserts that had once been the beds of primeval seas, now shrunk to marshy salt lakes glittering in the fierce sunshine. Even in 1813, land more than 50 miles from the small settlement at Sydney was unexplored. Then Lawson, Blaxland and Wentworth crossed the Blue Mountains, which had until then proved an impassable barrier. For the first time, settlers were given a hint of the vast territory that lay inland, awaiting exploration.

Water was the first need of the pioneers, as it is of the graziers, farmers and manufacturers to-day. Water meant life to the 300,000 Aboriginals who inhabited Australia before the white man came. These primitive black men held the secrets of their "soaks" or waterholes; secrets which they passed on to the white settlers, who often cruelly betrayed the black man's trust. Many of the early settlers were brutal people, made more cruel by fear of the unknown land in which they found themselves. These men faced a desperately hard life in a land completely alien to them. There were no domestic animals; the soil had never been cultivated; droughts might last for years and floods wash away the small beginnings of civilised life. Only the tough and resolute could survive. And when you remember what the pioneers faced in their new country, little more than a century ago, you begin to appreciate the outstanding progress Australia has made.

DISCOVERY OF GOLD

The story of Australia's transformation really starts in 1850, when the first gold-strike brought people in their thousands to this empty land. People mean progress, and communities of people form the nuclei of civilisation. As populations increase, we see the development of water supplies and public services, of agriculture and industry, of communications and transport. It has been said that "Civilisation is just a slow process of learning to be kind"; from this, the idea of social services is born, with care for the sick and the weak, for children and old people.

For eighty years after the discovery of Australia, its population did not rise above 500,000. Seven years after the gold-strike, it had increased to a million. As the gold-fever died down, people tired of the diggings and flocked into the young towns. New industries developed, and by 1901, Australia was peopled by a vigorous stock of nearly four million people.

The hard Australian earth with its brightly-coloured rocks hides a wealth of many different minerals. Fortunes were made and lost as people strove to develop this vast expanse of virgin land.

MINERAL WEALTH

Gold was found at Kalgoorlie in Western Australia and at Ballarat in Victoria. Lead, zinc and copper are mined at Mount Isa.

Steel-making is an important industry, and coal is mined in increasing quantities. The search for oil continues in many parts of the Australian continent; it has already been found in Queensland.

The mines producing the beautiful black opals, found only at Lightning Ridge, are almost worked-out. Now, with so much other employment available to them, the "fossickers" no longer seek new fields. The "milk" and the white moonlit opals are still found at Whitecliffs and at Coober Pedy, where miners and their families live underground in the desert heat. "Boulder" opals, clear and brightly coloured, are found only in Queensland.

POPULATION INCREASE

Through the years the population of Australia has gone on rising. At the last census, the total population had reached 11,928,889. Immigration between October, 1945, and December, 1967, brought 2,247,612 New Australians; most

The aborigines of Australia vary physically according to whether they are from the desert or coastal regions. Above is an aborigine about to throw his boomerang.

When a call is made to the Flying Doctor Service, friends or relatives of the patient mark out a rough landing-strip for the plane. Smoke, or a piece of material held aloft, shows the pilot the direction of the wind.

were Britons, but many were displaced persons, including Poles, Italians and Netherlanders.

Australians like to own their homes, and the Government helps them to do so. Modern homes are up-to-date and labour-saving. Since the end of World War II over 1,000,000 homes have been built, but there is still a housing shortage. Each State deals with its particular problems of housing and public health. In 1950, town-planning began, and a year later the Federal Government subsidised building.

Standards of living have increased rapidly in Australia, and social services are among the most advanced in the world. In 1948, the 40-hour working week was introduced; Government spending on Social Services was six times as much as before World War II.

EDUCATION IN THE OUTBACK

Australia's educational systems are often unique, being designed to deal with the special conditions of sparsely-populated areas. There are several methods of educating outback children. Correspondence courses, conducted through the post, have given a sound education to many children.

There are also " schools of the air," which use the two-way radio equipment developed originally for the Royal Flying Doctor Service. Alice Springs was the first centre to use this method. For the only child of an isolated family it can mean very much more than a formal education; it is a way of making friends over the air.

There are fourteen universities, including at least one in each State Capital. In 1950, the Institute of Technology opened, adding to the facilities for higher education already existing in the National University, which was opened in 1946, for postgraduate research in medicine and physical sciences and Pacific studies.

WATER SHORTAGE

Australia is not an easy land. As the population rises, so does the demand for increased water supplies. Water is the life-blood of this land, where strange rivers wind like wounds across the face of a land as arid as a moonscape. Many of these rivers alternate between extremes; one month they are in flood, and the next month they are dry, sandy watercourses.

The first settlers were usually called squatters, a name used for men with no legal title to the land they claimed. To-day, the owners of big cattle and sheep properties are known as " graziers ". These men echo the explorers' cries for water. In times of drought, they watch in despair as sheep and cattle die around them. It is a fact that the total run-off of *all* Australian rivers for one year is less than the total run-off of the Danube basin for the same period. Australia is so flat that there are only a few sites on which big reservoirs can be created.

WATER FROM THE SNOWY MOUNTAINS

The Snowy Mountains Scheme is the largest civil engineering project in the world. Approved by the Federal Parliament in 1949, it is designed to provide water and power to vast areas of N.S.W. and Victoria. In the summer, the snow-capped mountains drain into the Snowy River which flows into the Tasman Sea. The Snowy Mountains Scheme will divert the Upper Snowy River westward, providing extra water which is badly needed on the inland plain.

The life-giving water from the Snowy will bring increases in population and industry. As the water of the river flows through man-made tunnels in the mountains, it will generate colossal amounts of electric power. The scheme will involve construction of nine big dams and at least ten smaller ones, eleven power-stations and more than a hundred miles of tunnels, nearly a hundred miles of aqueducts, and shafts that are up to 1,100 feet deep, plus hundreds of miles of roads through rough alpine country.

This giant project will take many more years to complete. To make it possible, engineers and workmen have been brought in from abroad. Russians, Canadians, Greeks, Britons, Germans, Swedes, Maltese, Americans and South Africans are all working side by side.

The State of Tasmania has its own Hydro-Electric Commission. The power of water is being harnessed by dams at Tungentinah, Catagunya and the Great Lake Power Developments.

THE RABBIT MENACE

Two of the greatest scourges of Australia were imported by man. A hundred-and-seventy-five years ago, when Captain Phillip's ships brought the first settlers, they also brought five rabbits. The rabbits multiplied so fast that they became a pest which eventually cost the country five hundred million pounds a year. Science took a hand in attacking the Australian rabbits, but it was not until ten years ago that the pest was controlled; and now land that once carried only a hundred-and-twenty-five sheep can carry five hundred.

ARRIVAL OF THE CACTUS

The second pest arrived less than eighty years ago, when a sailing ship brought two cactus plants from California to Queensland. In their native soil these plants grew only a couple of feet high; under the Australian sun it was a different matter. The seeds were carried by bird and breeze, and in no time at all the cactus had made itself at home. Monstrous growths towered to a height of fifteen feet; round, fleshy leaves rose like prickly hands. Thousands of bushmen were ruined by this " green octopus " or " prickly pear ", as it is called. By 1925, the cactus covered an area larger than the British Isles, and direct attacks against it, by cutting it down or burning, were quite useless.

Then, in South America, entomologists from Queensland found a tiny insect called cactoblastis, whose grubs devoured the cactus with great enthusiasm. Imported into Australia, the grubs enjoyed a gargantuan meal, and the cactus was defeated. Grateful Queenslanders built a memorial hall and dedicated it to the myriads of tiny grubs of the cactoblastis that had cleaned their land of the unwanted plants.

EARLY EXPLORERS

To-day, we remember these giants of the nineteenth century. Men of immense courage, like Sturt, who hoped to discover a great inland sea, only to find that he was many millions of years too late for that. There was McDouall Stuart who, after terrible hardship and disappointment, became the first man to blaze a route from south to north through the centre of the continent. There was Giles, who twice crossed Australia; and Burke and Wills, who crossed from south to north on a more easterly line than Stuart's, only to die on their return trip.

Horses were the only transport for these men; and so wise did drought and hardship make their animals that the horses would often find water which saved their own and their masters' lives. The names of these great horses live to-day; Australians remember Sturt's " Punch ", Stuart's " Warlock " and his grey mare " Polly ", and at least eight of the horses in Giles's party. Without their fine mounts the Australian pioneers could not have explored such a terrible and arid wilderness. Horses have played more than their part in the exploration and discovery of Australia.

In 1860, twenty-four camels arrived in Melbourne from Karachi. These strange beasts could carry great burdens and live on scanty food. They were able to do without water for longer periods than a horse is able to. They were intended for use in the exploration of Central Australia, and were taken on the ill-fated Burke and Wills expedition. Wills was a man of poetry as well as a man of action and he wrote of what he saw; " Rocks so old, they have forgotten the singing and the shouting of the sea, the violence of the earth in the making."

Thomas Elder imported a hundred camels and their Afghan drivers in 1866 to transport wool. These brave and patient beasts were the ancestors of wild camels that still roam the Australian inland. They played an important role in the exploration of the continent.

To-day, with the harbours of the State capitals crowded with shipping, it is difficult to think back little more than a hundred years, to the time when sailing ships took from four to six months on the journey between London and Sydney. Then came the beautiful clipper ships, the greyhounds of the sea, which cut the time to less than three months. After the clippers came the steamships, which did the journey in two months. Midway through the nineteenth century the Suez Canal was opened, shortening the distance and the time of the journey.

FIRST COMMUNICATIONS

Less than a hundred years ago, Aborigines carried pieces of delicately-patterned wood called " message sticks ". These were a means of communication between tribes, and were so important to the Aborigines that even in war the stick-carriers were allowed to pass.

A flourishing modern nation must have efficient lines of communication. This is particularly important in a big country like Australia, isolated from the markets of the world. Communications were speeded up in the middle of the nineteenth century when the first electric telegraph was installed between Melbourne and Williamstown, Victoria. Subsequent to the installation of the telegraph, the Australian Government approached the Colonial Office in London and asked them to send someone to be Superintendent of Telegraphs. Charles Todd was appointed.

In 1857, an undersea cable stretched from Launceston, Tasmania, to Melbourne, Victoria. By 1870, all States, except Western Australia were linked. The cable link with Tasmania fired Todd's imagination. He was a dynamic man who refused to be deterred by the stiffest obstacles, and he planned to build an overland telegraph from Port Augusta, South Australia, to Port Darwin in the north-west. Only that man of great courage, McDouall Stuart, had ridden the 2,000 miles of unknown country through the centre. Todd planned to build his line to connect with a cable from Banjoewanji in Java to Port Darwin in northern Australia, which would link-up with the European cable. When this was done, Australia, the isolated continent, would be in direct touch with Europe.

The army of workmen employed to build the line needed many tons of material and food, which had to be transported in wagons or on horseback. Sheep and cattle for food were driven on the hoof. The heavy telegraph poles, made of metal to defeat the all-devouring white ants, had to be manhandled over hundreds of miles through desert country.

The wild Myall blacks were a constant hazard; but the bitterest enemies were the climate and the terrain. The men were plagued by burning heat, sandstorms, and clouds of flies and mosquitoes. In the north, months of monsoonal rains swamped the holes dug to hold the poles. Horses were drowned, and fever was rife among the men. Even crocodiles became a serious menace.

When poling began from the northern end of the line, material and men were shipped round the coast to Darwin. The men worked courageously and hard against fearful odds. John McKinlay, sent north by the Government with a party of men and forty-five horses to explore the territory, became lost during the dreaded wet season. For five months

Air-conditioned trains drawn by diesel engines were introduced into the Queensland State Railway in 1953 with the Sunlander *and the* Inlander. *Above is the* Westlander, *a modern, fully air-conditioned express, with hot and cold showers, sitting cars with wash-basins and refrigerated drinking water. The gauge of the Queensland State Railways is 3 feet 6 inches.*

the party struggled on, until only twenty-five horses remained. McKinlay decided they must kill the horses, make a raft from their hides and try to float down the river. Crocodiles tore at the raw hides of this weird craft, but finally the men reached the coast and found help.

The telegraph wire on its line of poles ran like a great nerve across the terrible land; the Myalls called it " the singing string." Australia was now linked with Europe, and the development of the continent had taken a stride forward.

ROAD AND RAIL TRANSPORT

Meanwhile, rail and sea communications were making rapid progress. Railways have increased through the years until to-day over 400,000,000 passengers are carried annually on lines run by the Government. Between Western and South Australia, 297 miles of perfectly straight track cross Nullabor Plain. The Northern Territory needs more rail transport to move its live cattle and frozen beef. Road trains are one answer to this problem, but the cost is high and the road-making is expensive.

There are over 500,000 miles of made roads in Australia, and endless uncounted miles of winding bush tracks that served men well before roadmaking began. 78,000 miles of air routes and over 25,000 miles of rails have brought together the empty spaces where, before, the "great Australian loneliness" brooded.

INCREASE IN AIR TRAFFIC

Almost every family owns a car, but the country is one of the most air-minded in the world. Stringent safety rules ensure a very low accident-rate. Many graziers have their own planes and landing strips. The Royal Flying Doctor Service, begun in the Territory, has been so successful that other countries with scattered populations have followed Australia's lead.

A web of fine red lines criss-crosses the airmaps of the continent. Along these lines fly the Government-owned Trans Australian Airways, and A.N.A., run by private enterprise; Empire Airways Ltd. and Quantas operate round-the-world services. This air traffic has conquered the great distances separating the centres of population and the

scattered homesteads in Australia, bringing immense changes in this vast land.

In the old days, settlers usually built their wood and bark huts many miles apart. A cluster of several huts became a township, but even this might be a hundred miles or more from the nearest railway. The only means of transporting heavy goods was by horse or bullock wagons. Stores were brought three or four times a year; sometimes prolonged drought or heavy floods would make even this impossible. At such times, families on the land had to manage the best way they could; they were often glad of the rabbits that were later destroyed.

AUSTRALIAN " STATIONS "

The big tracts of land on which cattle or sheep run free are known as " stations ". Some are of great size; Alexandria Downs in the Northern Territory, for example, has 11,262 square miles of cattle run. The biggest Merino sheep stud in the world is in N.S.W., where about 70,000 sheep run on 240,000 acres of land.

To-day, the big graziers have comfortable homesteads with electricity generating plants, running water, cooking stoves operating on " bottled " gas, and other modern equipment. Most stations run several cars and many have aeroplanes. When the grandfathers of the present graziers established their stations, they probably began with a few head of stock. Their womenfolk washed and cooked and made their own bread; they carried water in buckets from wells or casks; they baked and bottled and also looked after live-stock. When supplies could not get through, they lived for long periods on little more than tea and bread and home-made jam.

Farmers fared the same way, using a single horse to winnow their wheat; neighbours from perhaps fifty miles away would help shear the sheep, and would be helped in their turn. Now, the shearers travel in their own cars and take their own cooks with them; they use electric shearing machines and have forgotten the hard but splendid past, when men fought and won their homes from the difficult earth with the help of their women and their children. In the lean times, so much molasses was eaten by farmers' families

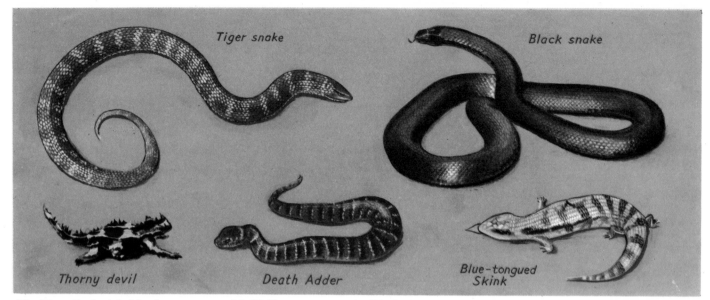

The Tiger Snake inhabits dry country and is highly venomous; the Black Snake is also poisonous and grows to about 7 feet long; the Death Adder, also known as Deaf Adder because of its habit of lying still until trodden on, is also poisonous. The Thorny Devil, a lizard of the desert areas, lives on ants. Another inhabitant of desert regions is the blue-tongued skink.

that it is still called " Cocky's Joy," because the small farmers were known as cockies.

Cattle produce many things in addition to beef, including milk, butter and cheese. The hides are turned into leather, and the skimmed milk is used for feeding pigs. The foremost breeds of cattle are Herefords, Shorthorns and Polled Angus. Cattlemen are now experimenting with zebu-cattle crosses, which withstand tick and will graze through the heat of the day, putting on beef quickly. The two most favoured cross-breeds of this kind are the Santa Gertrudis, from the King Ranch in America, and Australia's own breed, the Drought-master.

The Australian Aborigine is a fine horseman and an expert at working cattle. In the north, he drives the great herds to the Channel Country to fatten. White and black and red beasts pour over the plains in a great flood, dominated by a handful of stockmen. The cattle fill the burning air with their moaning cries, which sounds for all the world like the murmur of a great sea.

In 1967, there were about 18,270,000 cattle and 164,237,000 sheep, many of them Merinos, in Australia. Nearly two hundred years ago, Merinos were introduced to the country by Captain Waterhouse; he brought in thirteen Cape Merinos, for which he paid four guineas a head. This was the beginning of Australia's wool industry. Captain J. Macarthur bought some of these Merinos and his interest in his Merino stud brought dividends for Australia.

WOOL EXPORT

Sheep established Australia in the world's markets; wool is her finest export. Long ago, the fine quality of Australia's merino wool was recognised by the experts of Yorkshire's great textile industry. Macarthur may have been an arrogant man—he quarrelled bitterly with the then Governor Bligh—but his experiments in sheep-breeding, begun in 1791, paid off handsomely in quality and weight of wool by 1803.

To-day, cattle and sheep are both being bred to flourish in their tough environment. Science helps the settlers to wage unceasing war on pests such as the blowflies which cause great losses in sheep. Merinos, bred with deep folds in their hides to increase the wool-producing area, offered

a wonderful opportunity to the blowflies which laid their eggs in the folds. The maggots burrowed into the flesh, the fleece was damaged, and eventually the sheep died. Geneticists (experts on breeding) bred the skinfolds out of the sheep, and the blowflies lost their cosy breeding grounds.

Wool used to be shipped to England for sale, but in 1843 wool auctions were held in Sydney and later in other States. The first Commonwealth wool, 175,400 pounds of it, was exported to England in 1821. Nine years later, export wool weighed two million pounds. In 1967, the value of the wool exported from Australia was about £400,000,000.

Prosperity and security are things for which Australians must work. Eleven million people spread over Australia's empty spaces are not enough. If Australia is to develop her full potential, she must expand her population, but there are many problems. More water is needed, for example, if food production is to keep pace, and industry to expand. Science, which has already done so much for Australia, must play an even more vital role in the years to come.

GROWTH OF INDUSTRY

Wool-production, grain-growing and dairying are three of the great industries. Wheat is Australia's most valuable crop, which is exported to the United Kingdom and to Asia. Rice, sugar-cane and tobacco are smaller, but important, crops. Fruit is exported in increasing quantities, much in the form of dried and canned fruits, jams and juices. These are all products of a soil that first came under the plough only a little more than a century and a half ago.

In 1911, there were 368,000 people working in Australian industry. In 1967, there was a total work-force of more than 4,000,000, producing machinery, textiles, chemicals, dyes, paints, paper, foods and many other commodities for home and for export.

Science and technology are carrying the world rapidly into the space age, and Australia is playing a vital role in the exciting field of space research. In South Australia, the little town of Woomera has had a rapid rise to fame. Its name is apt; it is the Aboriginal word for a throwing stick that increases the flight of a hunting spear. In 1946, Woomera became the site of a rocket range which extends over desert land for a thousand miles north-west, followed by two thousand miles of Indian Ocean. Great missiles now soar over waste land where the Myalls still live as their Stone Age ancestors lived. The shadows of huge rockets have now replaced the shadows of the hunting eagles that once sped over the sandy wastes of salt bush and stunted shrubs.

Woomera is a neat, pleasant town supplied by water brought through 400 miles of pipeline from the River Murray. Salisbury is another town forming part of the Woomera administration, and Maralinga (meaning " thunder " in the Aboriginal language) is part of the testing ground. These names, which meant little to the world less than 20 years ago, are now familiar to all who are taking part in the great venture into space.

SNAKE-MILKING

Australia has a hundred and forty species of snakes, but few people die of snakebite; many city dwellers have never seen a snake. Among the most venomous snakes are taipans, unwelcome migrants from Malaya; brown snakes, possessing short fangs which inject the most lethal venom known; death-adders and others. Snake-catchers take their bag to laboratories where the snakes are " milked " of their venom by being allowed to strike at rubber-topped glass beakers. It takes seventy-seven brown snakes to fill a small beaker to a depth of two inches with the deadliest venom known. Serum is made from the venom, and is used for treating people bitten by snakes. This is is a big step forward from the days, not so long ago, when bushmen would cut out the fang-marks, pack the wound with gunpowder and put a match to it.

In the tropical north, deadly sea-snakes are a menace to pearl-divers. Serum is now available for the treatment of a diver who is bitten. The highly-coloured sea-snakes are savage and deadly in the sea, but do not bite when taken out of the water.

Australian Aborigines, most primitive of men, have made their contribution to science with a narcotic they call " pituri " obtained from a small shrub. The wild men chew it, and they also dip their spear-heads in it to stupefy the fish they hunt. During the war when drugs were in short supply, chemists made seasick pills and other tranquillisers from pituri.

ARTS FLOURISH

A hard-won civilisation would be a poor thing if it resulted only in commercial advancement. Australians, endowed with great energy and adaptability, take a keen interest in the arts. They are twelve thousand miles from the old and basic arts of Europe, but are more inclined to be " doers " than " lookers-on ".

Dame Nellie Melba and Joan Sutherland are only two of the great singers that Australia has produced. The Australian Robert Helpmann has become a famous name in modern ballet. John Antill's native ballet, "Corroboree", is only one of the successful productions of the National Ballet Company. It is an elegant interpretation of the true corroboree, performed by tall black men painted with ochre and the scrapings from the white bark of ghost-gums; this ballet is danced to the accompaniment of the didgeridoo, a long wooden trumpet, and the thumping of sticks on logs. The Arts Council organises seasonal tours of ballet, opera and drama.

One hundred and fifty years ago, art in Australia consisted of Aboriginal designs scratched on stones or on rocky surfaces. This primitive Aboriginal art has now developed into the great work of modern artists such as Albert Namatjira, a full-blood Aborigine of the Arunta tribe who died in 1959, and of other native painters.

There is a richness about modern artists such as Dobell with his strange portraits, and Russell Drysdale whose paintings show the harsh, incomparable beauty of wild landscapes. Sidney Nolan, with his intense romantic feeling for his homeland, is as famous abroad as he is in his native land.

Poets such as Christopher Brennan, Judith Wright, Kenneth Slessor, and Douglas Stewart (who is novelist, critic and dramatist as well), are among many who have become internationally known. No longer does the Australian lyre have to be " strung with horse-hair ".

Writers of a hundred years ago included Henry Kingsley and Marcus Clarke. Born in 1870, Henry Handel Richardson, author of the trilogy " The Fortunes of Richard Mahoney " is often regarded as Australia's greatest writer. Since the 1940s, many Australian writers have become world famous; Chester Wilmot, Patrick White, Alan Moorehead, Christina Stead, Russell Braddon, Katherine Prichard, Miles Franklin and many others, have achieved distinction through their work.

Artists depend for support upon the flourishing commercial and economic life of the community in which they work. And Australia, with great industries like shipbuilding, engineering, chemistry and oil refining is in a position to sustain a flourishing culture. To-day, this great country has become one of the great modern nations of the civilised world. Yet development has been so fast that there are still plenty of people who remember the hard Australian pioneering days. Communications, water conservation, transport, agriculture, housing, shipbuilding and chemistry are only about a century away from message sticks, water soaks, camel pads, yam patches, bark huts, pituri-tipped spears and sailing ships. Australia is a thriving, modern country whose prosperity grows as its population increases. Its people can claim with pride that their young nation has advanced along the path of true civilisation.

The Commonwealth Observatory is at Mount Stromlo, near Canberra in Australia. It has a 74-inch reflecting telescope, the largest in the Southern Hemisphere.

PRINTING AND THE PRESS

One day, while Gutenberg was watching an artisan cutting some wooden letters it occurred to him that he could compose the letters in the form of words and so make an entire page. Records show that by the early 1440s, Gutenberg, then living in Strasbourg, was experimenting in the art of printing. About ten years later he produced printed copies of a letter written by Pope Nicholas V, copies of which exist to this day. Then, in August, 1456, he completed the famous Gutenberg Bible which consists of 1,282 pages, each of forty-two lines printed in Latin. Meanwhile, Johan Fust, also of Mainz and a former partner of Gutenberg's, had set up a little printing works of his own. Fust's most famous publication was a 350-page Psalter with initial letters in red and blue. It came out just one year after the Bible and is the first book to bear the name of its printer on the title page.

THE FATHER OF ENGLISH PRINTING

The art of printing now spread to France, Italy, Spain and Austria. Its immense possibilities were realised by William Caxton, who held a post on the Continent in the service of Margaret, Duchess of Burgundy, a sister of King Edward IV. The Duchess had asked Caxton to translate a history book about ancient Troy which interested her. It was a long task which caused Caxton's pen to become worn, " his hand weary, his eye dimmed ". So, while living in Cologne in 1471-2, Caxton decided to learn the new technique of printing, and a few years later Margaret was presented with her *Historyes of Troye*. This was the first book to be set in English. It was printed in Bruges, which town Caxton soon left to return to England and establish a press in Westminster. Here he published about one hundred works of varying importance before his death in 1491. One of the most

memorable of these was *The Myrrour Of The World* (1481), and this was the first illustrated book to appear in England. It was intended for all persons who could read, as also were Chaucer's *Canterbury Tales* and Malory's *Morte d'Arthur*, issued in 1484-5. The quality of Caxton's genius was shown by the fact that he worked in the mother tongue of his readers, while the continental printers were all using Latin.

Latin was the language most commonly used in the written manuscripts of that time. Caxton had to translate many of the works he published from this and other languages,

Before the invention of movable type, books were printed by the wooden block process. Short texts and pictures had to be laboriously hand cut. The Chinese were block-printing as early as the 8th century.

The famous Gutenberg Bible was the first book to be printed using movable type. First published about 1456, copies of this famous book still exist to-day.

mainly French and Dutch. Fortunately, he was a good and diligent translator; twenty-four of his publications, some of which were extremely long, were taken from other languages. Each volume bears the initials W.C. on the title page, the rarest of them being worth a small fortune to-day.

Caxton's printing press was a very primitive affair compared with the modern presses of Fleet Street. Built of wood, it was equipped with a screw-press and platen which brought the paper down on to the inked type; a hand operation which would produce at most a thousand sheets a day. These old hand-presses remained in use until the beginning of the last century. It was then that Friedrich Koenig's invention of the flatbed steam-press startled the publishing world. *The Times* of London printed its issue of 29th November, 1814, on one of these machines, describing it as the greatest improvement of its kind since the discovery of the art itself. Cylinder and rotary machines came later, and they were to be followed by those multi-colour presses used in the production of modern illustrated books.

SETTING TYPE BY HAND

In every printing works, large or small, there are two separate departments. One is for composition, and those who work in it are called compositors; the other is where the printing is done. In most cases composition is to-day a mechanical operation.

For hand-set work metallic types made of lead, tin and antimony are used. These are called type letters and they are selected from cases by the typesetter and arranged one by one to form the required words. They include all the letters, numbers, punctuation marks, special rules and blank metal slugs of various widths for making spaces between the lines. The type and spaces, which differ according to the kind of work, are measured in points, each of these units representing one seventy-second of an inch.

Printed type varies in size and form. Each of these different sizes is known as a fount, which is a complete set of all the metal type needed to compose a harmoniously printed page. Even ornaments, floral decorations and little flourishes differ between one fount and another. Their production is the task of special factories known as type foundries.

For commercial printing, hand typesetting has been replaced by machines. Hand setting is still used for display work.

Hand setting is slow and the invention of the linotype machine by Mergenthaler was welcomed by newspaper publishers.

The Monotype machine, operated by compressed air, is composed of two units, the keyboard and the caster.

The page of a hand-set book—and such works are rarely produced to-day—would consist of perhaps 2,000 individual letters all packed closely together in a single tray called a galley. When the page is ready, an inked impression is taken: the galley proof. Its purpose is to show whether mistakes have been made in setting up the type. Should there be any, the compositor has to correct them by picking out the wrong letters and replacing them with the correct ones. A second proof is taken and so on until perfection is attained. The only difference in correcting type is that, with linotype (but not monotype—which casts single characters), a whole line must be replaced instead of a single letter.

TYPESETTING MACHINES

Typesetting by hand was used from Caxton's day until the introduction of composing machines in the middle of the last century. The process was slow and tedious—a page or two a day from each compositor—and imposed a severe strain on the eyes and patience of the typesetter. It is now only used for the setting up of special advertisement and publicity matter or display work.

Machines embodying the principles of mechanical composition were invented about a hundred years ago. The most successful of them was developed in the 1880s by a young German immigrant to the United States, Ottmar Mergenthaler. One day in 1886, the inventor was demonstrating the uses of his machine in the offices of the *New York Tribune*. He tapped out a few words, and a slug of metal type of the same width as a newspaper column fell from his machine. "A line of type!" exclaimed the enthusiastic editor, and the new word "linotype" was born.

The linotype machine casts the words on slugs of hot metal which are assembled to form a page or newspaper column. The keyboard of the machine looks rather like a gigantic typewriter, on which the operator sits tapping away from his copy. Another machine was invented at about the same time as the linotype; this was the monotype machine which is operated by compressed air and produces a ribbon of paper punched in a pattern which supplies the necessary information for casting the letters.

The monotype and other hot-metal composing machines are, for certain purposes, even more useful than the linotype machine. But it was the linotype that really represented the greatest step in the progress of printing. It reduced publishing costs by doing the work of ten men. And newspapers, as we know them to-day, owe their origin to the wide use of Mergenthaler's linotype machines, which reached Europe in perfected form in the 1890s.

MODERN PRINTING PRESSES

When the type has been set up by the compositors, it is then used for the actual printing process. The first machine to be used was the old hand-press, which probably developed from the presses used in Southern Europe for crushing grapes when making wine. Printing devices of this type continued in fairly common use until the beginning of the present century and are even found in small printing works to this day.

The old hand-press left its imprint on only one side of the paper. What was obviously needed was a machine capable of printing both sides at once, and this came with the invention of the cylinder press. This was the invention of

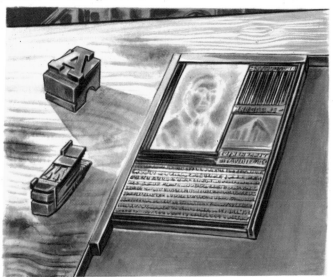

Blocks and type, assembled in a frame called a chase, show the production at page-proof stage.

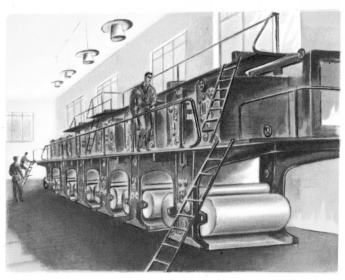

At one time, rotary presses were used exclusively for newspaper printing. Books can now be printed by this method.

Friedrich Koenig, whose firm, Koenig and Bauer, still manufacture printing machinery in Germany to-day. The merit of the cylinder press was that a cylinder revolving over a flat, moving bed could now make an inked impression on both sides of the sheet. Hence the name flat-bed cylinder press. This discovery made possible the cheap printing of popular books in large numbers, and the works of Sir Walter Scott, Dickens, Thackeray and other Victorian novelists were enabled to reach a very wide public.

Another great development took place in 1869, when *The Times* of London was printed on a continuous roll of paper from stereotypes which fitted over the revolving cylinders of the printing machine. This was the prototype of the great rotary presses that now turn out millions of printed and folded newspapers at all hours of the day and night. Modern improvements have adapted them for colour printing, a separate curved plate being necessary for every additional colour impression. Rotary presses run at an immense speed and can consume up to twenty miles of paper an hour.

FINAL EDITION

The work of newspaper offices, from the editorial department to the stereotyping room, where the curved plates are cast in molten metal, is all geared to the speed and productive capacity of monster printing presses. Newspapermen must work at high speed to keep pace with the hungry machines. Reports are phoned to the editorial offices, typed out, cut to appropriate length by sub-editors, and enlivened with headlines. The copy, as it is called, passes on to the copytaster, who assesses its news value. It is then set, proofed, and corrected, after which a stereotype is made and the curved plates are cast in page form. Meanwhile the rotary machines are waiting impatiently for the latest items of news which are to appear in their final edition.

Modern newspaper publishing represents a pinnacle in the development of the art of printing: an art which started with the calligraphers of ancient China and wood block engravers of Caxton's days. Its benefits have been incalculable, for it has enabled man to acquire a knowledge of the world and its happenings which our medieval forefathers did not have. By bringing education within the reach of all, the printed word has stimulated us to new thoughts, new ideas and new aspirations.

THE ART OF BOOKBINDING

How seldom we really think about the familiar objects that we use from day to day. Take books, for example. This book you are reading is only one of tens of millions that are produced every year. Have you ever wondered how a book like this is made?

The pages of a book are printed as large sheets, which are folded to form sections of perhaps 16 pages. These sections are then collected in the proper order, and must be held together permanently and enclosed in protective covers. This is the basis of the ancient craft of bookbinding, which has been in existence since the days before paper was used for keeping written records.

Books are bound not only to keep the pages firmly together in their proper places, but to give the book itself a neat and handsome appearance. Books must be clothed, as we are, in a manner which is decent, respectable and at the same time pleasing to the eye. More attention used to be paid to the artistic side of bookbinding than is now the case. Designers, engravers, artists and jewellers would all contribute their skills to the binding of books, and the results would often rank as works of art. Some bookbinders would even add their signature or cipher to a work of distinction, and such books are now treasured as much for their appearance as for their contents.

Bookbinding has a long and interesting history of which few people are aware. It dates back to the earliest days of the written word, to a time before books began to take the place of parchment rolls. The word then used for a collection of written sheets was *volumen*, which means a scroll. We find the same term in the word " evolution ", which really means an " unrolling "; it comes from the Latin verb *volvere* to " roll ". To preserve them, old papyrus scrolls were sometimes sewn together and pressed between two wooden boards. The Romans stored their documents in

this way, but when the material was of special importance they gave it a better binding. It was the custom of the Roman emperors, for example, to send their provincial governors four volumes of instructions bound in leather and adorned with metal clasps.

For longer works, a form of binding called the " codex " came into use at the beginning of our era. Christianity did not spread only by word of mouth; the writings of the fathers of the Church were bound together as rough books, the sheets being written on both sides (this was not the practice with pagan scrolls). Parchment or vellum was used for the pages, and since this material is extremely durable a number of examples of the codex still exist. Among the most famous are the *Codex Vaticanus* and the *Codex Alexandrinus* of the fourth and fifth centuries A.D. Another is the *Codex Sinaiticus* which was bought in 1933 from the Russian Government, and is now in the British Museum. It cost £100,000 and, like the other two mentioned above, is written in Greek.

So bound, manuscript copies of the Gospels and missals containing the services of the Church existed at the time of St. Augustine. One of these is to be seen at Monza, near Milan, in northern Italy. This volume forms part of the treasured relics of Queen Theodelinda, who ruled over Lombardy in A.D. 600. The binding is set with cameos, precious stones and decorations in gold. It is the oldest known book to be presented in this style. If any books of this type existed before, they were probably stripped of their precious covers and destroyed in times of war and revolution.

Throughout the Dark Ages, western culture was kept alive by religious communities and powerful princes. These custodians of civilisation maintained scribes to copy and illustrate the scriptures, and artists to bind them into volumes. Sheets of embossed ivory, gold and silver were sometimes

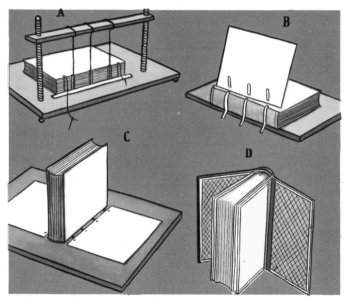

The sections are sewn together (*A*), boards are added (*B*) and the book covered and decorated (*C*, *D*).

Modern machinery has now replaced the older, more expensive hand-binding methods shown above.

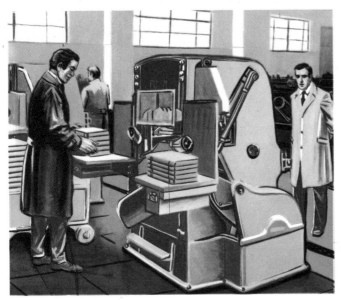

A modern cutting machine is used for trimming the three open sides of the quires.

The hard, board covers of the book are covered in fabric and glued into place, and the spine strengthened with a paper strip.

used for this purpose. A splendid specimen of this type of work is the *Gospels of Charlemagne* which were bound in beechwood overlaid with gold. Gems and rare enamel-work adorn the exterior.

Printing had not yet been invented, but the number of manuscript books in existence was quite large. The most economical way of binding them was to enclose the sheets between two wooden panels. Sometimes these panels were given to artists to paint with beautiful miniatures relating to the contents of the book. A number of these, now preserved in Siena, were painted by the great Italian artist Duccio di Buoninsegna; they provide a valuable pictorial record of life in his day. As time went on, it became the custom to cover these boards with tooled leather. Embossed figures were cut in wood, and the leather, well soaked, was pressed over the dies until it took their shape. It was then glued to the panels between which the leaves of the book were held.

While the art of leather binding was still developing, the practice of using fine velvet and damasks came in. The works of Latin and Greek authors were often bound in this form. Some of these volumes were fitted with gold clasps. Of all the materials available, leather was to prove the best, and with the invention of printing it became an essential item in book production. It was obvious that books would now be made in greater numbers, and craftsmen vied with one another in producing fine leather bindings.

RARE LEATHER BINDINGS

Venice was one of the great European centres of the craft of leather making. The commercial prosperity of the city acted as a strong stimulus to the arts, and did much to foster the Italian Renaissance. Venetian wealth had been built up over a long period of trade with East Mediterranean countries. The people of Venice had always been quick to absorb artistic techniques from those with whom they traded. It was from the Near East that they learned the art of gold-tooling, which is seen on the leather bindings of many old books.

To make these rich bindings, patterned dies were dipped into a small quantity of heated gold and then stamped on to the leather. A similar technique was used by the Moors of

Cordoba in Spain for decorating Moroccan goatskin; it gave rise to the term "Moroccan" binding. This method was adopted in Naples, whose craftsmen were called upon by Matthias I of Hungary—then considered the greatest king in Europe—to bind a large collection of books in his library at Budapest.

Meanwhile, Venetian leather bindings were becoming well known all over western Europe. This was largely due to Aldus Manutius, whose famous aldine bindings were bordered with golden friezes in the Renaissance style. Gold-tooled bindings executed "in the Venetian manner" were made in England by Thomas Berthelet for King Henry VIII. In France, the royal court also had its own bookbinders, and they excelled in producing designs of great elegance for Francis I and Henri II. One design, famous during the reign of Louis XIV, featured a large rose in the centre, four smaller roses in the corners, a lace pattern round the edges, all stamped in gold on the finest leather.

BOOKS ARE STILL HANDSOME

By 1600, the great days of Italian bookbinding were over. France had won a reputation in this field which she never lost, although gold-tooled leather was in growing demand among the nobility of England. Samuel Mearne, who bound books for Charles II, was perhaps the best-known English designer. It was he who introduced the "cottage" design, specimens of which are now greatly treasured. Other names associated with fine English bindings are those of Roger Payne, who worked at the end of the eighteenth century, and William Morris, the Victorian poet and artist, who owned the Kelmscott Press.

Since then, a modern English school of bookbinding has grown up, and its influence on this branch of the decorative arts has been considerable. But the products of these dedicated bookbinders are only a trickle compared with the flood of cloth-bound and paper-back books that now pour from the presses. Leather-bound volumes go mainly to collectors, or are used as presentation copies.

The production of books in everyday bindings is now a mechanical operation, carried out with the help of ingenious machines.

BOOTS AND SHOES

As man broke away from his wild beginnings, and set out on the long road towards a civilised existence, he looked for ways of protecting his body from heat and cold and from damage by the rough terrain in which he lived. He began wearing simple clothes in the form of animal skins; and he devised simple methods of protecting his feet from stones and thorns, and the bites of vicious insects. Rough-hewn pieces of wood, strips of tree bark, and crude soles cut from the hide of an animal: these were the raw materials from which primitive footwear was made.

The Chinese had developed the art of shoemaking to a high degree at a time when our ancestors in Europe were wearing simple clogs or pattens fastened to the feet by leather bands. Decorative sandals made in the Far East five thousand years ago are still providing inspiration for shoe-designers to this day.

THE FOOTWEAR OF THE GREEKS

The ancient Greeks, who favoured the simple life, wore shoes that were both practical and elegant. Most popular of all was the sandal, which was at first worn only by women. Later, the Greeks developed a shoe in which the leather was drawn over the back of the heel and the sides of the feet. This led in turn to ankle boots which gave greater support and protection to the foot, and to military boots in which the soles were studded with nails.

Women's footwear became more colourful and elegant, especially in the province of Lydia. Red- and purple-dyed leather, raised soles and metal buckles adorned with precious stones were worn by Greek women who also favoured cork-soled shoes which became known as " squeakers ".

The Greeks were lovers of the theatre, and the actor's dress was part of his stock-in-trade. When acting in a tragedy he wore thick-soled buskins called *cothurni*: for comedies, he wore the *soccus*, a light shoe or slipper from which comes our own word "sock ". " Sock and buskin " is a very old expression; in Shakespeare's time it was used of the theatrical profession as a whole.

MEDIEVAL SHOE FASHIONS

The character of past civilisations is reflected in the shoes worn by their people. The severity of the Latins of the Middle Ages, the ostentation of the Byzantines of Constantinople, the Teutonic heaviness of northern Europeans and the romantic gaiety of French and English knights of Norman times are clearly seen in the shoes they wore. Compare the hefty jackboots favoured by the Germans, for example, with the delicate, multi-coloured shoes of the easy-going Byzantines.

Footwear is, of course, greatly influenced by climate. Sandals originated in the sunny countries of the Mediterranean. Galoshes, mentioned in Chaucer, were invented by the French; the original galoshes were made of wood thick enough to keep the feet out of the mud. The Slavs once favoured shoes with wooden crosspieces, which gave added support when walking in the snow. The Italians of the thirteenth century modified this style, adorning the broad wooden toepiece with decorative carvings. Medieval courtiers wore the *poulain* of Polish origin—also known as the *crakow* —holding up its immensely long points with two chains like dog leashes.

At the beginning of the sixteenth century, the rich wore footwear indoors and good, stout hunting-boots outdoors.

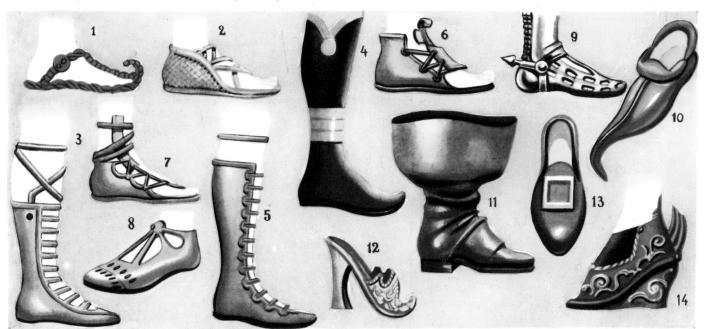

Ancient and medieval footwear: 1. Egyptian; 2. Assyrian; 3. Assyrian; 4. Etruscan; 5. Greek; 6. Greek; 7. Roman; 8. Early Byzantine; 9. 13th century Italian; 10. 14th century Italian; 11. Musketeer's boot; 12. Venetian slipper; 13. French shoe (Louis XVIth); 14. Chinese woman's shoe.

In France, the latter—called *haut de chausses*—were made of leather: full-length for men, and knee-length, with buttons up the sides, for women. In France, too, high, red heels were introduced at the end of the seventeenth century. This was the golden age of Louis XIV, an age which is described as the " red heel " age in many French history books.

During the eighteenth century, the height of men's heels returned to normal. It became the fashion to decorate the uppers with a silver buckle. The women now took a turn at wearing high heels, and Venetian ladies shown in eighteenth-century paintings often seem to be standing on tiptoe. The French Revolution brought drastic changes in fashion. Footwear became practical, and people began wearing boots and shoes, light or heavy according to the season, which were comfortable rather than ornamental.

In the early 1900s new fashions began to appear. Women, in particular, looked for smarter and more stylish shoes, for example with pointed toes. They bought more shoes than ever before, changing them to match their clothes or to keep abreast of current fashion. Production methods, raw materials and machinery changed to meet this growing demand. In the 1930s, for example, a revolutionary new process was adopted, in which the sole was cemented to the upper part of the shoe instead of being stitched.

THE IMPORTANCE OF TANNING

One of the most important things to consider when buying a pair of shoes is the quality of the leather. This depends partly on the region of the animal's hide from which it has been taken, and partly on the way it has been tanned. The aim of tanning is to protect the leather from deterioration and to give it greater strength and flexibility. Several processes are used: vegetable tanning with the extracts of certain trees and plants; tanning with salts and alum; chrome tanning and oil tannage. Methods vary according to the type of leather to be treated, and the tanner must use great skill in deciding how to get the best out of any particular batch of hides.

Hides for the boot and shoe industry come from a wide variety of animals. Soles are made usually from the skins

The basic material for the uppers of shoes is still leather. Here you see one of the processes of tanning leather.

Although the bulk of modern shoes are mass-produced, there is still a place for the maker of hand-made shoes.

of cattle; in special cases, other animals like the buffalo may be used. The uppers, which are usually cowhide, may also be of calf, kid, goat, pony, antelope, reindeer or chamois. Alligator, snake, lizard, kangaroo and shark skins are difficult to obtain in quantity, but are used for making luxury footwear. Good-quality cowhide or calfskin is preferred for normal everyday shoes; in some countries horse-hide and sheepskin are used for rougher wear.

Wherever the hide may have come from it must first be tanned before it is put to practical use. There are special tanning machines for every animal hide, and even for the different qualities and textures of various parts of its skin.

SOME MANUFACTURING PROCESSES

After the leather has been tanned, the uppers are cut and stamped with the numbers of their respective sizes. They are then passed on to the assembly department to be sewn together and to have the linings, facings and eyelets inserted. The next stage is to attach the uppers to the inner soles and the outer soles and, in most shoes, to a strip of leather sandwiched between them to give rigidity and solidity to the shoe. This may be done by machine-stitching, using a curved needle and a strong waxed thread.

Another method is now widely used in the shoe industry, in which a strong adhesive solution of natural or synthetic rubber is used to cement the leather. The cement is spread over the parts to be joined, which are then squeezed together under great pressure. Finally, the heel is added either by cementing or by nailing. Other operations such as trimming, buffing, waxing and polishing complete the process.

You can see that making a shoe is a complicated process; many different skills are involved, and a great variety of machines are used to ensure that every shoe will be of the exact shape and size required.

WHAT SIZE DO YOU TAKE?

The standard sizes of shoes, 8, 8½, 9 and so on, were established by a decree of Edward II in 1324. Someone had found that the length of the largest man's foot was equal to that of thirty-nine barleycorns. Since three barleycorns equalled one inch, it was decided to call the largest size of shoes " thirteens ", and then to work downwards, one barleycorn or one-third of an inch, to each size. This system is still used in Britain and America, but many countries use a different size unit based on two-thirds of a centimetre.

RUBBER
The Most Useful Tree in the World

As you cycle to school, or catch the bus into town, or go for a drive in the family car, do you ever think about the strange material on which you are rolling along, the material we call rubber?

Rubber is such a familiar substance that we tend to take it for granted. Yet it really is extraordinary stuff when you think about it. Consider how you can stretch a rubber band to several times its length, and let it snap back to its original size. What other material will do this?

Think, too, of the way in which a rubber motor-car tyre will absorb the shocks as it runs on the road, and yet retain its shape. Imagine what a state our transport system would be in if we had no rubber for making tyres!

Nowadays, we use some 2 million tons of rubber every year. Some of this huge quantity is made synthetically. But much of it is natural rubber that comes from the sap of certain trees, in the form of a milky fluid called latex. Rubber is found in trees of many species, but commercial supplies of rubber are obtained from a tree called the *Hevea brasiliensis*, a native of the Amazon Valley. When the latex flows from the tree, no actual rubber is to be seen in it. But, as it stands, the latex coagulates to form a dough-like material which is the crude rubber of commerce.

PUSH-BALL WITH THE INDIANS

The peculiar properties of this milky fluid were well known to native Indians, long before the first Spaniards arrived in South America. One day, Spanish soldiers noticed a group of Indians crouching round the trunk of a tall, smooth, grey-barked tree. They were allowing the sap to drip slowly over their limbs, forming a sticky film which they peeled off in threads and wound up in hanks. The Spaniards were curious to know what the Indians used it for, and were greatly amused when, in one of the villages, they discovered a large rubber ball which was used by the Indians for games of push-ball.

The Indians knew how to use latex for waterproofing clothes. They showed the Spaniards how to coat their cloaks with a layer of rubber by smearing latex on the cloth. The waterproofed cloaks were excellent for keeping out the rain, but when the sun came out the rubber melted. The Spaniards found that rubber would burn, and weapons dipped in rubber

In South America, Spanish soldiers noticed that the Indians collected milky fluid from a certain tree.

The process of vulcanisation of rubber was discovered accidentally by Charles Goodyear.

could be hurled as flaming projectiles against an enemy. These discoveries are referred to by a 16th century Spanish author, Fernando de Oviedo y Valdes.

In the 1730s, Charles de la Condamine was sent by the French Government to Peru, on a geographical expedition. Condamine had already seen a specimen of rubber, and was so intrigued by it that he devoted most of his time to searching for the fabulous tree from which it came. His explorations led him into the Amazon Valley, but locating the rubber tree in those vast forests abounding with savage tribes and animals was like looking for a needle in a haystack. Condamine decided on another plan, and went next to French Guiana.

In French Guiana there were then many native Indians who had fled from Portuguese rule in Brazil. Condamine talked to some of them who knew the tree he was looking for. He persuaded the natives to sketch it, made many copies of the drawing and sent these to French agents in all the most likely parts of South America.

Soon, replies were coming in. The rubber tree was well known in several regions, one of them not far distant on the River Maturani. Before long Condamine reported back to France, describing his investigation of the tree, and its strange product, which he called caoutchouc. The natives, he wrote, dip bottle-shaped clay moulds in the latex, allowing a layer of rubber to form on the surface. Then " when the resin is dry they smash the mould, take the pieces of earth out through the neck, and have an unbreakable bottle which is useful for preserving all kinds of liquids." . . . The first rubber hot-water bottle! Condamine's report aroused great interest in Europe. Crude rubber brought home by explorers sold for as much as a guinea an ounce. In 1759, the Brazilian state of Para made a waterproofed rubberised garment which was presented to the King of Portugal.

In 1770, an Englishman called Nairne, who had obtained a small piece of crude rubber, tried mixing it with powdered substances like pumice stone and emery. He was thinking of making it into small bars for cleaning metals. By chance, he tested it on a piece of paper covered with pencil marks. They at once vanished, and the first india-rubbers were soon on the market, selling at five shillings a piece: a large sum in those days. It was in this way that the name " india-rubber " was acquired; it was a material that rubbed out pencil, and it was associated with the Indians of South America.

Rubber was also studied by Joseph Priestley, the discoverer of oxygen, and by Samuel Peal who, in 1793, took out a patent for making fabrics waterproof by coating them with a solution of rubber in turpentine.

At that time many people referred to rubber as " gum ". This is the origin of the term " gum-boots ", for the rubber boots which in the 1830s and 1840s were extremely popular with American pioneers. They were made of what we would now call unvulcanised rubber, the sort of rubber used for making crepe soles. One man who saw the immense commercial possibilities of rubber was Charles Goodyear, who had been born in Connecticut in 1800. Goodyear's name is now linked for ever with the rubber industry, through his efforts to find a way of treating rubber so that it would remain tough, flexible and resistant to the effects of heat.

THE SECRET OF VULCANISATION

Goodyear faced formidable difficulties. Without any real knowledge of chemistry, and no money to support his family, he was ill-equipped for a long and unrewarding period of research. But he persisted until, at last, by a combination of good luck and hard work, he achieved success. Goodyear's discovery of the process we now call vulcanisation was an accidental one. A rubber sack intended to be used as a mail bag fell on to the kitchen stove and burst into flames. The room was filled with foul-smelling fumes, and Goodyear threw the burning material out of the window. Next morning, he picked it up and found that the rubber had lost its stiffness. It was more flexible, more springy; the heat of the stove had caused a reaction between the rubber and the sulphur with which it had been mixed. It had become vulcanised by the process that we now use in the manufacture of virtually all rubber products, from the production of motor-car tyres to football bladders. Charles Goodyear in America and Thomas Hancock in England patented the vulcanisation process in the early 1840s.

Rubber vulcanisation consists essentially of heating the raw rubber with sulphur, usually in the presence of other substances. It made possible the commercial development of the rubber industry on a huge scale, and this in turn stimulated the production of natural rubber. It is estimated that in Asia alone there are now about two and a half million people earning their living in rubber plantations. The largest plantations are in Malaya, Ceylon and Indonesia. Others are to be found in India, Borneo, Sarawak, Thailand and Indo-China. The trees in these plantations came originally from seeds brought by Sir Henry Wickham from Brazil. The seedlings were raised in Kew Gardens, then shipped to Ceylon, where they flourished. Soon, it became possible to extend their cultivation to many countries in the Far East.

TAPPING THE RUBBER TREE

Work in a rubber plantation starts at the crack of dawn. The men arrive with buckets, sharp knives and tapping cups or small bowls. They cut the bark slantwise at heights up to about six feet. This requires great skill, as the latex tubes must be opened without the wood being penetrated. If

Pictured above are some of the many products of a rubber factory: toys, balls, tyres, wellington boots, raincoats, sou'westers and lifebelts.

this should happen, the bark takes much longer to heal. The bowl is then placed at the bottom of a groove into which flows the milky fluid that oozes from the latex vessels. Slowly, it drips into the bowl, which is emptied periodically into a bucket. The buckets of latex are then taken to the estate factory, where the latex is coagulated into crude rubber. This is passed through a mill like a huge old-fashioned mangle, forming sheets which are dried and wrapped in bales of about two hundredweights each for shipment.

The method described is used on big rubber plantations in the East. In the Amazon regions, an older and more picturesque technique is practised.

EVERYONE'S SHOCK ABSORBER

Rubber is made into thousands of different products, and it is difficult to think of a modern industry that does not use rubber in one way or another. Tyres, boots, crêpe-soled shoes, toys, balloons and rubber bands are familiar, everyday examples of rubber products. Sports equipment, groundsheets, hosepipes, bottle rings and housewives' gloves are things we use every day. Rubber belts are used for driving machines, and for conveying all manner of raw materials. Apart from tyres, rubber goes into cars, vans and lorries in many different forms.

Your raincoat may have been waterproofed with rubber, just as the cloaks of the Spaniards were hundreds of years ago. You probably sleep on a mattress of foam rubber, and wear rubber boots when you walk in the rain. It is extraordinary, isn't it, when you think that all this began when a milky liquid ran out of a tree!

THE BICYCLE

Almost every boy and girl in every country of the world must have longed to own a bicycle. This wonderful machine, simple, efficient, cheap to run and easy to look after, opens up the world to our exploration. With a bike, we are free to ride a couple of hundred yards to the nearest shop, or take a much longer journey around the countryside.

By riding a bicycle, we learn the road sense that will stand us in good stead when we begin to drive a car. A bike is many things to most of us; it is a handy form of transport, and a form of exercise; it is the basis of an exciting sport, and the means of seeing how the rest of the world lives.

The " steel horse ", as the bicycle was called in the days of its greatest popularity, is to-day a most important form of transport. In many countries, special tracks are provided alongside the roads for the exclusive use of cyclists. It has taken many years for the importance of cycling to be fully appreciated, for the bicycle was not born in a day. Like so many other devices of our modern age, it reached its present state of perfection by slow degrees.

HOBBY-HORSES

It is impossible to name any one person as the inventor of the bicycle. The machine, as we know it, is really a descendant of the old hobby-horse, a primitive model of which was constructed in France by M. de Sivrac. In the Buckinghamshire village of Stoke Poges, where Thomas Gray the poet is buried, one of these contraptions is to be seen in a stained-glass window of the church. Perhaps the designer of the window had been to Paris and seen M. de Sivrac, or M. Ozanam, a professor at the Sorbonne University, experimenting with simple two-wheelers in the 1690s.

The hobby-horse made little progress until the beginning

In 1815, Karl Drais added handle-bars and a saddle to the hobby-horse and called it a draisine.

As the boneshaker, or velocipede, developed, the front wheels became larger, sometimes as much as five feet in diameter, with a corresponding reduction in the rear wheels to as. little as twelve inches.

of last century, when a German land-surveyor named Karl Drais added handlebars, a padded seat and other improvements. The people of Mannheim, where the machine first appeared in 1815, called it the " draisine ". They were greatly amused by its inventor's antics, but everyone was impressed when he rode from Karlsruhe to Strasbourg in four hours— a quarter of the time that it took on foot.

These hobby-horses had no pedal or other device for propulsion. Except when going downhill, they had to be pushed along with the feet. They attracted the attention of the London " bucks " of Byron's day, who christened them dandy-horses. The machines were bought from Dennis Johnson in Long Acre, who supplied one to the Prince Regent in about 1818. The best that can be said of these clumsy and expensive toys is that they gave their owners plenty of exercise.

FIRST BICYCLE SHOP

The next stage in the development of the bicycle took place in Scotland, where two enterprising young men added pedals, crank shafts and other devices to the old dandy-horse. Kirkpatrick MacMillan and Gavin Dalzell were the true pioneers of the bicycle, and MacMillan even earned the distinction of being fined for " furious driving " on the roads around Dumfries. Between them, these two Scotsmen were responsible for most of the progress made in bicycle design between 1840 and 1865. In the latter year, a Frenchman named Pierre Lallement, who worked for M. Michaux in Paris, built the first velocipede with rotary cranks attached to the front wheel. A smaller wheel followed behind. Bicycles of this type were soon selling in M. Michaux's shop at 29 Avenue Montaigne—the first bicycle shop in the world—for 200 francs apiece. Lallement, who

The first safety bicycle had rear wheel drive and wheels of nearly equal size, and was perfected by J. K. Starley.

sold his patent to his employer, went off to develop the business in the United States.

THE PERILOUS " PENNY-FARTHING "

The Industrial Revolution was at its height in the middle of last century. Iron had become the most important metal for the construction of machinery, and it was natural that M. Michaux should use it in his bicycles. Some of the frames were made for him in Coventry, and when the Franco-Prussian war broke out the firm concerned was left with 500 of them on their hands. Their sale in England stimulated new interest in the bicycle and manufacturers now produced the strangest-looking juggernaut ever ridden by man.

In this weird machine, the diameter of the front wheel was increased to four feet, then five feet, and more, while the back wheel diminished in size to that of a small pram wheel. It looked like a farthing chasing a penny, and our great-grandfathers called it the " penny-farthing ". The wheels of these bicycles were little more than iron hoops, and they bumped sickeningly over the rough roads of the pre-tarmac era. Solid rubber tyres were fitted, but these did little to increase the comfort of the rider. It could not have been pleasant to be pedalling along high above the ground, with the chance of flying head over heels into the hedge every time the front wheel hit a stone or pot-hole. The rider had to be an acrobat and an athlete to stay in the saddle. Even so, the expert could attain a speed of twenty miles an hour—and more downhill. Such was the bicycle of the 1870s and early '80s before the " safety " model came along.

THE " SAFETY " MODEL

Several attempts had been made, especially in France, to build a " safety " bicycle. But the first machine which really merited the name was built and sold by two Englishmen, Starley and Sutton of the Rover Company, in 1885. With wheels of nearly equal size, a crossbar and tubular framework, it was a crude version of the modern machine. Moreover, the pedal, chain and cogwheel were now used together for the first time. The new two-wheeler created a tremendous sensation; by 1893, only seven years after the " safety " bicycle appeared, nine out of ten models shown at British exhibitions were of this type.

Early " safety " bicycles had certain defects compared with later ones. They were heavy and tiring to pedal, the cogwheels wore out quickly, and the rims bumped uncomfortably on the unmetalled roads of the day. One of the biggest problems was overcome by John Boyd Dunlop of Belfast, who invented the pneumatic tyre. With W. du Cros, Dunlop started manufacturing his revolutionary tyre on a large scale in 1890. This, too, created a sensation. Within five years, solid tyres had disappeared, and 90 per cent. of all bicycles were fitted with " Dunlops ". The remainder were equipped with cushion tyres which enjoyed a brief spell of popularity. By the turn of the century the main features of the bicycle as we know it to-day, including the use of ball bearings in the wheel hubs, had been firmly established.

THE BICYCLE INDUSTRY DEVELOPS

In the manufacture of bicycles, Britain was at a great advantage. Many of the patents were in the hands of British firms. The technical skill and raw materials needed for their manufacture—apart from rubber—were readily available. Immense numbers of machines were built in Britain, both for home consumption and for export, during the first half of the twentieth century. As production expanded, it became the practice to make the different parts of the bicycle in different factories, each specialising in its own particular type of work.

Cold-drawn steel tubing for the frame would be made at one factory, ball bearings at a second and handle-bar lengths at a third. These and other parts would be ordered by the bicycle manufacturers, who would then use them to produce a machine of their own general design. The tubes would be cut, fitted with angle joints and brackets and welded into a frame. Bending machines would be used to shape the handlebars and some parts of the frame, expecially on women's bicycles. With many of the parts arriving at the factory ready-made, the bicycle manufacturer's main job was to assemble, finish and test the machine. Mass production had begun.

Over the years, great advances have been made in bicycle construction. The frames are better designed and much

J. B. Dunlop helped to make cycling even more popular with his invention of the pneumatic tyre.

An important annual event in the calendar of the cycle-racing enthusiast is the Tour de France. *Held over a course of some 2,782 miles of mountains and valleys, this takes a cyclist 25 days to complete.*

lighter than they used to be. Hub or coaster brakes, less likely to cause a skid, have replaced the rim and calliper brakes of older models. Oil and acetylene lamps were abandoned long ago in favour of battery and dynamo lighting. Multiple-gear changes and semi-automatic devices now make cycling a pleasure on all but the steepest hills. The tyres are much lighter than they used to be, and when these are cemented to the rim, as on racing models, the cyclist thinks nothing of carrying the entire feather-light spare wheel.

As a result of these improvements, cycling has grown in popularity in many parts of the world. Despite the vast numbers of cars, motor-cycles and scooters that are now on the road, millions of men and women still go to work every day on their bicycles. This is particularly so in countries like Holland and Denmark where hills are few and far between. In the agricultural districts of Europe the bicycle is widely used, and it is an uncanny experience to drive through the French and Italian countryside in the early hours of the morning, when peasants and farmworkers are pedalling silently out to the fields. The developing countries, too, are great bicycle-users; thousands of machines are to be seen in the young countries of Africa and Asia, where the bicycle provides a cheap and handy means of transport.

CYCLING AS A NATIONAL SPORT

Sport and recreation have been well served by the bicycle. This was foreseen more than eighty years ago when the British cycling organisations, C.T.C. and N.C.U. were set up. The latter was the first to erect danger signs on the roads, and both did much to improve the lot of touring cyclists. Bodies of this kind have always interested themselves in cycle racing, more especially the Union Cycliste Internationale which operates on the Continent, where people regard cycling as one of the leading sports. Most west European countries go in for track racing, and the world championships are held under the direction of the U.C.I. But the greatest cycle race in the world to-day is undoubtedly the *Tour de France* which has been held every summer since 1903, except during the war years. The *Tour de France* lasts twenty-five days, covers a distance of 2,800 miles, and takes competitors from Paris to the Pyrenees and back via the Swiss border. Political and other events lose their importance during this marathon,

as anyone knows who has been in France at the beginning of July. A similar race, the *Giro d'Italia*, is run every summer in Italy where enthusiasm for cycle racing of this sort is intense.

SIX-DAY TRACK RACING

As with motor racing, track and road trials have been of the greatest importance in developing the bicycle to its present state of perfection. In 1940, Raymond Bryan rode the 3,149 miles from New York to San Francisco in 27 days 11 hours. During the previous decade, six-day track races had been immensely popular in New York, Chicago and other American cities. Everything possible was done to produce bicycles which were fast and light, with gears providing maximum efficiency on all gradients. In those years, the modern racing " bike ", weighing a mere fifteen or sixteen pounds, was developed. Compared with the " crocks " of last century it was a precision instrument. But it is worth remembering that it was on one of those " crocks " that the first mile-a-minute record was set up. Charles Murphy reached this speed riding behind windshields on a Long Island track in 1899.

A GOOD COMPANION

The bicycle may be a simple device compared with the motor-cycle or the car, but it remains a vital cog in the world's transport system. It has given millions of people their first taste of speed. It has taught many of us the meaning of *road sense*. It takes us to school and to work in all weathers.

In Britain to-day there are as many bicycles as there are cars. The mechanisation of transport has not diminished the popularity of the humble bicycle. It is still ideal for short journeys where the car or motor bicycle may be nothing but a nuisance. And it does many of us a lot of good to get a spell of regular exercise.

A cycle ride sets the blood tingling in the veins; it brings the sweat to the brow; it builds up muscle and fills the lungs with fresh, sweet air. Poets have written of the joys of cycling. If you would like to share their inspiration, to catch the thrill that they expressed in beautiful words, just go for a ride in the country and see what freedom a bicycle gives you as you coast down a long, steep hill.

ALUMINIUM – THE LIGHT METAL

For many thousands of years man has been extracting metals from the earth in ever-increasing variety and quantity. The discovery and use of new metals have become important landmarks in the progress of civilisation.

The Stone Age was followed first by the Copper Age and then by the Bronze Age; after a long period, these were succeeded by the Iron Age. Steel came much later; it was not produced on an industrial scale until little more than a hundred years ago. Iron and its alloy steel are still our most important constructional metals. But in recent years, they have been joined by many others which are playing an increasingly important part in our modern world. Among these are the *light metals*, of which the best known is aluminium.

WHAT IS ALUMINIUM?

Exceptionally light and of a shiny greyish-white colour, aluminium is one of the most abundant elements in the earth's crust. But we do not find it in the form of the metal itself. Gold is found in the sand of some river beds, and the tiny particles are recognisable as the gold we all know. Aluminium, on the other hand, occurs most frequently as an oxide present in kaolin, corundum, bauxite, cryolite, leucite, feldspar and certain clays and micas. Deposits of these minerals exist in all parts of the world, but only a few are rich enough in aluminium oxide to make its extraction profitable.

ALUMINIUM ORES

The most important aluminium ores are bauxite, leucite and cryolite, and it is these minerals that industry uses as its raw materials. They are found in abundance in Green-

Aluminium is the third most abundant element on the surface of the earth. It is present in most rocks, animals and vegetation, but is not found as the free metal.

land, the United States, the Ural mountains of Russia, and in France, Italy and several other European countries. Commercial bauxite is also largely mined in Jamaica, Equatorial Africa, the East Indies and Australia.

WORKING THE METAL

Aluminium is a malleable and ductile metal, and is easily worked. It melts at a temperature of about 659°C. By comparison with other metals, like copper, tin and iron, it is very light in weight; pure aluminium weighs only 2·7 grammes per cubic centimetre. Aluminium resists corrosion on exposure to weather, due to the formation of a coating of oxide on the metal's surface, which protects it from further corrosion. It is, however, attacked by hydrochloric acid.

Another useful characteristic of aluminium is that it can be worked hot or cold and, by means of certain techniques, it may be made into sheets of foil measuring as little as one hundred-and-fiftieth part of a millimetre in thickness. Aluminium is also a good conductor of heat and electricity.

HOW ALUMINIUM IS OBTAINED

The discovery and development of aluminium goes back little more than a century. It is generally believed to have been isolated for the first time in 1825 by the Danish physicist Oersted. A method of preparing the metal was invented by Wöhler in 1827. His process was not followed up, however, for another twenty years, when it was perfected by Sainte-Claire Deville who produced aluminium of a fair degree of purity.

A much purer aluminium was needed for the metal to become of industrial importance. And it was not until 1887 that Héroult in France and Hall in the United States invented the electrolytic cell which is still used in the production of aluminium to the required standard of purity.

Bauxite, which is the most common source of aluminium, takes its name from Les Baux in France, the area in which it was first found. Bauxite is mined extensively in tropical regions, but is found also in many other parts of the world. It results from the weathering of many different rock types.

Let us see how the *alumina* obtained from aluminium minerals is used in producing the metal itself.

The industry relies mainly on three processes: *Bayer's*, by which alumina is obtained from bauxite; *Haglund's* which also makes use of bauxite; and *Blanc's*, which is for the production of alumina from leucite.

THE THREE PROCESSES

In the *Bayer Process*, bauxite is crushed and ground and then passed on to an autoclave. Here it is treated under pressure with a concentrated solution of caustic soda. This results in the formation of sodium aluminate, which is then treated with carbon dioxide, or with aluminium hydrate which has already been made. Alumina is formed, and isolated as a precipitate. In the next stage the alumina is mixed with cryolite and placed in special electrolytic cells. It dissolves in the molten cryolite, and is decomposed by the electric current by the process called electrolysis. The molten aluminium which is released sinks to the bottom of the electrolytic cell.

The *Haglund Process* consists of smelting bauxite in electric furnaces with sulphide of iron and carbon. As the mixture melts, metallic iron is formed, and the *alumina* is transformed into aluminium sulphide. Two distinct layers are formed at the bottom of the furnace: the lower layer consists of the heavier ferrosilicon compounds; the upper layer contains *aluminium sulphide* and *crystalline alumina*. The latter is treated with water, when the sulphide reacts leaving a mixed residue of aluminium hydrate and alumina. This residue is dried and then treated in electrolytic cells, as already described.

Blanc's Process makes use of leucite, which is finely ground and placed in tanks where it is subjected to a continuous flow of concentrated hydrochloric acid. The strength of the acid must be sustained, as it is weakened by reaction with the mineral. Hydrates are precipitated, and they are decomposed by electrolysis to release the metal as in the case of bauxite.

It should be noted that all the above processes depend upon an adequate supply of cheap electricity. Without this, aluminium could never have been produced economically in commercial quantities.

ALUMINIUM AND ITS ALLOYS

Aluminium made by the industrial processes just described is not absolutely pure. Impurities such as iron, copper, silica, zinc, titanium and other minerals—differing in proportion depending on the source of the ore—cannot be removed completely from the alumina. Aluminium produced from European ores, for example, commonly contains iron and silica as impurities. Traces of other minerals are also found, but in insignificant quantities.

It is not necessarily desirable that aluminium should be extremely pure for many industrial applications. Certain " impurities " may, in fact, improve the properties of the metal. When highly refined metal is required, for example in electrical applications, the aluminium produced by electrolysis is refined in a special refining cell.

For many industrial purposes, pure aluminium is unsatisfactory, and the properties of the metal can be modified to meet particular requirements. This is done by mixing the aluminium with small quantities of other metals to form an alloy. Aluminium alloys are of great importance to modern industry. Zinc, copper, nickel, manganese and titanium are

The rolling of aluminium hardens the metal, increasing the tensile strength with each successive rolling. Pure aluminium is the easiest form of the metal to work because of its softness and yielding properties. Above is an aluminium rolling mill in operation.

commonly alloyed with aluminium to provide materials suitable for various industrial purposes.

ALUMINIUM IN EVERYDAY LIFE

Aluminium plays an important part in the everyday life of all of us. During the past fifty years this lightweight metal has largely replaced iron and copper as the raw material from which we make our pots and pans and cooking utensils. Aluminium is a familiar metal to the housewife.

But aluminium is not used only for domestic purposes. Its unique properties have brought it into use in many fields of human activity. Electricity, as we have seen, was largely responsible for making the large-scale manufacture of aluminium possible. If electricity was the " father ", aluminium has been a dutiful " son ", for aluminium is second only to copper as a conductor of electricity, and it is widely used in making equipment for power transmission and distribution.

It is difficult to find any branch of engineering that does not make use of aluminium, either as pure metal or as an alloy. It is used in precision instruments, electric motors, cars, ships, aeroplanes and railway rolling stock. Architects and designers use it in construction work and for making home and office furniture. Aluminium has spread far and wide during the present century, bringing lightness and grace in place of the ugliness and crudity that had previously been associated with many consumer goods.

Few people realise that the by-products and compounds of aluminium have many uses too. Alum and aluminium sulphate are used as fertilisers in agriculture, for the purification of drinking water, and in the manufacture of many commodities; paper, abrasives, paints and varnishes, and even explosives. We celebrate Guy Fawkes Day with fireworks containing aluminium compounds. In addition, they are used in tanning and dyeing, and in the processing of waterproof fabrics such as raincoats and groundsheets.

European countries are able to produce all the aluminium that they need, but about half of the total world output is produced in Canada and the United States.

DIVING FOR SPONGES

Harvesting the depths to supply the markets of the world

Free-diving for sponges in calm, or inshore, waters.

Fishing for sponges in deeper water requires more elaborate equipment.

A diver gathering sponges in water too deep for free diving.

Sponges are simple multicellular creatures belonging to a sub-kingdom of animal life known as Metazoa. They are classified in this group under the family name of *Porifera*.

These simple animals we know as sponges grow for all the world like vegetables on the bottom of the sea. A tangle of fibrous branches, formed from a material resembling silk, supports and protects the inner structure of living cells. Tubes and cavities in the sponge form a simple digestive tract through which the animal feeds on bacteria and other tiny organisms suspended in sea water. The digestive processes of the sponge can be seen by feeding a live sponge with coloured substances such as milk. The liquid can be followed as it enters via the pores and passes into a system of thread-like channels and minute cells which trap the food particles.

Sponges multiply by fission, or splitting; some more highly-developed species reproduce by the fertilisation of egg cells.

The sponge fishers of ancient times were usually slaves

The sponges are taken to the surface where they are cleaned.

On shore the sponges are squeezed, rinsed in clear water, and dried in the air.

Most of the sponges for domestic use to-day are made of synthetic materials.

who would dive naked to great depths, tearing and cutting the sponges from the sea bottom. The Eastern Mediterranean is a prolific source of *porifera*, and the vinegar-soaked sponge which a Roman soldier offered to the crucified Christ would have come, almost certainly, from this region. Roman soldiers habitually carried sponges, which they would moisten and chew on long marches in hot weather. The Greeks used sponges dipped in honey as a " comforter " for babies who would not stop crying.

In some parts of the world, sponges are still gathered by naked divers swimming unprotected under water. But this is a risky occupation owing to the effects of water pressure at great depths, and to the danger of attack by sharks, barracudas and other voracious fish. Most modern sponge fishers are equipped with diving suits which enable them to stay submerged for long periods. Individual divers are able to " scout " for sponge banks on the sea-floor, and the discovery of a good crop of sponges is exploited by a team of divers.

Laden with its haul, the sponge divers' boat returns to shore. Here, the divers work through their sponges, stripping off the fibrous structure and squeezing out impurities. After a thorough washing and drying in the sun, the sponges are ready for the market. And it is a market which has been growing rapidly, if only because most motorists like to keep a sponge handy for washing down their car. The type used for this purpose is called the wool sponge. It comes mainly from the Caribbean Sea, which supplies 80 per cent. of the demand in America and Western Europe. But the sponge most favoured for the bath is the the soft, durable sponge of the East Mediterranean, known as " Turkey Toilet ". A good specimen of this sponge will cost two guineas or more.

SAILING SHIPS

If you have sailed a dinghy at the seaside, you will know the wonderful sense of freedom that comes from being carried along by the wind. And you will know too that you cannot relax for an instant when you are under sail. The wind never flows at a steady speed, or from the same direction for very long.

Until a century or so ago, the wind was the "engine" that carried our ships to every part of the world, and the story of the sailing ship is the story of man's efforts to build great ships that could make the most effective use of the ever-changing wind.

On 15th March, 1493, the forty-ton caravel *Nina* tied up in the quiet little port of Palos in south-west Spain. None of the dockers or sailors who were present had any idea what an important occasion it was. No one would have imagined that the log book which the master carried beneath his arm, as he stepped ashore, contained information which would influence the future of navigation and of man's knowledge of the world. The name of the ship's master was Christopher Columbus, and he was just back from his first voyage of discovery to America.

FAIR-WEATHER SHIPS

Until the time of Columbus, the boundaries of the inhabited world had been clearly understood. The sailors of Europe knew the sea routes of the comparatively calm Mediterranean by heart. Their ships were galleys, lateeners, caravels, carracks and other vessels with long-forgotten names. The old Viking tradition had disappeared, and the ships were slow and clumsy. The ships that Columbus used were ill-equipped for long ocean voyages. They were fair-weather ships built for coastal trading, and not for the rough seas of the Atlantic.

As news of the great discovery spread, the effects on shipping must have been eagerly discussed in the ports of London, Lisbon, Genoa, Bristol and Cadiz. It was one thing to design ships to sail in coastal waters, or in the Mediterranean, but quite another thing to build vessels that could make long ocean voyages. Much larger ships would be needed, with three masts or more, and a much greater spread of sail.

THE FIRST GALLEONS

The discovery of the New World gave a great fillip to shipping. New types of ships, like the stately galleons of the sixteenth century, were born. Built entirely of timber, up to one hundred feet in length and forty in the beam, the galleon carried on the poop a quarter deck that was constructed like the wing of a house. This was for the captain and his officers, a tradition maintained in the "admiral's stern walk" of modern battle-cruisers. The galleon bore three masts, main, fore, and mizzen or aftermost mast. In the bows, there was a tower set on a raised deck, providing a base from which to attack and board an enemy ship.

These old galleons look awkward to modern eyes, but they were the most advanced vessels built during the great age of discovery. Armed with cannon peeping from stout wooden hulls, they served both as merchant vessels and as warships.

In those days, the countries of western Europe were engaged in never-ending fights at sea. Moreover, it was more than likely that a cargo ship would be attacked by pirates as she returned, laden with rich cargo, from a long voyage.

THE THREE-DECKERS APPEAR

Until the first galleons were built, sea-going vessels had altered little since the time of the Phoenicians. These older ships were more graceful than the heavy galleon with its cumbersome superstructure and broad beam, and British shipbuilders began to favour a more slender type of three-masted vessel with an improved sail plan. Naval engineers studied the problems of seaworthiness, tonnage, armament and the size of a vessel. They invented the helmsman's wheel, which took the place of the tiller. The masts were heightened and strengthened, carrying sails that could be trimmed to make the most of every breeze that blew. The ship that now appeared on the high seas was the famous three-decker.

Throughout the eighteenth century, British, Spanish, French and Dutch three-deckers and frigates ventured into every sea; they took part in the explorations that opened up the world. This was the golden age of the sailing ship, just as it was of the stage coach on land. Sailmaking became a minor industry, and thousands of acres of linen sailcloth were produced in dockside sail lofts. Main square sails, fore sails, aft sails, triangular lateen and stay sails were tailor-made to the required size by chalking out the pattern on the workshop floor. Cutting, sewing, hemming and reinforcing the points of greatest strain were all done by hand, requiring great patience, thoroughness and skill.

SAILING CONDITIONS

The seaman in those days had to be able to manipulate his sails in every kind of weather. Sailing, which was a relatively

An English sixteenth-century sailing ship of the type similar to those that sailed at the time of Elizabeth I of England. English ships of this period were small and fast.

simple matter in brigs and small schooners, called for increasing skill as frigates, merchantmen and three-deckers grew in size and carried more sail. The sailors lived their lives in a world of their own, with a language of the sea that set them apart from the landlubber. The seaman of the day knew what it was to sail *before* the wind and *by* the wind, *down*, *into*, *near* and *off* the wind. *Up* the wind meant one thing to him, *under* the wind another. The growth of British sea power depended on these seamen of the eighteenth century, who knew how to handle their ships with consummate skill in fair weather and foul.

From the moment she left port, the old sailing ship was at the mercy of the waves. Day and night, the sailor would have to be ready to go aloft to furl or spread a sail as the ship tossed in a heaving sea and the wind tore at the rigging. Down on deck the crew must always be on the alert to brace the yards and trim the sails at every shift and turn of the wind. In a ship of the line, sailors and gunners would work together as the officers brought the vessel into position to fire a broadside into the enemy hulls. Discipline was hard, the pay miserable, and many a man was broken in health by long voyages to tropical climes and disease-infested ports. Yet in spite of it all, the adventurous youth of Britain and western Europe turned eagerly to the sea. Who could resist the lure of the fabulous lands that lay on the other side of the world?

NAVAL AND MERCHANT VESSELS

At the beginning of the eighteenth century, three-deckers were graded first, second and third class. The largest of them, 200 feet in length and weighing up to 6,000 tons, went into battle carrying one hundred pieces of cannon. The frigates, with a maximum displacement of 3,000 tons, carried between thirty and sixty guns. Smaller craft included corvettes, brigantines, cutters: all had one or two masts and a single row of guns to give supporting fire. From 1700 onwards, naval vessels acquired a character of their own and were no longer indistinguishable from merchantmen (as had previously been the case).

Merchant vessels developed along several lines, according to the country of their origin. They were of all types and

The frequent naval battles of the seventeenth century marked the adoption of the frigate as a standard class of vessel. Above is a 32-gun frigate of the late eighteenth century.

Clipper ships were developed principally by American shipbuilders. These ships were renowned for their speed; in early vessels as much as 18 knots. British shipbuilders quickly followed the American style and one of the best-known names was the tea-clipper, the Cutty Sark.

sizes: big three- and four-masted ships for ocean voyages, small brigs and schooners to work as tramps round the coasts of Europe. Built of wood throughout, painted more brightly than most ships are nowadays, they depended for their motive power on the uncertain wind, and the skill with which their crews could handle them. Improvement in performance could be achieved only by the development of better design of hull and sails. Ironically, perfection in the sailing ship came nearest to being achieved just as the steamship was becoming established. But perhaps the most wonderful sailing vessels of all time were the clipper ships of the mid-nineteenth century.

THE CLIPPER SHIPS

Clipper ships reached the peak of their fame just over a hundred years ago. Hundreds of thousands of prospectors were carried by them to the gold fields of Australia and California. The clippers, with their swept-back rectangular sails, sped over the waves beneath billowing clouds of canvas. British and American shipbuilders vied with one another in building these beautiful ships. The American *Lightning* once logged 436 miles for a single day's run; the British-owned *Cutty Sark* maintained a regular and speedy service between England and China that made her name a byword among travellers of the day.

The winds of the Roaring Forties and the Bay of Biscay tested the crews of the clippers to the utmost. For thirty years, the ships carried the tea and spices of China and the East round the Cape of Good Hope. Virginian tobacco, West Indian sugar and other perishable commodities filled their holds. But their days were numbered. In 1870 the Suez Canal was opened. Steamships were claiming the cargoes of these magnificent vessels, and they disappeared from the trade routes almost as suddenly as they had invaded them thirty years before. The clipper ship is now as dead as the dodo. So, too, are all the old fully-rigged ships, including those that sailed in the Australian " grain race " of more recent times. This is the price of progress, and the steamships are in their turn facing competition from the air-lines that carry passengers and freight swiftly to every corner of the world.

MERCURY
The Quicksilver Metal

Mercury has two properties that give it a special place in the field of metallurgy; it is a liquid at normal temperatures and it will dissolve certain other metals forming amalgams.

Mercury freezes at the temperature of —38°C. and boils at 357°C. It is a heavy, silvery-white liquid, which takes the chemical symbol Hg from its Latin name *Hydrargyrum.* It is also called quicksilver.

Gold, silver, lead and zinc dissolve in mercury, no heating being required. Iron, nickel and cobalt do not dissolve in this way. Mercury has always been associated as a solvent (i.e. something capable of dissolving another substance) with gold and silver; it was used in the past for extracting these precious metals from their ores. A solution of a metal in mercury is called an amalgam.

Pure mercury is very rarely found in its natural state. Sometimes it forms tiny drops on the surface of certain ore deposits, and occurs with gold and silver in rocks containing these metals. But it most commonly has to be extracted from its compounds, the most common of which is mercuric sulphide.

Two common sulphide ores of mercury, both of a fine red colour, cinnabar and hepatic cinnabar, are mined and used in the commercial production of mercury. Cinnabar is also a source of the rich red pigment used as colouring matter in sealing-wax and vermilion paint.

FROM ALCHEMY TO AMALGAM

No one can say exactly when man first succeeded in extracting metallic mercury from its ore. But it is a well-established fact that the Ancients used it, particularly as a solvent for gold and silver.

In the Middle Ages, mercury acquired a mysterious aura on account of its strange qualities. The alchemists of that

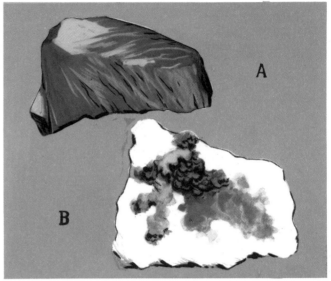

A. The principal ore of mercury is a red sulphide, cinnabar.
B. Cinnabar also occurs in other rocks, including limestone.

period thought that quicksilver occupied a place somewhere between matter and spirit. They regarded it as one of five magic " principles " which formed the basis of all earthly substances. They named it mercury after the planet and carried out strange experiments with it in vessels called alembics. Not until the second half of the eighteenth century was this metal properly identified, when the French chemist, Lavoisier, declared it to be an element, or elementary form of matter. Nowadays, there is no mystery about mercury. It has become an important industrial raw material in its own right.

Some of the main applications of mercury are familiar to

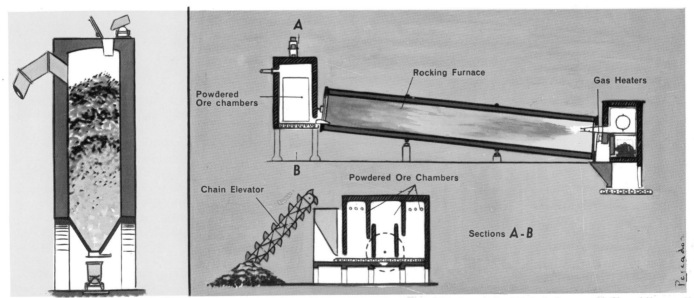

Two processes used in the extraction of mercury. Large lumps of ore are roasted in the vertical Spirek furnace (left), while small lumps and powdered ore are roasted in the inclined rotary Moeller-Pfeiffer furnace (right).

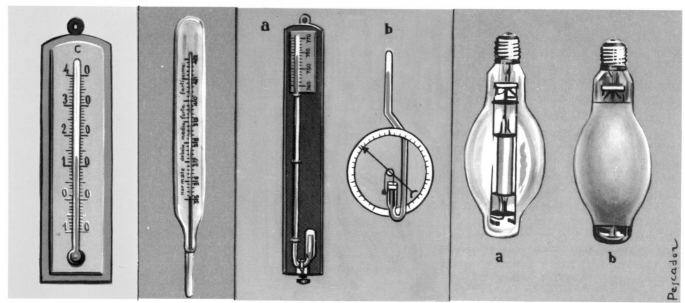

Mercury is liquid over a temperature range of minus 38° to 357° C., which makes it suitable for use in thermometers, barometers and scientific instruments. At 357° C. it vaporises, and when an electric discharge is passed through the vapour a light is emitted which is rich in ultra violet rays (a and b).

all. It is used in making a wide variety of scientific and semi-scientific instruments: thermometers, barometers, hydrometers and gauges of various kinds. The expansion and contraction of mercury has been used as a method of measuring temperature for some 250 years. Prior to that alcohol and linseed oil were used.

Mercury is also used to-day as an electrode, for example in the electrolysis of alkaline chlorides. Mercury vapour provides us with special types of electric lamps which emit a characteristic light.

There is a clear relationship between an amalgam and an alloy. An alloy is commonly formed by the fusion of molten metals to form a material of desired properties. Bronze, for example, is an alloy of copper and tin. An amalgam can be regarded as a mixture of one or more metals with mercury. A typical amalgam is the amalgam of silver and mercury used in filling teeth. This ability to dissolve certain metals has led to the use of gold or silver amalgams for gilding or silvering statuettes and other ornamental objects.

Mercury is widely used with zinc in the manufacture of electric battery plates, and in certain printing processes. Mercury has been used for centuries in the form of an amalgam for plating the backs of mirrors. This technique has now been largely superseded by other processes.

MERCURY FROM CINNABAR

Mercury is produced from the mineral cinnabar, which is mined in great quantities in southern Europe. Italy and Spain are leading producers and are together responsible for three-fifths of the world's cinnabar output. The largest mines are at Monte Amiata in Tuscany and in the Italian province of Grosseto.

In the first stage of the process, the rock lumps are broken up and sorted; one type of furnace is used for treating large lumps and another for small ones. The ore is usually wet, and must first be dried, either in the sun or in a hot air-stream. The ore is then roasted at 500/600°C. Special furnaces are employed in which the sulphide ore releases mercury in the form of vapour.

The mercury vapours are cooled in condensers, forming drops of liquid mercury which collect in special vessels. The mercury is contaminated with dust and dirt, and is very impure. It must undergo further purification before it is suitable for use, for example, in a clinical thermometer.

At one time, people employed in the extraction and processing of mercury suffered serious illness owing to the effects of the mercury. Men suffered from a form of chronic poisoning, just as they did in the lead industry. Precautionary measures have since been taken and the disease is now an extremely rare one.

Mercury compounds are used in medicine. But mercury and its compounds are highly poisonous, and are used medicinally only in small dozes and under strict supervision. Great care must be used when handling them. Mercuric chloride, for example, is a white crystalline substance that has, in the past, been mistaken for sugar. Few people have survived after swallowing a dose of this dangerous poison.

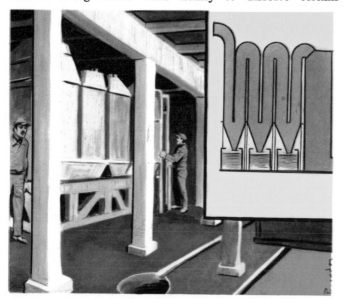

In the condensers (right), mercury vapour from the furnaces (left) is cooled. Liquid mercury is run off into vessels below for further purification.

CORK AND ITS USES

Millions of bottles are made every year to hold medicines and wines and all manner of liquid products. And millions of stoppers are needed to make sure that the liquids stay inside their bottles.

Nowadays, we use plastics, metals, rubber and other materials for making these bottle stoppers, but for many purposes we still rely on the old, familiar cork that has served us well from time immemorial.

Corks are made from the bark of a tree, the cork oak, which flourishes best in a warm climate and at low altitudes. It is found mainly in southern Europe and North Africa; in Spain alone, cork forests cover an area of two million acres.

With its strong trunk and dense mass of evergreen foliage, the cork oak (*Quercus suber*), is a handsome tree. Robust and sturdy, it seems the very essence of strength and permanence. These qualities appealed to primitive peoples, who thought highly of the cork oak even before they had learnt to make practical use of it. The Greeks, in particular, regarded the tree with special veneration.

According to Theophrastus, the cork oak was growing in Greece and other Mediterranean countries at least five centuries before Christ. The Greeks dedicated the tree to Jupiter, and no one was allowed to cut it down without permission from the priests. At Dodona in Epirus, it was believed that the cork groves were populated by wood-nymphs called hamadryads: friendly creatures who passed on the words of the sky and weather gods through the rustling of branches and leaves.

This deep reverence for the trees was felt also by the people who lived in Italy before the days of the Roman Empire. On a hill which now forms part of the Vatican State, there was once a very old cork tree. Pliny describes how in his day—about A.D. 50—it was still engraved with inscriptions sacred to the cult of tree worship.

Not all ancient civilisations held the cork tree in such

Jars such as these, with the corks still in place, were found among the ruins of Pompeii.

great respect. The Chinese were making fishing tackle and life-buoys from cork five thousand years ago. The Armenians followed suit, while in Sardinia there is archaeological evidence that the island people were making use of cork at a very early date. Nor were the Romans squeamish about felling cork oaks. We know from Pliny that these trees were being grown in Italy for commercial purposes at the beginning of the Christian era. Tall jars containing wine and oil, with the corks still in them, have been found among the ruins of Pompeii which was destroyed by Vesuvius in A.D. 79. Cork appeared some centuries later in Arabian furniture, and towards the end of the Middle Ages it was being used for decorative purposes in European countries.

The cork tree belongs to the oak family, in which botanists

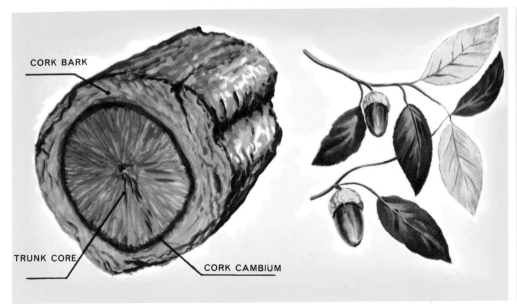

CORK BARK

TRUNK CORE

CORK CAMBIUM

Quercus suber, the cork oak, is a native of the Mediterranean area, with Spain the chief producer. Stripping of the cork takes place regularly, the interval between each stripping being between 8 and 11 years. Horizontal cuts are made around the tree, then a longitudinal cut is made from one encircling cut to the next and the piece of outer bark is carefully removed. Great care is taken at this stage not to damage the cambium layer where new cells are produced to re-create the protective layer of cork round the tree. The acorns of the cork oak appear only every other year.

After stripping, the cork is usually steamed or boiled. This process removes the soluble tannins.

include over 300 species. Among these are several kinds of cork oak, including the Spanish variety, and the *Quercus occidentalis* which is native to western Mediterranean countries. The height and girth of the trunk vary according to the species and the age of the tree. In exceptional cases it grows to seventy feet, but the normal height is between thirty-five and forty-five feet. The trunk, from which the cork is obtained, averages about eight feet in circumference, with a maximum of thirteen feet.

The evergreen leaves of the cork tree are dark on the top and whitish underneath. They are tough and leathery, oval in shape and slightly indented. In general, they hang diagonally from the twigs and branches, allowing plenty of sunshine to reach shrubs and undergrowth which flourish on the ground beneath. This benefits the tree by helping to conserve moisture. Cork trees flower in April and May, their acorns forming once every other year. Like those of the common oak, which appear every year, the acorns of the cork tree are enjoyed by pigs and cattle.

Although it will grow in dry and even rocky places, the cork oak prefers deep, damp soil and an altitude of less than 3,000 feet. It grows best in a temperate climate with warm, dry summers and wet winters. Ideal conditions are found in Spain and Portugal, where the best species of cork oak flourishes. This is the Spanish variety, whose cultivation is of great value to the Iberian peninsula. The same tree is grown to some extent in parts of France, Algeria, Greece and Turkey, but it does not flourish, as a rule, outside this region. Cork grown in Sicily and Sardinia is sent for processing to factories around Milan, Genoa and Venice.

EXOGENS

If we were to examine a log of cork oak, we should see that it has a double bark; an outer one and an inner one, the cambium, at a depth of several inches. Trees of this kind are called exogens, a botanical word meaning growth by deposit on the outside. Exogenous growth is generally a form of protection; in the case of the cork tree it is protecting the internal tissue of the trunk. An inner bark is formed which produces a thick, surrounding shield of soft, spongy, cellular material. This is probably Nature's way of insulating the vital parts of a delicate tree against extreme temperatures

After being boiled and pressed flat, the cork sheets are sent to factories for the final processes of cutting, sterilising and stamping.

52

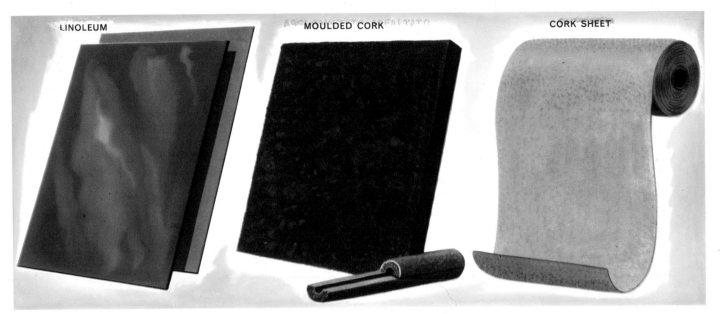

The original bark, or stripping, is usually not of a high enough quality for use as bottle-stoppers. It is ground up with cork waste and used for linoleum and insulating material, or moulded into sheets for use as packing for machinery.

during a time of severe climatic change. The shield provides us with our cork.

STRIPPING THE CORK OAK

Year by year, the layers of cork accumulate round the trunk of the tree, reaching maximum thickness (which may be anything between ten and thirty inches), in the fourteenth year. The cork is stripped off during mild seasons so that the tree will not suffer from excessive heat or cold. This is done very carefully to avoid damage to the inner bark, or cambium, which could prove fatal to the tree. A tree will withstand this drastic operation about once every ten years, and then only after it has reached the age of fifteen or twenty; by this time, it should have a trunk four feet in circumference.

The layers taken from a young tree at its first stripping are rough and knotty, and quite unsuitable for making corks. They are ground down for the manufacture of cork compositions. The second stripping produces good quality material, and subsequent strippings continue to do so until the tree is about sixty or seventy years old. After that, the bark becomes thinner and the yield smaller until, at the age of about 200 years, the tree stops producing the protective shield of cork altogether.

PREPARING THE RAW MATERIAL

The thick, spongy bark is removed from the trees in round sheets by making a long slit down one side. The stripped bark is then left for a time in the forest before being sent to the collecting depots. The cells of the bark contain organic matter which putrefies and creates unpleasant smells and acids that might contaminate bottled liquids. By exposing the bark to the sun and air these substances are partially evaporated and destroyed.

On arrival at the depots, the cork bark is prepared for the factory. The sheets are first boiled in copper vats. This extracts the tannin and at the same time increases the bulk and flexibility of the material. After being dried in the open air, the sheets are scraped to remove the woody crust from the outer surface. Next, they are cut into strips which are graded according to size, quality and thickness of the cork. These are auctioned or sent direct to industrial buyers.

CORK AS BOTTLE-STOPPERS

If we exclude the first strippings, which are largely used for cork compositions, about nine-tenths of world production goes into making corks and stoppers for all kinds of bottles, flasks and other vessels. Cork has been used for this purpose, in modern times, since the seventeenth century. It is an ideal material for the purpose. Cork is an excellent insulator against heat and cold; its cells are chemically inert and practically odourless; it is elastic, watertight and has no effect on the liquids with which it comes into contact.

To make the finest quality cork, such as that used for making wine-bottle stoppers, a number of operations are necessary. The strips from which it is cut are treated with sulphuric acid, steamed and dried in the open air for at least six months. They are then thoroughly sterilised, to make sure that the cork contains no impurities which might harm the wines and medicines it is intended to preserve and protect.

OTHER USES OF CORK

Cork waste, and the first strippings from young trees, are used for making cork compositions. This is an important branch of the cork industry, and the compositions are used for many valuable products. Powdered cork mixed with pitch, bitumen and other substances provides insulating material for refrigeration chambers. Pulverised cork, size, and other ingredients go into the cork board used in the building trade. A similar material of finer quality is used for making gaskets in engineering and as jointing and padding in the furniture and clothing industries. Thin sheets of cork provide us with the tips on our cigarettes.

The most important of all the modern cork products are cork insulation boards and linoleum. Insulation boards are made from cork chips or powder heated and compressed with binding materials. They are extremely light, and are used in building the partition walls of many modern buildings. Linoleum, which is familiar to us all, contains a high proportion of powdered cork or cork dust, which contributes to the flexibility and hard-wearing qualities. Every year, some twenty million square yards of linoleum are produced throughout the world.

SHIPBUILDING

On days when gale warnings are being issued on the radio, when the Atlantic breakers are beating against the Irish Coast and swirling around the lighthouses of the Channel, steamships do not hesitate to leave the shelter of their ports and harbours and thrust their way into the boiling sea.

Each of these ships, large or small, carries a team of men—its crew—who challenge the elements in vessels that must strain and struggle with mountainous waves and lashing spray. It seems incredible that man is prepared to entrust his fate to the fragile craft that sail the sea. Yet seafaring peoples have such faith in their vessels that they sail through the fiercest storms. Let us see how this faith is justified by visiting a shipyard and following the construction of an ocean-going vessel from the moment that its hull is laid down to the day of the launching ceremony. We shall then see what care is taken to ensure that the ship is seaworthy, so that its crew will handle it with ease and confidence.

THE KEEL IS LAID

Blueprints showing the design of the ship in white lines drawn on blue paper are prepared in two series. The larger ones give an overall picture of the vessel, and the smaller ones include every detail to a scale of 1:50 or 1:100. They are laid out in sheds on immense tables where designers will continue the work of checking every section and fitting as construction proceeds. There is not a single plate, not a single piece of piping, not a nut and bolt that has not been designed and measured accurately before it is made.

Building begins with the laying down of the keel blocks. These stout wooden sleepers are laid on the floor of the shipyard in a line corresponding with the length of the ship's keel. Above them tower the moving cranes, while on the ground materials pile up for the construction of the main framework: the hull, the bulkheads and the decks.

Everything is made from steel, and it is an interesting fact that a steel boat weighs less than a wooden one of the same size. Steel has other advantages too. It is more easily worked, its quality does not vary, it is fireproof and less likely to spring leaks than is wood. Large ships, which would require a whole forest of timber if made from wood, are built from steel provided in any quantity from the rolling mills. Sections are delivered to the yard in two forms: as girders and as shell plates.

The girders form the ribs of the ship; if they are not an exact fit, they can be cut to size on the spot. Seen sideways, or in cross-section, these girders are of various shapes and thicknesses. They may run to 150 feet in length, or they may be only six or seven feet long, according to their functions. They are a vitally important part of the ship, giving strength to the hull and enabling it to resist the fiercest storms.

No less important are the metal plates forming the outer hull. The plates come from steel mills equipped with hydraulic presses and planers which reduce the sheets to a thickness of between 0·3 and 0·5 of an inch. They are cut to the required size and pierced by batteries of drills which bore the holes for the rivets or bolts that will hold them together. All this takes place in the steel mills.

THE SHIP TAKES SHAPE

Returning to the shipyard, we find that the keel, which may be called the spinal column of the ship, is now in position. Built throughout of mild steel for extra strength and elasticity, it forms a base on which the rest of the main structure is erected. Stout cross-arms and bent shell plates are welded together to give shape to the hull bottom. Next come the floor plates and the side frames, the latter being added as the walls begin to rise. With the erection of the side frames, the ship really begins to take shape behind a

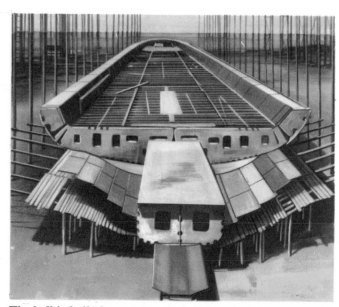

Keel blocks are laid one on top of another and fastened together before the building of a new ship commences.

The hull is built from stout cross-arms and girders encased in steel sheets known as shell plating.

Metal plates being welded to the iron girder framework.

necessarily on the site of the building yards. These sections, which may weigh fifty or sixty tons each, are hoisted into position by gigantic cranes. Naturally, the whole ship cannot be prefabricated in this way, but the method works very well for those sections that make up the double bottom, the watertight compartments, the bows, and certain units forming part of the superstructure.

STANDARDS OF PERFECTION

Progress on our ship is going ahead rapidly, though what we see still looks like a huge, elongated workshop; it echoes from end to end with the rattle of pneumatic hammers and rivet guns, the screech of planes and metal shavers, and the deafening hiss of oxy-acetylene flames burning brightly round the goggled welders. Hundreds of mechanics, carpenters, electricians, plumbers, toolmakers and other skilled workers bustle round an open network of corridors, hatchways and compartments distinguishable amid the sprouting girders and spreading area of welded sheet steel. To the untrained eye it is all rather puzzling, but we may be sure that every job

maze of props and buttresses that carry scaffolding and platforms for the drillers and welders.

Little by little, the shell plating is welded round a forest of ribs and side frames to make a great watertight shield. An advantage of welding over the use of rivets is that it does away with the need for caulking up the seams. A ship which is welded throughout weighs about one-eighth less than a riveted one as there is no overlapping between the plates and no strapping with cross pieces. While all this is going on, a labyrinth of metal trestles is being fitted inside the ship to support the decks, the superstructure of cabins and the living quarters for passengers and crew.

Another system now widely used was first developed by British yards in 1917. This is the method of constructing a vessel out of prefabricated sections. Ships can be turned out much more quickly in this way, as was shown in the Second World War when liberty vessels of over 14,000 tons were assembled by American shipbuilders in forty days. Compare this with the six or seven months that it normally takes to build a ship of that tonnage. Prefabrication involves the erection of whole sections in special workshops, not

The upper decks of most vessels are made of wood, while the lower decks are of metal.

is performed to a carefully worked-out plan; every step is supervised by engineers and designers whose main concern is to see that each man's work reaches a required standard of perfection.

Most young people are keenly observant, and often ask why a ship is always built with its aftermost part facing the water. This is because the rounded shape of the poop, or stern, gives greater support and stability at the moment of launching, while the stresses of torsion, or twisting exerted on the framework by this operation, are borne much better by the slender bows. Already the great vessel seems eager to slip into the water, but the time for its launching has not yet come. The hull, still wrapped in scaffolding, towers over the surrounding workshops. Workmen are still busily closing every joint and seam with molten metal. Where necessary they are driving home the last rivets. The long arms of cranes, now installed inside the hulk, reach out to grapple with huge sections of superstructure. They are hauled aboard and set in position, while all over the ship technicians are making a final inspection to see that all is in order before the launching.

Prefabricated units, built in special factories, are swung into position by shipyard cranes.

One more task remains, and this is an important one—painting. The ship is given several thick coats of specially mixed paint to protect her from clinging seaweed and shellfish which, if allowed to build up freely on the hull, would reduce the vessel's speed and efficiency. While this is going on, more inspections are made and at length our ship is declared ready for her launching.

THE LAUNCHING CEREMONY

Six months have gone by since the keel was laid down, and the soaring prow is at last ready to cleave the waves. Freed of its scaffolding, the great hulk crouches in its stocks balanced on a low wooden cradle which keeps it steady until the moment for launching comes. If the day is fine and the vessel an important one, this traditional ceremony will be attended by a large crowd all eager to watch some very important person—perhaps a member of the Royal Family—christen the departing ship with a bottle of champagne.

As the bottle cracks against the bows and the liquid flows down the side of the ship, the last links with the slipway are torn away. Hydraulic jacks give just sufficient push to start her moving. There is a breathless hush as the echoing cheers of the onlookers die away, followed by a creaking noise. Everyone cranes forward to watch. Almost imperceptibly at first, then gaining speed, the ship slides sedately down a slight gradient of not more than 1 : 20. Again the cheers burst from the crowd and the sirens scream from every vessel in the harbour. As the new ship hits the water a great wave springs from her stern enfolding her in the embrace of the element which is to be her home. The name of the ship passes from mouth to mouth. It is like the whispering of the sea greeting her as she starts on the adventures of many voyages that lie ahead.

Watching from the shore, the builders know that their newly-launched vessel is by no means ready for the sea. It will be some time before she is passed A1 and registered for insurance purposes at Lloyds. So, perhaps with a groan from deep down in her hold, she surrenders to a team of powerful tugs that take her in tow and haul her to the fitting-out basin. There is much to be done, and the men who now come aboard are not the same as those who crawled about her

It takes many months, sometimes years, to build a modern ocean-going liner. Before she can go into service she has to have trials and any defects noted during these trials are corrected before the ship is delivered to the owners.

sides when she lay on the slipway. She remains only an empty shell.

FINISHING TOUCHES

The engines have to be installed. There are still many additions to be made to the superstructure. The masts must be set with the aid of hoisting tackle known as shears. At least one funnel will be necessary. Then come the electric motors and the ventilating plant, to say nothing of navigational instruments, radio and radar installations. Meanwhile a mountain of equipment has been accumulating for the passenger and crew quarters, and all this has to be brought aboard. Depending on the type of ship, some builders wait until this stage before fitting the propellers and the anchor gear.

These specialised jobs keep hundreds of men busy for several months. Others on duty in the fitting-out basin manipulate the cranes, the power controls and conveyors which facilitate the work of the men on board.

The sea trials are held in the presence of the company officials and the engineers responsible for construction. Several days of testing may be necessary before the engines are properly adjusted and all mechanical parts have been checked. The builders are not satisfied until they are certain that every component of the ship is in perfect working order.

HER MAIDEN VOYAGE

On a fine summer's morning the ship sails out of harbour to the accompaniment of a long and powerful blast from her own siren. Flags are flying from masthead, stern and bows. Triangular pennants flutter in the breeze as she sets off, " dressed overall ", on that maiden voyage for which some of those who came to the launching ceremony booked their passages many months ago.

Such is the story of the birth of a ship, of all those ships that we see, whether lying at anchor in harbour or moving slowly along the line of the horizon. And we should remember that every one of them has a life of its own which it shares with those who travel aboard her: the captain and his officers, the passengers and the crew.

It is usual for the shaft and propeller to be fitted to the ship before launching.

HOW RADIATION HELPS US

On 8th November, 1895, Professor Wilhelm Röntgen of Wurzburg University in Bavaria was carrying out experiments in which electricity flowed through gas at low pressure. The glass tube containing the gas was covered entirely with black cardboard, so that no visible light could be seen. And yet, as electricity flowed through the tube, some crystals of a chemical lying nearby began to glow with an eerie light.

INVISIBLE RAYS

Röntgen was intrigued by this discovery. He turned off the current, and the glow disappeared. Then he turned it on again, and the crystals glowed once more. It seemed that some invisible influence was coming from the glass tube, passing through the black cardboard and making the crystals emit light.

" I tested it," explained Röntgen later. " In a few minutes there was no doubt about it. Rays were coming from the tube which had a luminous effect on the crystals . . . It seemed at first a new kind of invisible light."

Announcing his discovery in a paper " On a New Kind of Ray ", on 23rd January, 1896, Röntgen described how the rays would penetrate objects which were opaque to ordinary light. They would pass through a bound book of 1,000 pages, or a double pack of cards. In a footnote to the paper, he said, " For brevity's sake, I shall use the expression ' rays ', and to distinguish them from others of this name, I shall call them ' X-rays '."

Röntgen explained, " If the hand be held between the discharge tube and a screen coated with crystals, the darker shadow of the bones is seen within the slightly dark shadow image of the hand itself." He went on to describe how X-rays would affect a photographic plate in much the same way as light rays do.

DISCOVERY OF THE X-RAY

Röntgen showed how X-rays were able to penetrate opaque substances to varying degrees, depending on the density of the material. The bones of the body, for example, absorbed more of the rays than the flesh and tissues surrounding them. So, by placing a photographic plate behind a portion of the body, it was possible to take a " shadow " photograph by allowing X-rays to fall on the plate after passing through the body. The places where X-rays were absorbed least, opposite the fleshy parts of the body, were exposed much more than those places where absorption of X-rays had been greater, opposite the bones.

Unlike so many scientific discoveries, Röntgen's discovery of X-rays was accepted and welcomed throughout the world. And almost immediately, the rays were brought into practical use. Within a few days of the news of the discovery reaching America, doctors had used X-rays for locating a bullet in a patient's leg. In France, surgeons used X-rays to diagnose a diseased thigh bone, only a few weeks after Röntgen's announcement.

Some of the early X-ray experimenters were carried away by their enthusiasm. A British textile firm, for example, announced that it had developed " X-ray proof " under-clothing for the modest woman. An inventor declared that he could make his dog hungry by using X-rays to throw the shadow of a bone into the dog's brain! And in America, a bill was introduced with the object of prohibiting the use of X-rays in opera glasses in theatres.

APPLICATION TO MEDICINE

From the very beginning, X-rays have played an important role in medicine. The ability to " see " inside a patient's body was a wonderful aid to the doctor, and within a year or two X-rays were in widespread use in the medical world. Unfortunately, these early workers did not realise that X-rays can damage and ultimately destroy living cells. And it was not long before people using X-rays found that they were developing a form of skin disease.

This discovery stimulated research into the effect of X-rays on living tissues, and showed how essential it was to protect people from unnecessary exposure to the rays. To-day, X-ray equipment is shielded by lead and other dense material that absorbs rays which might otherwise affect the operator.

The ability of X-rays to destroy living cells is now put to good use by the doctor who uses them to attack cells that he wishes to destroy. X-rays are used, for example, in the treatment of cancer and similar diseases caused by abnormal cell growth.

X-RAYS IN INDUSTRY

Most of us are familiar with the important part played by X-rays in modern medicine, but we seldom hear about the many ways in which the X-ray helps in industrial life.

As in the case of medicine, the X-ray got away to a flying start in industry. A month after Röntgen had announced

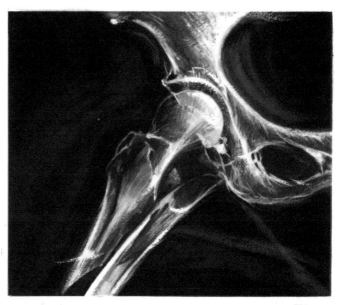

When a broken bone is suspected, a radiograph is taken of the affected part. This is an artist's impression of an X-ray plate showing a broken thigh bone.

the discovery of his rays, Professor A. W. Wright of Yale University showed how X-rays could reveal a hidden fracture in a weld. And by the turn of the century the rays were being used for detecting sand in sugar, catching smugglers, distinguishing between natural and artificial diamonds, and picking out oysters that contained pearls.

Wherever the ability to " see inside " something can be useful, the X-ray has come into its own. In recent years, we have learned how to generate X-rays with greater and greater penetrating powers. And this has given them much greater scope in industry than they had before.

In heavy engineering, powerful X-rays are used for examining forgings and castings to detect any faults which may have occurred during manufacture. This is especially important in products which could cause disaster if they failed; X-rays will show up flaws, for example, in high-pressure steam boilers, or railway-engine wheels.

INSPECTION RAY

This sort of inspection and testing, which does not involve any damage to the object being tested, is particularly important in the aircraft and atomic industries. In aircraft, everything is done to keep weight to an absolute minimum, so that it is not always possible to make an important part several times stronger than it needs to be, to ensure safety. X-rays, however, will peer into the heart of the metal and show up any flaw that might mean danger.

Similarly, X-ray examination will reveal any imperfections in the welding of atomic reactors, where failure could mean disaster.

In the art world, X-rays can look beneath the outer layers of paint on a picture, and show up any forgeries or alterations. The pigments used by painters centuries ago were more opaque than those that have been used in modern times. The famous " Madonna " by Geertgen van St. Jans, for example, was examined by Dr. Heilbron of Amsterdam with the help of X-rays. The penetrating rays were able to see beneath the outer layers of paint, and showed that the figure had originally carried an infant in her arms.

When X-rays are passed through crystalline substances,

The penetrating power of the X-ray microscope allows the scientist to see microscopically into opaque materials.

they are deflected and scattered by the orderly rows of atoms in the crystal. By measuring the angles through which the X-rays are deflected, scientists can work out how the atoms are arranged. This technique of X-ray analysis, as it is called, enables us to probe into atomic structures, and to relate the properties and behaviour of substances to the arrangement of the atoms in their molecules.

X-RAY MICROSCOPE

The X-ray has now been harnessed to the microscope. By using X-rays instead of visible light we can travel farther into the world of small things than we do with an optical microscope. And the penetrating power of the X-ray allows us to see microscopically into the interior of " opaque " materials. Scientists have used the X-ray microscope, for example, to study the way insects' muscles work!

When Wilhelm Röntgen discovered X-rays in 1895, he did not know what they were. They appeared to be a form of " invisible light " which could travel through materials opaque to ordinary visible light.

To-day, we recognise X-rays as a form of electromagnetic radiation which is fundamentally similar to light, but of very much shorter wave length. The rays are generated when substances are bombarded by a stream of electrons, the tiny particles that form one of the constituents of every atom.

Many scientists took up the study of X-rays soon after Röntgen's discovery, and among them was Professor Henri Becquerel of the Museum of Natural History in Paris. In 1896, Becquerel was studying the strange glow that was emitted spontaneously by certain salts. This natural fluorescence had an obvious similarity to the glow that came from the salts which were stimulated by Röntgen's X-rays.

One of the substances which Becquerel prepared was a salt of the element uranium, which glowed spontaneously. It had been assumed that the glow was caused by stimulation of the salt with visible light. But Becquerel wrapped the uranium salts in black paper, placed the packet on a piece of silver foil and then on a photographic plate. To his

Industrial use of X-ray equipment, showing a test being carried out on an aircraft.

surprise, he found that the plate was " exposed " beneath the place where the salts had been. Apparently, some sort of ray had been emitted by the uranium, penetrating the paper and the silver foil to affect the photographic plate.

Obviously, the rays were not being caused by stimulation of the salt with visible light—the black paper prevented light reaching the salt. And there were no electrons to cause the rays, as in the case of X-rays. The uranium salt was emitting its penetrating rays without any form of outside encouragement.

DISCOVERY OF RADIUM

In Paris at that time, there was a young Polish scientist, Marie Sklodowska, who was married to a French physicist, Pierre Curie. She made the startling suggestion that the rays were caused by the breaking-up of the uranium atoms.

Marie Curie's idea was followed up by Lord Rutherford, the famous British physicist, who showed that her theory was correct. The atoms of certain elements, like uranium and radium (which Madame Curie had discovered) were disintegrating spontaneously, emitting electromagnetic rays similar to X-rays, but much more powerful. These became known as gamma rays. In addition, there were two other kinds of ray consisting of particles released as a result of the break-up of the atom.

One of these " particle-rays ", called the beta ray, consists of electrons; the other, known as the alpha ray, consists of relatively heavy sub-atomic particles identical with the nuclei of helium atoms.

RADIOACTIVE ELEMENTS

Materials which disintegrate spontaneously in this way are now known as radioactive substances. Their atoms are inherently unstable, and undergo a continuous disintegration which results in the formation of atoms of different elements. The rate at which radioactive disintegration takes place is constant and is characteristic of any particular element.

Some elements which occur naturally are radioactive— like uranium and radium. But in recent years, scientists have been able to create radioactive forms of virtually every element, for example by bombarding other elements with streams of atomic particles.

These substances are known as radioactive isotopes; they behave chemically in the same way as the non-radioactive form of the same element. That is to say, they will combine with other elements in the same way, forming substances with the same chemical properties. But they differ in that they are undergoing a spontaneous and continuous disintegration, throwing out atomic particles in the form of alpha or beta rays, and electromagnetic radiation in the form of gamma rays.

This strange characteristic of radioactive isotopes has proved of immense benefit to modern science and industry. The rays emitted by a radioactive isotope can be detected and measured very easily by simple instruments, and by using a radioactive isotope in place of its non-radioactive twin, we can follow the progress of a substance as it makes its way through all sorts of complicated processes.

THE DETECTIVE TRACERS

We can put radioactive elements into fertilisers, for example, and follow their movements through the plant. We can make a radioactive drug and discover what happens to it inside the human body. Radioactive isotopes used in this way, known as tracers, have been of immense benefit to modern science.

The great penetrating power of the gamma rays emitted by radio-isotopes enables them to be used for locating objects buried deep in the ground. Small amounts of radioactive material fixed to underground pipes will mark the position of special places in the pipe; even after many years deep in the ground, a simple detector will locate the radio-isotope without difficulty.

Radioactive substances can be used for finding leaks in water mains. The radioactive isotope is dissolved in water and the solution held under pressure in a section of the main. After a short time, the pipe is cleared of solution, and a detector above the ground will soon locate any radioactive solution that leaked from the faulty joint into the ground.

Radioactive steel piston rings will enable a car manufacturer to measure engine wear continuously without dismantling the engine. Oil from the engine sump is circulated past a radiation detector, and the amount of radiation in the oil gives a measure of the metal that has been worn away.

STERILISATION USES

To-day, radioactive isotopes are used in all manner of " tracer " applications of this type. The radiation is essentially a means of detecting and measuring what is going on in the process under test. But radiation is also being used to bring about changes on its own account. Heavy doses of gamma rays, for example, will sterilise food or medical products by destroying micro-organisms. And the material can be sterilised in this way after it has been sealed into a container. The rays penetrate the interior of the container, and the sterilised material remains sterile until the container is opened.

Radiation is also used for creating new varieties of plants, and for killing insects in corn; it encourages chemical reactions to take place, and is used for improving the properties of plastics.

Wilhelm Röntgen and Henri Becquerel would be astonished if they could see how their discoveries are being applied to-day, after little more than half-a-century of the Atomic Age.

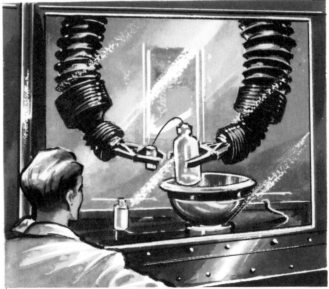

Preparation of radio-isotopes in a "hot cell" for use by doctors, hospitals and research laboratories. Radio-isotopes are used as tracers in medicine.

THE STORY OF ZINC

Zinc is an important and useful metal which is used for many purposes; but it has only a short individual history behind it. Zinc oxide has been known since Roman times, and has been used throughout the centuries for making alloys. With copper and tin it yields orichalc, a kind of golden copper, while with copper alone it produces brass. The manufacture of these alloys has long flourished in Europe, especially in France and Germany during the late Middle Ages. But zinc was not isolated as an element until well into the eighteenth century.

The chief mineral sources of zinc are blende, calamine and smithsonite. Blende is zinc sulphide, a compound of zinc and sulphur; calamine is a carbonate of zinc and smithsonite is its silicate. (In some countries, for instance America, these definitions of calamine and smithsonite are reversed.) Zinc-blende which is very similar in appearance to lead sulphide, was often confused with galena, the ore of lead. In ancient times, zinc-blende was called *galena inanis*—" useless galena "—and was thrown away because it yielded no lead.

It is, in fact, quite easy to distinguish zinc blende from lead-bearing galena by scraping the surface of the ores with a penknife. The interior of the lead ore is dark like the colour of lead itself; the blende, or zinc ore, is light, its external appearance being due to impurities which discolour the surface. Mineralogists have a special word for ores whose powder is of a different colour from that of the same ore in bulk. They call them allochromatic.

HOW ZINC IS OBTAINED

Two very different processes are used for separating zinc from its ores: one is chemical and the other electrolytic. The chemical method is the old process, and it presented

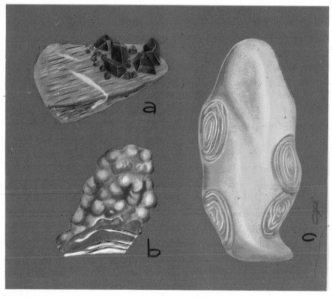

Zinc is found in its natural state in the mineral ores (a) blende; (b) calamine; (c) smithsonite. In blende it is combined with sulphur as a sulphide; in calamine, with carbon and oxygen to form a carbonate; in smithsonite with silicon and oxygen to form a silicate.

so many difficulties that zinc extraction was in a relatively primitive state until about thirty years ago.

First the zinc ore is roasted in the presence of an ample flow of air, the zinc forming zinc oxide. This is a compound in which zinc is united with oxygen. The zinc oxide is then " reduced ", a chemical process in which oxygen is removed from the zinc by burning it with coal; the oxygen in the oxide forms carbon monoxide gas, leaving zinc. The zinc produced by this method is relatively impure.

Chemical extraction tends to be expensive. The cost of the fuel, of refractory or heat-resisting materials with which to line the furnaces and of skilled labour is considerable. Much more economic, especially in countries where hydro-electric power is plentiful and cheap, is the electrolytic method now in general use.

Our illustration shows how zinc is extracted by electrolysis. A solution of zinc sulphate, produced in the early stages of treatment, flows into tanks fitted with electrolytic equipment. Here, the zinc sulphate is decomposed by the action of the electric current, the metal accumulating around the negative electrode.

Apart from the fact that the electrolytic method is comparatively cheap, the zinc it produces is extremely pure. This alone has given zinc a new importance in the metallurgical industry. Its low price and high purity has even brought it into competition with aluminium for certain applications where the lightness of aluminium is not an important factor.

THE METAL AND ITS ALLOYS

When zinc is exposed to the air it acquires a patina, or sheen, due to oxidation. Once formed, this thin layer prevents the oxygen in the air from attacking the metal beneath, so that corrosion cannot continue. For this reason zinc sheeting is often used as a protection against the weather —on roofs, for instance—where the heavier lead is also commonly used. Zinc is applied as a film or coating on iron, protecting it from the atmosphere and so preventing rusting. The common trade name for this product is galvanised iron, even though electricity, with which "galvanised" is associated, is not necessarily used in coating iron with its layer of zinc.

Zinc is widely used in making alloys. A mixture containing half copper, quarter nickel and quarter zinc forms the important alloy nickel silver, or German silver. The best known of all zinc alloys is brass, or perhaps we should say " the brasses " as there are many different types. Ordinary brass is a mixture of copper and zinc, 70 per cent. of the former and 30 per cent. of the latter. When more zinc and less copper are used brass acquires greater strength and resistance.

The properties of special brasses produced by varying the proportions of the two metals depend, however, on two further processes: annealing and hardening. In annealing brass, it is heated until it recovers mechanical properties, such as ductility, which were lost in making the alloy. In hardening it, the brass is first heated and then suddenly

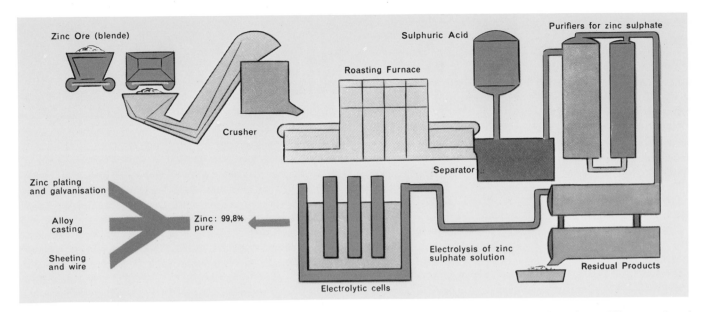

The raw blende is crushed, roasted and treated with sulphuric acid. The zinc sulphate formed is an electrolyte. When an electric current is passed through it, pure zinc is deposited at the electrode.

cooled. By these means copper and zinc are bound together to form one of the most useful of all alloys, for brass resists many forms of metal corrosion. It is also cheap and easy to work on simple equipment.

ZINC COMPOUNDS

There are many compounds of zinc in commercial use. One of the most valuable of these is its oxide, zinc-white, which is used as a pigment in white paint. The advantage of zinc-white is that it does not darken in contact with traces of hydrogen sulphide in the air, as does white lead which is also used for paints and varnishes. Zinc-white is used in the rubber industry and in the manufacture of linoleum and oil cloth.

Another compound is zinc chloride, a salt obtained by treating the metal with hydrochloric acid. This substance, which is sometimes called " zinc butter", decomposes at a comparatively low temperature, giving off hydrochloric acid.

1. Printing plates; 2. electric battery; 3. zinc-white paint; 4a. wire; 4b. bucket; 5a. plain, 5b. corrugated sheeting; 5c. tube; 5d. roof gutter.

When this " butter " comes into contact with other metals, the liberated acid combines with metallic oxides which may have been formed as impurity. For this reason, zinc chloride is often used in soldering metals. One of its other uses is as a preservative of wood against wood-worm.

When zinc reacts with sulphuric acid we obtain zinc sulphate which is an ingredient of collyrium, better known as eye-salve. Zinc sulphide, a compound of zinc with sulphur, emits a green or blue fluorescence when exposed to light. This is most pronounced when there are traces of copper or other heavy metals in the compound. Fluorescent paint is made in this way for poster and publicity purposes.

One of the many applications of zinc which we should not forget is suggested by the word zincography; that is to say, the use of an engraved zinc plate for printing designs and photographs. Such prints can also be obtained from stone by the process called lithography, but zinc plates are lighter and much easier to handle. The design is etched on to the zinc by treating the metal with acids; the job is performed quickly and economically.

Most of the world's supply of zinc comes from the United States, which is the largest producer. Belgium comes next, zinc now being one of her traditional exports. Zinc is also produced in most other European countries; in Italy, for example, the electrolytic process has been in use for a long time, using electricity which is produced cheaply and in abundance by hydro-electric installations.

CADMIUM

Cadmium is a metal found in the blende and calamine ores of zinc. It is chemically and physically similar to zinc, and it is often difficult to distinguish between the two metals and to separate them from one another. In practice, it is only when extracting zinc by the electrolytic method that cadmium can be isolated in quantities sufficient for industrial use. Cadmium forms low-melting alloys. It gives even better anti-rust protection than zinc, and iron and steel plated with cadmium are used for special applications, such as the manufacture of surgical and medical instruments. Cadmium sulphide is used as a pigment; it is familiar to us as the bright yellow often found in paint boxes.

61

THE STEAMSHIP TRIUMPHS

When we hear of nuclear-powered submarines sailing round the world without coming to the surface, and watch destroyers cutting through the waves at breathtaking speed, the days of the old sailing ship seem very far away indeed. Yet it is, in fact, only about a hundred years since warships finally gave up their sails and accepted the steam-engine as a reliable means of propulsion.

The steam-engine had been making slow headway in ships since late in the eighteenth century. James Watt, the Scottish inventor, constructed his first steam-engine and patented it in 1769, and in doing so he laid the foundations of an industrial revolution that brought great changes to every form of transport, on sea and on the land.

Before Watt's time, many experiments had been made in building mechanically-propelled boats, but none had been a success. In 1707, Denis Papin launched a small man-powered paddle-boat on the River Fulda, near Kassel in Germany. But it was not until the steam-engine provided a source of power that boats propelled in this way could hope to be successful. One of the first steam-powered boats was built by the French Marquis de Jouffroy d'Abbans. In his 182-ton *Pyroscaphe*, which was fitted with paddle-wheels and a double-ratchet mechanism driven by a steam engine, he made several successful trips up the Saône, near Lyons. Had it not been for the French Revolution, he might well have developed his first steamboat into a practical sea-going vessel.

At about this time, the American inventors James Rumsey and John Fitch built and operated steamboats on the Rivers Potomac and Delaware. Fitch even maintained a regular service, with a timetable that was published in the Philadelphia papers of 1787. But lack of finance, and the loss of one of the boats in a storm, put an end to those early ventures. In addition, the pioneers had to contend with the opposition of shipbuilders and seamen alike. This attitude reached extremes in France, where the Marquis d'Abbans was regarded as being out of his mind because he was trying " to placate water with fire ".

Man's progress has always depended on the creative resources of individuals determined enough to go ahead in spite of opposition and indifference. Every new generation has new ideas it wishes to put into practice, but it must first overcome the objections of people whose livelihood is bound up with old and well-tried methods. The development of the steamship is a case in point. But, despite the difficulties and frustration that hindered the pioneer steam-power enthusiasts, progress was made. By 1802, William Symington's steamboat *Charlotte Dundas* was being used for towing ships in the Forth and Clyde Canal. Here it was seen by Robert Fulton, the great American engineer who dedicated himself to the advancement of steam-navigation.

STEAM-DRIVEN PADDLE WHEELS

Fulton's first experiments were made on the Seine, and were treated with derision even by the logical French. Returning to America, Fulton continued his work in company with Robert Livingston. Together they built a paddle-wheel steamer and equipped it with Boulton and Watt engines sent out from England. It was launched on the Hudson River in 1807 and given the name of *Clermont*. Such was the success of this little passenger boat as it plied between New York and Albany that Fulton decided to construct a larger and more powerful vessel of similar design. While it was being built, John Stevens, another American engineer, put his *Phoenix* into service; with it, he made the first steamboat sea voyage by travelling round the New Jersey coast in 1809. Fulton's second boat, the *Paragon*, was launched in 1811. There were now three steamers on the Hudson River, an achievement of which the young American nation could well be proud.

The steamboat was now at a stage of development com-

The Clermont, *which went into service on the Hudson river between New York and Albany in 1807, was built by Fulton.*

The Comet, *built on the Clyde in 1812 by Henry Bell, carried passengers between Glasgow, Greenock and Helensburgh.*

Fitted with an auxiliary steam engine, the sailing packet Savannah *was the first steam-assisted vessel to make the Atlantic crossing from east to west.*

parable with that of the aeroplane before the First World War. Primitive engines required huge quantities of coal to fuel them, fragile paddle wheels buckled when they struck submerged objects, and failed to grip the water in choppy seas. Difficulties of this sort plagued the engineers who tried to make their boats seaworthy. Every steamboat carried a set of sails for use in case of an engine breakdown. The hull of the ship in those days was made of wood, and great care had to be taken to prevent the ship going up in flames. Shipbuilders who believed in the future of steam realised that they must do everything possible to increase the stability and safety of the ship that was going to be propelled successfully by steam.

Industrial supremacy 150 years ago was centred in Britain and Europe rather than in the United States. Between 1812 and 1816, several steamers were built on the Clyde, among them Henry Bell's *Comet* which went into service on the Glasgow-Helensburgh route. The *Elise*, also built in Scottish shipyards, steamed across the Channel in 1816, continuing up the Seine to make headline news in newspapers of the day. Two years later, a Neapolitan steamboat called

Naval authorities were slower than merchant lines in going over to steam. (Left) Steam frigate Austerlitz, *with escort vessel.*

Ferdinand I started a regular service between Naples, Genoa and Marseilles.

Initiative now passed to the other side of the Atlantic, where the Americans were building the 350-ton *Savannah*. Propelled by steam and sail, using her engines only when the wind dropped, the *Savannah* made the crossing from New York to Liverpool in twenty-four days in May/June 1818. This was the first crossing of the Atlantic by a steamship.

FROM WOOD TO IRON

All the early steamboats were built with wooden hulls. The suggestion that the hull of a ship might be made of iron had not yet been accepted as a practical proposition. But the advantage of an iron hull was demonstrated in 1824 by Aaron Manby, a British shipbuilder, who built an iron vessel.

It was not until ten years later that the advantages of the iron hull were made apparent. A violent storm swept Britain at that time, playing havoc with coastal shipping and wrecking almost every craft in its path. Only one ship rode the storm

Originally designed for service between Britain and India, the Great Eastern *was a failure as an Atlantic steamer, but excelled in laying the cable across the Atlantic.*

and escaped serious damage; this was the ship with the iron hull.

Shipbuilders were impressed, and when a new transatlantic steamer was laid down at Bristol in 1839, it was decided that it should be built with an iron hull and with iron decks and framework. This was the *Great Britain*, launched a year after Charles Dickens crossed the Atlantic in a wooden paddle-wheel steamer. A description of the voyage on the *Britannia* is contained in Dickens's *Notes on America*, compiled during a journey which was to give him the material for *Martin Chuzzlewit*. In America, Dickens travelled on many of the early river steamboats.

THE GREAT EASTERN

The *Great Britain*, designed by the famous engineer I. K. Brunel, was the first large steamer to be driven by the screw propeller system newly patented by F. P. Smith and J. Ericsson. She was 322 feet long with a tonnage exceeding 3,000 and a maximum speed of eleven knots. Her many successful runs and her ability to withstand the worst Atlantic gales encouraged Brunel to design a more ambitious vessel with a four-bladed screw propeller and closed-in paddle wheels.

The name given to this ship was *The Great Eastern*, as she was to be used for trading between Britain and India. Passengers and cargo, on reaching India, would be transferred to sailing vessels going to Australia and the Far East. Lack of coal held up the use of steamships in eastern waters.

LAUNCHING DIFFICULTIES

In her hey-dey, *The Great Eastern* was one of the marvels of the world. Nearly 700 feet long, with screw and paddle engines developing over 8,000 horse-power between them, she displaced 27,000 tons. She carried sails extending in area to almost an acre and a half when fully set on her six masts. Misfortune struck the huge vessel, however, when she was launched. She became stuck on the river bank and the cost of righting her was so great that the company went bankrupt. *The Great Eastern* was bought by a North Atlantic line, and sailed for New York instead of to Calcutta. Brunel's health was affected by the worry and frustration, and he died while *The Great Eastern* was making her maiden voyage in September, 1859.

The Great Eastern had not been designed for the North Atlantic route, and she was not as successful as her designer had hoped she would be. Nevertheless, her performance demonstrated the power of steam, and gave a clear indication of the size of vessel that would be used on the transatlantic routes. She marked a stage in the triumph of steam over sail, in the great merchant fleets of the world.

SCREW PROPELLERS FOR THE NAVY

The development of steam-propulsion was watched with great interest by naval powers during the early nineteenth century. But naval engineers were not greatly impressed by the new steamboats. Experiments were made, and in 1832 the Royal Navy sent a steamer from Plymouth to the Barbados. Similar vessels had already been built in American and French naval shipyards, but it was found that paddle wheels made the big ships clumsy and difficult to manoeuvre. They were slower and more vulnerable than a well handled sailing ship. So at first the new engines were used only in small naval boats which served as escorts and for reconnaissance purposes.

The Russian navy built this strange saucer-shaped vessel of the iron-clad class.

The British ironclad, H.M.S. Warrior, *was one of the first battleships. It had an armament of twenty-six 68-pounders, ten 110-pounders and four 70-pounders.*

With the invention of the screw propeller, engineers saw at once that steam-propulsion had entered a new phase; the propeller was a great improvement on paddle-wheels, especially in naval vessels. Between 1840 and 1860, the Royal Navy installed engines and boilers in many of her ships-of-the-line. Steam frigates and steam corvettes were built, though with wooden hulls, and with sails and guns exactly as in the ships of Nelson's day. As late as 1860, the navies of the world regarded steam as an aid to wind propulsion, and never as a substitute for it.

THE FIRST IRONCLADS

The real revolution in naval construction came about a century ago. Great advances were made in arms and ammunition production during the Crimean War. The need for heavier battleships was obvious, and France and Britain now laid down their first armoured warships. The British *Warrior*, with her iron hull of 4½-inch-thick plates was commissioned in 1859. Shortly afterwards, two American ironclads proved their worth in a historic naval battle at the beginning of the Civil War. This was a cue for the general adoption of armour plate, and the leading navies of the world hastened to build warships protected in this way.

The "sixties" of last century were the great years of the clipper ships. Steam was to triumph just as the sailing ship reached the peak of perfection: in the merchant fleet with transatlantic liners like *The Great Eastern*; in the Royal Navy with ironclads of the *Warrior* class. These early ironclads did not bear any resemblance to the cruisers and destroyers we know to-day. They had no gun turrets, but fired from casemates and emplacements in the sides of the hull. And they *still* carried sails.

The first battleship to abandon sail completely and to use central gun turrets was laid down in 1869—her name was H.M.S. *Devastation*, and her appearance coincided with the opening of the Suez Canal; 1870 was indeed a great date in the annals of the sea. In that year, steam delivered a knock-out blow to sailing vessels. Merchant ships bound for the Far East could now pass through the Canal instead of making the long trip round Africa. In that year, too, the British Navy founded a generation of warships which were to reach perfection with the introduction of the steam-turbine engine.

THE STORY OF SOAP

Soap is one of the first things we get to know when we enter the world. And for the rest of our lives, day in, day out, we are never away from soap and water for very long.

Cleanliness, they say, is next to godliness. And if this is true, then the ancient Greeks and Romans must have been the saintliest of people.

The great poems of Homer tell us of the importance that the Greeks attached to hygiene. Greek heroes would not go into battle or take part in sacrificial ceremonies until they had anointed themselves with salves and ointments.

These lotions were made with resins taken from the trunks and stems of certain trees and plants, which were mixed with sweet-smelling oils distilled from their fruits. The commonest of them are still in use to-day in toilet preparations and perfumes; among them we find extracts of bay, juniper, myrrh, nard, myrtle (an evergreen shrub once sacred to Venus) and frankincense, or oil of Lebanon. These substances were well known two or three thousand years ago, and were present in the balsam oil used by the heroes of ancient Greece. This contained a selection of perfumes which were mixed with a form of liquid soap.

In Roman times, baths were already in widespread use. In Rome itself, the ruins of many bathing establishments, built both for public and private use, show traces of great luxury and magnificence. It was the practice of all Roman emperors, from Nero to Constantine, to erect baths which would outshine those erected by their predecessors. It seems certain that, by this time, soap was already in general use in Mediterranean countries. The Phoenicians were possibly the first to manufacture and sell it in this region. We know from Pliny's writings that soda soap was being made from goat fat and wood ash, and hardened with salt, in the first century A.D.

The process was very simple and basically the same as we use to this day. At that time, soap was probably made mainly

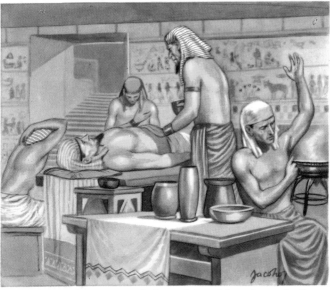

The Egyptians smeared themselves with resins and oils.

in the home. It was not until the thirteenth century that it became an industry, first in Italy and then in France and England. The Venetians acquired a great reputation for the quality of their soap. Its production was carefully supervised by officials of the Republic, and it was decreed by the Doge that in Venice and her provinces no one should use foreign soap. All Venetian soap was therefore branded with the mark of its origin, and its reputation grew as people associated the high quality with the brand-mark on the soap.

Soap is made by treating fats and oils with alkalis. The fats are split, forming soap and glycerine. Caustic soda is commonly used as the alkali, and, to a lesser extent, caustic potash. Tallow, or animal fat, has long been used for making hard soaps. Toilet soaps are made from a wide range of fatty

In 600 B.C., according to the Roman writer Pliny, the Phoenicians were making soap from goat tallow and wood ash.

The Romans built all sizes of baths, including the enormous "thermae" of imperial Rome.

materials, including olive, coconut, cotton-seed, palm and fish oils.

There are two main methods for making soap: the boiling process and the hydrolytic process. Boiling is the traditional method, in which caustic soda is boiled with the fats or oils in a large soap pan. After a time, the solution is treated with common salt. The soap forms a layer on the top of the pan; this neat soap consists of about 70 per cent. soap and 30 per cent. water. The bottom layer is a soapy liquid containing dissolved impurities. The boiling process takes anything from five to ten days to complete, the success of each " brew " depending on the expert soap boiler who, from time to time, tests the quality of his neat soap by tasting it.

During boiling the caustic soda converts the fats to soap and glycerine by a process called saponification. In the hydrolytic process, saponification is achieved by treating the fats with super-heated water at high temperature. This method can be adapted to produce a continuous flow of neat soap, the conversion of fat to soap taking place in a matter of a few hours instead of several days. To-day, about half of all soap produced is made by boiling and half by the hydrolytic process.

TOILET AND SPECIAL SOAPS

France was the first centre of toilet-soap production; the soap-makers of Marseilles have long been famous. The best Marseilles soap used to be made of pure olive-oil, but a mixture of olive, sesame and ground-nut oil is now commonly used. A tablet of hard white toilet soap will consist of about 85 per cent. soap and 15 per cent. water. Dyes and perfumes are usually added in small amounts.

During processing, the soap is first milled to a waxy consistency which lathers much better than ordinary laundry soap. A stream of molten soap is then poured between two rotating rollers, on which it solidifies as a thin film. The film is removed, ground up and treated with dyes and perfumes. It is milled again and again until the ingredients are thoroughly mixed, and then pressed and stamped into bars and tablets. Medicated soap is also made in a similar way, antiseptics, for example, being added with the perfumes. Camphor, salicylic acid and sulphur are examples of materials added to soap. Floating soap is made by aerating the neat soap before cooling.

FLAKES AND DETERGENTS

The introduction of washing machines in the 1930s created a demand for a type of soap different from the bar soap previously used for laundry purposes. Soap flakes were brought on the market, and have remained popular ever since. In making flakes, the soap is rolled out in very fine sheets which are then dried and broken up. In recent years, new types of soap-like material—which we call detergents—have been developed. These detergents have advantages over soap under many conditions of use; for example, they may be used effectively in hard water where soap will be converted into a useless scum.

Soap and other detergents are able to remove dirt by a process of emulsification. Fatty substances which are holding the dirt on to the skin or fabric are lifted from the surface and held in the water as tiny globules. These globules remain floating in the water, and do not settle back on to the fabric or skin; they are carried away in the dirty water that flows from the bath or wash-tub.

Several centuries ago, Venice was famous for its quality soap.

Which of us has not, at one time or another, dreamed of running away to sea? Who has not felt the lure of the Merchant Navy, inviting us to travel to new lands and meet new people? Yet how few of us realise our ambitions. We must be content to watch from the shore, as the great ships disappear slowly over the horizon.

Every ship that sails the sea in the peaceful interests of humanity, from the smallest fishing boat to the largest transatlantic liner, may be said to belong to the Merchant Navy. Every member of the crew, including captain, officers, mates, engineers, stewards, able seamen and cabin boys, belong to the brotherhood of the sea. They are sailors all, and all are bound to obey the strict regulations of International Maritime Law.

Each Merchant Navy sails under its own national flag, with its own traditions and regulations. But in some matters, all observe the same " common law of the sea ". Lights, signals, safety devices and loading regulations are controlled by general agreement. All nations treat one another with mutual respect in the great fraternity of the sea; any ship in distress can be certain that other ships will come to its aid, without regard to nationality.

MAIN TYPES OF MERCHANT VESSELS

The laws of the sea have evolved over the centuries, for merchant shipping has a history as old as that of man himself. Phoenician and Greek trading vessels, Venetian argosies, Elizabethan galleons and the clipper ships of more recent times all mark definite stages in the history of merchant shipping. Only in the last century, when steam-power began to replace sail, and ships were built of iron instead of wood, did the era of the modern merchant vessel begin. Let us look for a moment at the main classes of these ships now in use.

First, there are the great *liners* and *passenger ships* that serve the main sea routes of the world. Then come the *cargo boats* used for transporting every type of merchandise from iron ore to aircraft engines. *Oil tankers*, some of which are now among the largest vessels afloat—two tankers of nearly 150,000 tons are already in service—form a class of their own. In another category are the smaller vessels that make up the fishing fleet: *trawlers*, *drifters* and *smacks*. Finally, there is a wide variety of different types of auxiliary vessel: *lightships*, *cable-layers*, *salvage ships*, *dredgers*, *pontoons*, *lighters* and *tugs*.

MAP, CHART AND COMPASS

The modern freighter is a sturdy ship of smart appearance, equipped with all the essentials necessary to a life at sea. Dominating its decks is the captain's bridge, the brain and nerve centre of the vessel. Here the orders are given, and the ship's route is worked out. Here are the scores of maps, charts and diagrams that are carried by every sea-going vessel, showing in accurate detail the position of islands, rock shoals and other hazards. Contours on the charts show how the sea floor shelves away from the shore. Lightships, buoys and other navigation aids are clearly marked. With the aid of these maps and charts, the captain of a ship can take his vessel with safety anywhere in the world.

The captain's bridge resembles a veranda opening off the charthouse and wheel-house; its thick windows give an all-round field of view. In the wheel-house and charthouse are the navigational instruments, including the compass. Modern compasses are commonly of the gyro type, in which a rotor is spun electrically. Many merchant ships are equipped with the simpler dry-card compass invented by Lord Kelvin in 1876, or with a liquid compass of the kind carried by naval vessels. Alongside the compass is a special device which indicates any deviation made by the ship from the course laid down by the captain.

Cargo vessels ply the ports of the world, transporting goods in their vast holds.

Transatlantic liners are built not only for speed and safety, but also for the comfort of the passengers.

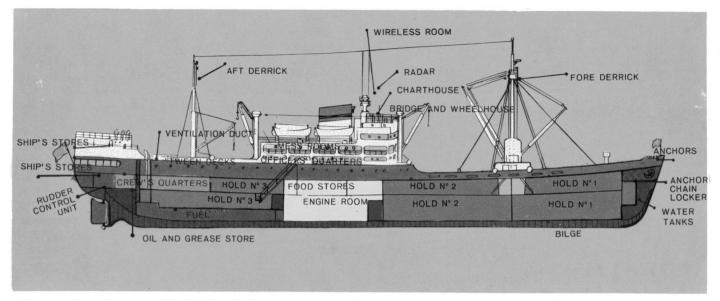

Cross-section of a cargo ship showing the large space reserved for cargo. The unloading of the cargo is done by the derricks, situated fore and aft. Bilge pumps draw off waste water which collects in the bilges.

SEXTANT AND CHRONOMETER

Every ship's officer must know how to use the sextant. Invented in 1731 by John Hadley, this instrument gives the angle of the sun or of a star above the horizon, and is used for estimating the latitude and longitude of a ship. Until the sextant was invented it was impossible to make an exact check on the geographical position of a ship at sea.

In 1714, the British Government announced an award of £20,000 for anyone who could produce an instrument to establish longitude, accurate to within half a degree after a six weeks' voyage. At that time it was realised that if the effect of temperature changes and of the ship's motion could be overcome, many calculations relating to the ship's position might be made by means of an ordinary clock. The development of the ship's chronometer, also kept on the captain's bridge, dates from the time that the British Government made its offer. Chronometers are now built to astonishing standards of accuracy, considering the unfavourable conditions they encounter at sea. They are made from special metals to protect the mechanism from the effects of atmospheric changes. Normally, the margin of error of a good chronometer does not exceed one second a day, and this can now be checked by radio. Compass, sextant and chronometer enable any trained officer to find the exact position of his ship, wherever it may be on the high seas. A sextant was used during Apollo 12's journey to the moon, to determine their exact position in relation to the Earth.

ON THE CAPTAIN'S BRIDGE

If the captain were to ask you up to the bridge, one of the first things you would notice is the helm or wheel by which the ship is steered. The man in control is an experienced sailor, who swings the wheel one way or the other to keep the ship on the course it must follow. The wheel is linked hydraulically or electrically with an engine set in the stern, which turns the heavy rudder in response to the slightest movement of the helmsman's hand.

On the bridge, too, you might see an instrument with a large dial divided into sections indicating various speeds from STOP to FULL AHEAD and FULL ASTERN. This instrument communicates with a similar one in the engine room. When the dial hand is moved, a bell rings and the engineers slow

down or increase speed accordingly. Most ships also have an internal telephone, so that an officer can give precise instructions to the engineer on duty.

MEASURING SPEED AND DEPTH

In navigating a ship, it is important to know the speed at which it is travelling. This is measured by its log which trails through the water on a line in the vessel's wake. The log consists of a double funnel through which the water rushes as the boat moves along. The greater the speed the stronger is the pressure that the flow exerts on the small propeller fixed in this instrument. The propeller operates a counter whose readings are transmitted via the line to a dial in the ship's poop or in the wheel-house.

When navigating in unfamiliar waters, it may be necessary for the captain to check the depth of water beneath the vessel. Underwater currents will often build up new sand banks, for example, which are not shown on the charts. The traditional method of estimating depth was to attach a lead sinker to a reel of strong wire and run it out at intervals as the ship moved forward. This system works well in shallow water and has been used, in fact, for taking soundings of up to 6,000 feet. Another method involves the use of an instrument which measures the pressure of the water as it is lowered towards the sea floor. These techniques have now been replaced by echo-sounders, which measure the exact time taken for sound waves travelling from the ship to the sea bottom and back again. As the speed of sound in water is known, the depth can be estimated easily and accurately.

THE WIRELESS OPERATOR

In the last half century, the wireless has become an essential feature of every ship. Wireless-telegraphy enables messages to pass between ships and shore, keeping the ship in constant touch with land. The wireless operator, known as "Sparks", has a cabin of his own which is commonly situated on the boat deck or near the wheel-house. Here he receives weather bulletins, storm warnings and important items of daily news which are posted on the ship's notice board.

The wireless operator transmits reports of the ship's progress to the company's headquarters ashore, and receives instructions in return. As only the largest merchant ships

Most passenger and cargo ships now use radar equipment, enabling them to "see" even in the worst weather conditions.

The engines are to be found deep in the heart of the ship, throbbing away in cavernous engine rooms full of switchgear and illuminated dials. Coal has now almost disappeared as a fuel, and fuel oil has taken its place. The older type of steam reciprocating engine is being supplanted by the more powerful turbine engine, which has long been used in naval vessels. Since about 1930, the diesel engine has also been installed in increasing numbers of cargo boats, and diesel-powered vessels can usually be spotted by their low, squat funnels. The function of the engine is, of course, to turn the propellers or screws, of which there may be one, two, four or even more. The engine transmits its power to the screws by means of a revolving shaft.

The din in a ship's engine-room can be unbearable to anyone who is not used to it. But the engine-room is home to the ship's engineers, who maintain a constant watch on the machinery that drives the ship. The chief engineer carries a heavy responsibility, and ranks equal to the captain of the ship. The engineers are also responsible for the power room, in which are generators which produce electricity for the ship. Electric current is required for lighting, for the radio and signalling installations, for scores of mechanical devices and for operating electric winches and derricks.

carry a doctor, he may have to ask for medical advice, or even call for a doctor from a passing ship should someone become seriously ill. In the event of a real emergency, his S O S. signals will bring other ships racing to the rescue.

If the ship runs into fog, " Sparks " will contact the marine radio stations, of which there are many scattered over the world. With the help of direction-finding equipment, he will be able to pin-point the position of the ship with great accuracy. A ship that carries wireless need never be lost at sea. Since World War II, radar has become a vital navigational aid, enabling the Captain to " see " vessels and other hazards even in the foggiest weather.

DOWN IN THE ENGINE-ROOMS

A modern merchant ship will often travel at between twelve and fourteen knots, or nautical miles, an hour, equivalent to a land speed of fifteen miles per hour. Powerful engines are needed to maintain even this modest speed in pushing a heavy ship through the water. And ships like the *Queen Elizabeth 2*, which average thirty knots, need engines which are very powerful indeed.

ACCOMMODATION ON BOARD

Every ship of any size and importance is also constructed so that it can be divided up into watertight compartments. In an emergency, the captain can seal off and isolate any compartment behind watertight doors. In this way, he can prevent the spread of fire, or ensure that the ship will not sink if damage causes a leak. The bilges, where waste water collects at the bottom of the ship, are themselves located in watertight compartments and can be emptied by means of the bilge-pumps.

The hull of a ship is designed according to the purpose for which the vessel is built; in a tanker, for example, two-thirds of the hull is divided into a series of large tanks to hold the oil. Tankers are easily recognised, since the engines, living quarters and superstructure are all concentrated at the rear; this is to minimise the danger of fire and leave more space for oil tanks. In passenger vessels, the central sector of the hull is used for cabins, lounges, dining-rooms and service quarters. Cargo boats are so constructed that the bulk of

The engine room, where the shaft (bottom right) connects the engines with the propellers.

their space is reserved for stowage. The freight compartments are called holds or bunkers.

In most ports, there are shore installations for loading or unloading cargo boats, including cranes of various sizes, overhead cable trucks for bringing up mineral ores, and chutes for handling grain and cereals. But in small ports it may be necessary for a boat to make use of its own derricks. These are usually worked by electric winches driven from the ship's power supply. It is customary to employ local dockers both for loading and unloading, even when the equipment used forms part of the ship's own gear. Cargo is stowed with great care under the supervision of experts, to ensure that it will not shift or slide in stormy seas. If badly-stowed cargo moved in this way, the freight might suffer serious damage, and the ship might also develop a list if the cargo were to pile up on one side of the hold.

THE CAPTAIN'S MEN

The ship's personnel can be divided into two categories. On the one hand, there are the deck officers and those members of the crew who are responsible to them; on the other hand, are the engineers and those of the crew who work under their orders. Passenger ships include a third important category consisting of cooks, stewards and others responsible for the welfare of the passengers.

The deck officers supervise the navigation of the ship and its handling in and out of port. They are responsible to the first officer, who is often called the " first mate ". The number of deck officers varies according to the size of the vessel; a minimum of three is needed to do two watches of four hours each per day. The larger vessels carry perhaps ten officers of this rank. In many of the world's merchant fleets, young cadets are attached to these senior officers and study for their examinations in nautical institutes ashore. In this way, the cadet can gain real sea experience during a two- or three-years' apprenticeship, before being given a position on one of the company's boats.

Able seamen working under the deck officers include the helmsmen, carpenters and storekeepers. Young deck-hands and boys come under the direct orders of the boatswain, who has access to the upper deck. They do the cleaning and

Cargo on a ship must be stored with great care as shifting cargo on the high seas can endanger the safety of the ship.

unskilled jobs necessary for the efficient maintenance of a ship.

INDEPENDENT PERSONNEL

A ship will usually carry three or more engineers, who are responsible to the chief engineer. The engineers enjoy absolute independence in their domain. Like the deck officers, they usually have apprentice engineers training under them. In the engine-room, the boatswain's place is taken by a leading stoker, who acts as a link between the officers and the men.

Apart from these important members of the ship's crew, we have the purser, who has a special administration job. The wireless operator, too, is a specialist who has been trained to fill his highly technical post. Finally, there are the stewards, cooks and kitchen boys; on passenger ships they come under the supervision of an officer, who will also be in charge of the cabin stewards and stewardesses.

There are special problems and difficulties to be faced in controlling a ship's crew, who must live in their own small, isolated world, often for long periods at a time. It is only by careful planning and organisation, and by maintaining proper discipline that these difficulties can be overcome. The crew of a ship must be prepared to accept the monotony that is inevitable on a long sea voyage and even to-day, with all the scientific equipment that is carried to ensure safety, there are hazards to be faced at sea. Every ship must carry lifeboats with places enough for everyone on board. Lifebelts are provided for the emergencies which everyone hopes will never come.

IMPORTANT NOTE:

When the tonnage of a naval ship is given, the reference is to *real tons*, each of 2,240 pounds. This is called *displacement tonnage*, a measurement based on Archimedes' Principle. With a passenger ship, however, tonnage is quoted in *gross tons*, each of 100 cubic feet of enclosed space contained within the ship. Cargo boats and tankers, on the other hand, express their weight as the difference between the number of real tons they displace when empty and when full. This is called *deadweight tonnage*. In other words, a liner's weight is really given in volumetric tons and a tramp's in the avoirdupois weight of its maximum load.

The powerful tugboat is essential for easing large ships in and out of port.

IRON AND STEEL

Iron is the metal on which our present civilisation has been built. With one of its alloys, which we know as steel, iron gives us our cars and ships, our railways and our bridges. We build our skyscrapers and our factories, our blocks of flats and public buildings on skeletons of steel. Without iron and steel, a country cannot prosper; with an ample supply, it has the makings of a great power.

THE PROPERTIES OF IRON

Iron itself is rarely used in its pure form, and it is never made as such on a commercial scale. The core of our planet may consist largely of molten iron, but the metal is found in a free state on the earth's surface only in meteorites. These masses of matter reaching us from space are believed to have been man's first source of iron. Primitive man did not know how to obtain iron from its ores, and had to make do with the metal he found inside the fragments of meteorites scattered about the earth.

In its pure state, iron has a specific gravity of 7·86. It is a shining grey metal which melts at 1,539°C.; if it contains carbon, it melts at lower temperatures. In the blast furnace for example, iron is molten at 1,130°C.

Iron is attacked readily by oxygen, forming flakes of rust when exposed to the air. For this reason, it exists in nature largely as an ore consisting of oxide combined with other substances such as silica and alumina.

Iron plays its part in the living matter of plants and animals. It is found in the liver, marrow and blood of human beings and other mammals. Lack of iron may cause anaemia, beri-beri and other deficiency diseases, and medicines containing iron are often used in their treatment.

ORE INTO ALLOY

Many minerals contain iron, but only a few are used in

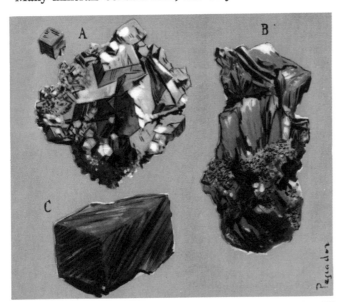

Iron pyrites (A) has a brassy appearance. Haematite (B) becomes reddish-brown when powdered. Magnetite (C) is sometimes called lodestone.

practice as a source of the metal. The most important iron-ores are haematite, magnetite (also called magnetic iron-ore), limonite, siderite and the iron pyrites. In one form or another, these ores occur in most parts of the world, especially in North and South America, in Britain, Western Europe and Russia. The famous Lorraine deposits on the borders of France and Germany, once neglected because of the difficulty of removing phosphorus from the haematite ore, contain ample supplies of iron. In Britain, the richest ironstone deposits have largely gone, but there are still 3/4,000 million tons of workable ores located in a broad strip running from Yorkshire to Dorset. This forms a useful part of the world's reserves, which are estimated at about 30,000 million tons; this does not include the huge untapped deposits of ore which have been discovered in the heart of Brazil. With an annual consumption of iron-ore in the region of 125 million tons, the world is not in any immediate danger of running out of supplies.

When smelted in blast furnaces, iron-ores produce a crude metal containing many impurities. This is commonly known as pig-iron. It is the raw material of steel. A typical carbon steel consists of 98/99 per cent. of iron modified by the addition of a small quantity of carbon. There are many kinds of *special steel*, which are made by including small amounts of various metals in the alloy: nickel and chromium, for example, are used in the manufacture of stainless steels; manganese gives a steel of greater strength; vanadium, tungsten, molybdenum or cobalt, are present in *high-speed steels* used in cutting tools and machine parts.

WHO FIRST MADE IRON?

The beginning of the *Iron Age*—about 1000 B.C.—coincides roughly with the beginning of recorded history. This is understandable, as the use of iron made possible the rapid development of human civilisation. Iron tools brought revolutionary changes in primitive agriculture, and stimulated the refinement of all manner of skills. It became possible to produce man-made goods much more effectively than before, resulting in the development of trade and commerce. These, in turn, sent man on his explorations across land and sea as he sought to make contact with the peoples of other lands.

Nobody knows when the first iron-smelting furnaces were set up. Specimens of ancient ironwork must have rusted to dust many centuries ago. We do know that the Egyptians were using iron in small quantities, and were perhaps even making a crude form of steel, during the second millennium before Christ.

The knowledge of how to smelt iron was probably fairly general in the Middle East at that time. There is a reference in the Book of Genesis to Tubal-cain, who instructed others in the working of iron. In King David's time, about 1000 B.C., iron tools and weapons were being made, and it is reasonable to guess that there were many small iron-smelters working in the mountain valleys of Anatolia, Iran, the Caucasus and other parts of the Middle East where iron-ore was to be found.

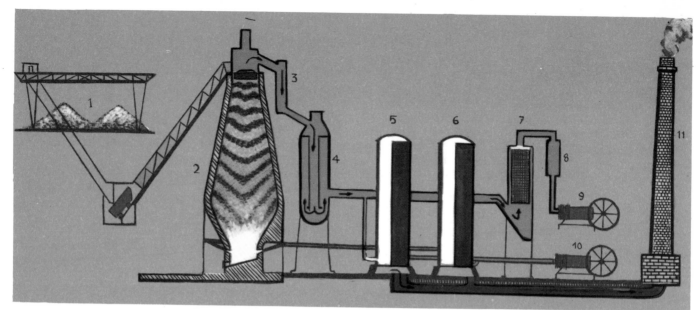

Smelting iron-ore. 1. Mixture of iron-ore, coke and limestone; 2. Blast furnace; 3 and 4. Outlets for hot gases, which are washed at this stage; 5 and 6. Cowper stoves; 7 and 8. Purifiers; 9 and 10. Gas engines; 11. Chimney for waste gases.

IRON INTO STEEL

In the early iron-smelting furnaces, wood or charcoal were used for firing the crushed ore. When enough crude metal had sunk to the bottom of the furnace, it was taken out, cooled and hammered; it was then reheated and hammered again and again. Hammering was the only way in which impurities could be removed and the metal bound into a solid mass. This practice continued well into the Middle Ages, until it was discovered that many of the impurities could be removed by mixing limestone with the ore and fuel in the furnace. Limestone is now an essential raw material in the smelting of iron in modern blast furnaces.

Throughout the early Middle Ages the Arabs made great progress in the art of smelting iron and converting it into steel. Their foundries in Syria and Spain became world famous, and are even now remembered in the terms, Damascus steel and Toledo blades. Metallurgy took a new turn in Western Europe in the fourteenth century, largely through Arabian influence. Large furnaces, using powerful bellows

Wrought ironwork of the Middle Ages. A. Tyrolean inn sign; B. fifteenth-century chest; right, wall lantern.

to create an artificial draught, were built in Britain, Germany and France. The foundries began to produce pig iron in greater quantity and at a lower cost; new methods were discovered for purifying the metal to provide the wrought iron which was much in demand (this pure form of iron rusts more slowly and is easier to work). Most important of all, the iron-workers were beginning to understand the advantages that lay in the alloying of iron to produce steel.

By a combination of circumstances, the economic development of steel production coincided with the height of the Industrial Revolution.

BESSEMER'S STEEL PLANT

The invention of the steam-engine enabled iron-smelters to increase the air pressure in their blast furnaces. Wood had already been replaced as fuel, first by charcoal and then by coke. The loss of metal was reduced when coke was used as fuel. Iron and steel founders began to use it in large quantities, especially when it became available as a by-product of the coal-gas industry.

In 1856, Henry Bessemer, an English inventor, read a report to the British Association in which he described a new method he had discovered for converting iron into steel.

The Bessemer process, which is now one of the most important steel-making processes, consists of blowing hot air at high pressure through a large mass of pig iron to burn silicon, manganese and carbon out of the metal. The oxidation products of these elements form a slag which floats to the top of the molten metal, leaving iron with only a small proportion of sulphur and phosphorus in it. Removal of the phosphorus presented a problem until Sidney Thomas and Percy Gilchrist showed how this could be done by mixing lime with the molten iron. This discovery, applied to the Bessemer process in 1879, proved invaluable on the Continent; until then, it had not been possible to make good steel from the huge iron-ore deposits of Lorraine, owing to the high proportion of phosphorus the ore contained.

THE OPEN-HEARTH PROCESS

The mid-Victorian age saw tremendous progress in iron

72

and steel production, and it was in this period that the first open-hearth furnaces were used. The Bessemer process had proved very successful in producing mild steels of low carbon content. But the process was protected by patents, and supply of this type of steel could not meet the growing demand for ships' plates, structural steel and railway lines. The open-hearth steel-making process, developed in Birmingham by the Siemens brothers, proved to be the answer.

In an open-hearth furnace, the charge is heated directly by the flames from the burning fuel. In making steel, a higher temperature is needed than in smelting iron-ore, and Friedrich Siemens showed how this could be achieved by making use of the hot fuel gases that would otherwise escape up the chimney. The air was preheated before entering the furnace, and fuel was burned in the air to heat the iron in the hearth of the furnace to the required temperature. The inner walls of open-hearth furnaces are lined with heat-resisting refractory bricks made of powdered magnesite and dolomite.

Sir William Siemens also built the first electric furnaces used in steel-making. The metal is heated by electric arcs struck between electrodes made of carbon or graphite.

BRITISH STEEL INDUSTRY

As we have seen, steel can be made in Bessemer converters, in open-hearth furnaces and in electric furnaces. These three methods are in current use, the Bessemer process being most popular in France and Germany, and the open-hearth in Britain and the United States, with electric furnaces gaining ground. Steel plants are commonly installed alongside blast-furnaces, so that the molten pig-iron is close at hand.

Without the blast-furnace there would be no pig-iron, and without pig-iron there would be no steel. This was the situation during the early years of the eighteenth century, when about 25,000 tons of iron were being produced from small charcoal furnaces scattered about Britain—and no steel. To-day, the British steel industry has a potential capacity of over 25 million tons, and this all comes from the iron-ore that is carried in a steady stream up inclined conveyors to the top of steel-plated towers. These ugly towers, sometimes more than a hundred feet high, we recognise as blast-furnaces

In the Bessemer converter, oxygen passes through the molten iron, oxidising the impurities which collect as slag, leaving pure iron.

A 500-ton press in a modern steel works, forging a large rotary unit.

when we travel through industrial areas. The blast-furnace is the birthplace of every article that is made of iron and steel.

INSIDE A BLAST-FURNACE

Like a huge metal pipe standing on end, the blast-furnace towers over its surroundings. Inside, its steel walls are lined with fire-brick; outside, it is festooned with equipment for feeding in the raw materials and drawing off the products. At the top is a double chamber which releases a constant flow of four parts of ore, two of coke and one of limestone into the twenty-foot-wide shaft beneath. Near the base of the furnace, a series of nozzles blow hot compressed air into the charge at a temperature of 700°C., and a pressure of 20 pounds per square inch. The coke burns in this fierce draught of hot air, releasing heat which raises the temperature of the charge. As the ore passes through the furnace it releases its iron, which trickles down to form a pool of molten metal at the base of the furnace. The metal is drawn off as pig-iron, white-hot and incandescent, ready for casting into solid " pigs " or for conversion into steel.

STEEL MEANS STRENGTH

If iron and steel are to be produced economically, unnecessary transport costs must be avoided. For this reason, the steelworks is usually built as near as possible to the sources of raw material. With coke as one of the main requirements, the works is commonly located on or near a coal field. Coal mines, blast-furnaces and steel works are almost always to be found together: in Britain, in the Midlands, South Wales, and Lanarkshire; in the United States, around Pittsburgh and Chicago; in Germany, mainly in the Ruhr and Saar districts; in France, in the provinces of Alsace and Lorraine; and in Luxembourg and Belgium. Russia has vast resources of iron and steel. At 23 million tons, the steel output of the U.S.S.R. in 1939 was equal to Britain's present annual total.

In a mechanical and industrial age, it is inevitable that living standards will increase most rapidly in those countries which are well provided with iron and coal. The United States, Russia, Britain, Germany, France, Belgium and Japan are rich in these essential minerals. Their strength in the world to-day is an indication of the power that comes from possession of the means to make iron and steel.

OCEAN-GOING PASSENGER SHIPS

Who has not thrilled to the sight of an ocean liner heading towards the open sea? Watch her as she makes for the distant horizon, marking her passage in the V-shaped wake that spreads across the surface of the water. A man-made floating city in which a few thousand people are inhabiting a private world of their own, cut off from the everyday life they have left behind on land. These greyhounds of the sea hold us in their spell just as, in the nineteenth century, the old clipper ships held our grandfathers spellbound. Built for speed and comfort, they are the pride of the merchant fleet. And they seem to know it. Their graceful lines and surging power remind us that there is no adventure like the adventure of the sea, no tradition as glorious as that which has been inherited by the sailor.

If you have sailed close to an ocean liner in a ferryboat or pleasure-steamer, you will have marvelled at the immense hull towering about you like a solid wall of steel. You may have felt that this is not really a ship at all; it is a floating palace enclosed in a shell of steel, with nothing but rows of portholes to link it with the outside world. And, in a sense, you would be right. Modern liners are the most palatial of all ships: they are the floating cities of the sea.

A LIVING ORGANISM

From the passenger's point of view, a liner is a complicated maze of corridors and passages, of decks rising one above the other, of dining-rooms, saloons, shops and offices. It is impossible to explore this complex world and get to know it quickly, and at first it seems that no one could ever hope to understand it all. Yet the plan of a liner is basically simple. The parts all combine to form a perfect whole, for a liner is designed to provide every amenity and comfort in the least possible space. She is like a living organism whose red corpuscles are the crew, whose white ones are the passen-

gers. Her brain is the captain's bridge with its array of nautical instruments. Her heart is the engine room in which the high-powered turbine or diesel engines keep four thirty-ton propellers racing round in the water.

After settling into his cabin the passenger begins his round of the ship. His first impression will be that he is inside a gigantic luxury hotel. There are lifts to carry him up or down, and he begins by exploring the decks which slope very gently towards the stern: the main deck, the promenade deck, the sports deck and the sun deck. On the sun deck, sometimes called "the lido", there is an open space for sun-bathing and recreation. There is a deck-tennis court, and a swimming pool with water drawn direct from the sea.

The passengers in a liner commonly travel in different "classes". There is nothing snobbish about this system, which dates back to the time when class distinctions were an accepted and important feature of the social order. In the nineteenth century, for example, hundreds of thousands of impoverished emigrants travelled steerage from European countries to America, making the journey the cheapest way they could. Their food was carried in baskets and bags. If the sea was rough, they would rope themselves together, tying one end of the rope to a firm support to avoid being washed overboard.

Cheap "steerage" rates are now a thing of the past in the transatlantic liner, on which accommodation is described as "first class", "cabin class", "second class" and "tourist class". The difference between these classes lies mainly in the quality of fittings and equipment, the position of the cabins and the number of berths they contain. The shipping companies try to provide accommodation to suit the means of all who are travelling in the ship. "Tourist class" on a modern liner for example, may be filled by young people,

Built in 1961, the P. and O. Steam Navigation Company's Canberra *has twin screws, weighs 45,270 tons and has an overall length of 815.5 feet.*

74

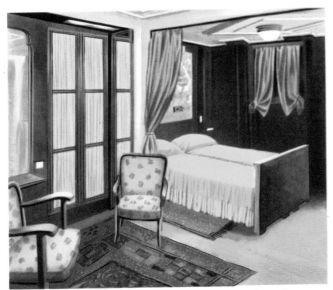

State rooms and first-class bedrooms on modern liners are extremely well furnished and decorated.

the busy executive can pick up the receiver and put through a radio " phone call " to New York, London or any other city in the world. The latest news is compiled from broadcasts and printed on the ship's own presses. Wherever the liner comes within the range of a television transmission, TV sets are turned on and passengers may watch their favourite programmes from the comfort of a deep armchair.

A VARIETY OF COMFORTS

One of the attractions of life on a big ship is the variety it offers. The traveller is mixing with people he has never seen before, and enjoying facilities that he would not find so easily on land. Long afternoons and evenings are spent in dancing, listening to concerts or going to the theatre. The most lively " show " of all is enjoyed when the Equator is crossed. Everyone turns out to watch passengers who have never before crossed " the line " being ducked in the presence of Father Neptune. This ceremony takes place in one of the swimming pools on deck.

The traditional ducking ceremony is not, of course, compulsory. If you were to tour the ship while Father Neptune is claiming his victims—he is usually an officer dressed up— you would find that many of the men were busy in the writing room, and the ladies had urgent appointments in the beauty parlour.

Life on board a liner has a special appeal to women. With no household chores to attend to, there is all the time in the world to go shopping on the ship and to enjoy dressing for the social events throughout the day. At mealtimes, there is a menu with a hundred different dishes—and not one that has had to be cooked by the person who enjoys it.

When supper and dancing is over and everyone has gone to bed, the only sounds to be heard are the occasional footsteps of the night stewards, the muffled throb of engines and the drowsy murmur of ventilators. The ventilating system of a modern liner is very carefully planned. Throughout the ship the atmosphere is kept at a steady spring-like temperature of about 65°F., no matter whether the ship is sailing the cold North Atlantic or cruising in tropical seas. Thousands of cubic feet of air must be changed every hour, an operation requiring the constant attention of the ventilation engineer and his mechanics.

students, ordinary families, and men and women who are making their way in life. The other two or three classes— some ships have done away with the " second " class—cater mainly for professional and business people, and for wealthy travellers who are prepared to pay extra for additional facilities and comfort.

SOCIAL LIFE ON BOARD

Many passengers come on board with no thought of taking physical exercise, except to stroll round the decks. But shipboard life soon begins to change their minds; the games that help to pass the time will also help to overcome the shyness that affects strangers of different nationalities. Friendships spring up, and the most unlikely people are soon splashing about in the swimming pool or throwing quoits to each other across a net.

An ocean voyage in a liner may not be quite as carefree as a cruise round the Mediterranean in a smaller passenger ship. The atmosphere in a liner is more purposeful; the people travelling in her are seldom making the journey just as a pleasure trip. But, despite this, an ocean voyage is still an opportunity to forget the worries and troubles of life ashore, to enjoy the wonderful meals and to make the most of the facilities provided in the lounges, writing rooms, libraries, cinemas, bars, ballrooms and other public rooms. The " floating city " offers an ample choice of attractions, not only indoors, but out in the healthy air and sunlight of the open deck.

CONTACTING THE OUTSIDE WORLD

There was a time when transatlantic passengers would cling to their cabin bunks or huddle in corners of the deck, suffering such agonies of sea-sickness that the dining-room was often empty for days on end. A long sea voyage was a hazardous adventure, and no one wanted to repeat it too often. The traveller in his ship felt isolated from the world he had left behind, and knew nothing of what was happening until he reached the other side.

To-day, there is not much isolation or adventure about a transatlantic voyage. Wireless operators are constantly in touch with the shipping offices ashore. Radio-telegrams may be sent at all hours of the day. In his comfortable cabin,

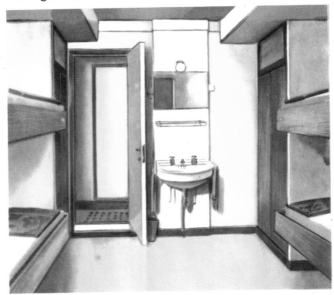

Although less luxurious than first-class cabins, tourist cabins have hot and cold running water and simple fittings.

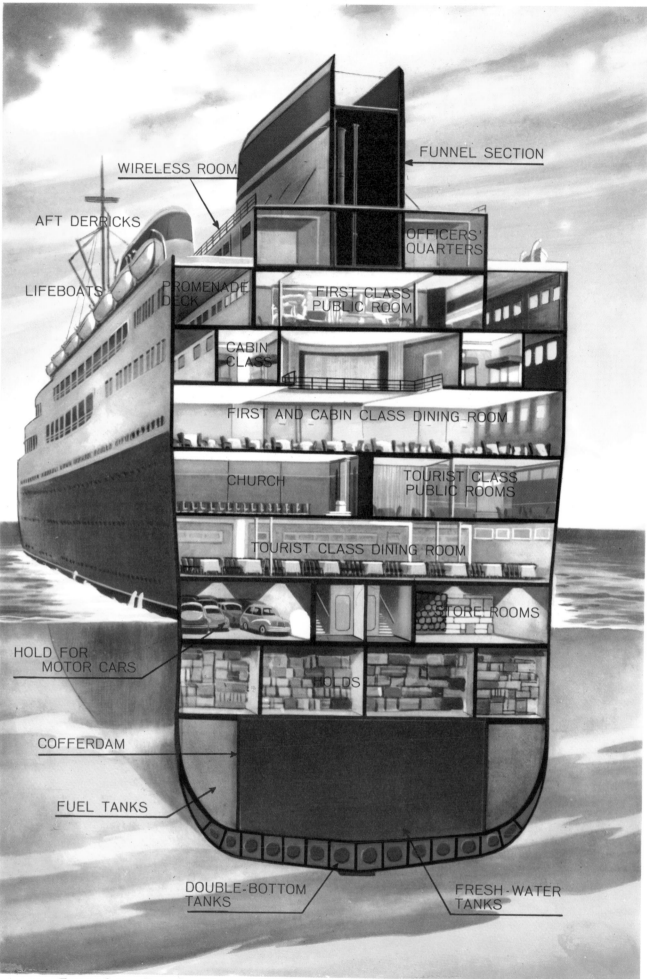

WIRELESS ROOM

AFT DERRICKS

LIFEBOATS

PROMENADE DECK

FUNNEL SECTION

OFFICERS' QUARTERS

FIRST CLASS PUBLIC ROOM

CABIN CLASS

FIRST AND CABIN CLASS DINING ROOM

CHURCH

TOURIST CLASS PUBLIC ROOMS

TOURIST CLASS DINING ROOM

STORE ROOMS

HOLD FOR MOTOR CARS

HOLDS

COFFERDAM

FUEL TANKS

DOUBLE-BOTTOM TANKS

FRESH-WATER TANKS

Even on luxury liners, careful use of all available space has to be made as this cross-section shows.

BIG NAMES IN SHIPPING

More than a thousand people may be needed to run a big passenger ship. The officers and crew include radio operators, engineers, electricians, mechanics, carpenters, cooks, stewards, stewardesses and waiters. The cost of maintaining and running a ship is very high, and a long journey by sea may often be more expensive than the same journey made by air. The passenger pays for the extra comfort and enjoyment of the sea voyage.

A modern liner costs many millions of pounds to build. The present high standard of comfort, speed and security has been reached only after a hundred years of steady progress. One of the greatest names associated with the development of the ocean liner is Cunard. It was Cunards who built the father of all liners, the *Gallia*, which went into service in 1879. Merging with the White Star Line, they built the old *Queen Mary*, the old 83,674-ton *Queen Elizabeth* and the 58,000-ton *Queen Elizabeth 2*, launched in 1968. The latter is now the most modern ship on the North Atlantic and cruise routes.

Cunard and White Star Line in Britain; North German Lloyd and Hamburg-American in Germany; the Compagnie Générale Transatlantique of France; the Finmare Group in Italy; the Home Line of America; these are some of the great shipping lines whose experience during the last century has combined to make ocean travel, especially between Europe and North America, as safe and pleasant as it is to-day. Huge sums have been spent in building such vessels as the French liner *France* and the 53,330-ton American liner *United States* that now holds the blue riband of the Atlantic. The establishment of the great ocean liner has cost not only money, but many lives too. The North Atlantic has taken a heavy toll of human life.

DISASTERS AT SEA

Few peacetime calamities shock the world more than the loss of a great ship. Fortunately this happens very rarely indeed. But fire and icebergs, rocks and fog are still the deadly menaces of the sea, and ships are still sunk from time to time despite the scientific equipment that they carry. When the Italian liner *Andrea Doria* ran into the Swedish ship *Stockholm* off Nantucket Island in 1956 she sank with fifty-two of her passengers and crew.

Thousands of fresh rolls and loaves are baked every day in the electric ovens of the ship's bakehouse.

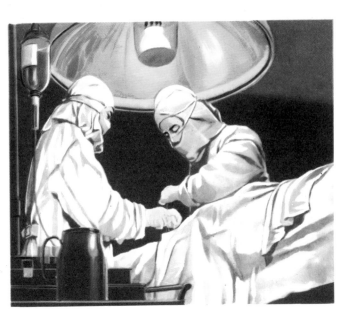

The medical service aboard a large liner is equipped to deal with all emergencies, including operations.

Much more mysterious was the fate of the *Normandie*, which in the " mid-thirties " gave France pride of place on the North Atlantic. When war broke out in 1939, she was lying in New York harbour and the Americans later took her over for conversion into a troopship. The day after she was transferred to the U.S. Navy, fire broke out on board the *Normandie*. This great ship of 83,423 tons capsized and had to be written off as a total loss. The same fate befell the British liner *Empress of Canada* in Liverpool docks in 1953.

Just before the First World War, two major disasters occurred, one of them due to fog and the other to an iceberg. While sailing in the St. Lawrence River in 1914, the Canadian Pacific liner *Empress of Ireland* struck a Norwegian collier and went down with a loss of over one thousand lives. At the time, the shock of the greatest of all sea disasters—the sinking of the *Titanic*—was still fresh in people's minds.

The *Titanic* belonged to the White Star Line. She was the largest and most splendid of that company's fleet, and had a great send-off when she left on her maiden voyage from England in April, 1912. Then, while travelling at full speed in the early hours of the morning of the 15th, the *Titanic* ran into an iceberg. Her 2,224 passengers did not believe that the wonderful new 46,000 ton liner could sink. But the water poured in, the ship's list increased and before dawn broke she sank to the bottom of the Atlantic, taking with her 1,513 men, women and children. Had there been more lifeboats on her boat deck, many more passengers would have been saved.

ACHIEVEMENT THROUGH SACRIFICE

So we see that, as so often in the history of man, the way to success lies to a great extent in anticipating the unexpected. When a ship is facing disaster at sea, we pin our faith upon the experience of the captain and his crew, and on the skill of the naval engineers and dockyard workers who have built the ship.

The hazards of the sea have always been a challenge to the British people, and the sea has always played a vital part in the history of Britain. People who live by the sea are ever reminded that the price of achievement is sacrifice.

COFFEE

We tend to think of the coffee bar as a novel sort of café that has appeared quite recently in our modern chromium-plated world. But, in fact, the coffee bar is simply a development of the " coffee house " that has been in existence now for hundreds of years.

Coffee drinking has always been more popular on the Continent than in Britain; the average Continental drinks nine cups of coffee to every cup of tea. But in Britain, the opposite is true.

THE ART OF COFFEE-MAKING

Until quite recently, the art of making coffee was not really understood in Britain. But the modern coffee bar is changing all that. Who can resist the fragrant smell that comes from the coffee trickling from the " espresso " machine? Who does not enjoy the stimulating effect of the first few sips, and the gossip and chatter that is so much a part of drinking coffee with friends?

In Britain now, as in most Continental countries, the coffee-break is part of the regular routine of life. This gentle stimulant helps to carry us through the day, and so long as we do not drink it to excess, coffee does not do us any harm.

FROM ARABIA TO BRAZIL

In the 17th century, the only coffee to reach Europe came from the Yemen in the Arabian Peninsula. Cultivation later spread to Ceylon, Java, Haiti, Jamaica and Brazil. As the popular song says, " There's an awful lot of coffee in Brazil ". This country has now become the greatest producer of coffee in the world; between fifteen and twenty million bags of coffee, each of 132 pounds, are exported from Brazil every year. So immense was this country's coffee output before the war that there was a surplus and, in the 1930s, 68 million bags of coffee were either burnt or thrown into the sea.

Brazil now supplies two-thirds of the world's coffee, which is grown mostly in the region of Sao Paulo, a fine city dominating the sea of plantations that stretch for miles and miles around it. The coffee tree, about fifteen feet tall, spreads out into a bushy crown of foilage with leaves like those of the laurel—dark green on top and lighter underneath. Against this foliage the white, sweet-smelling, star-shaped flowers stand out sharply. They are still on the tree when the little clusters of coffee cherries begin to appear. Each cherry contains two leathery green beans encased in a pulpy red skin. Growing in long rows from a dark, reddish-brown soil these trees make a pleasant sight. There are over 2,000 million of them in Brazil alone.

THE PLANTER'S " HACIENDA "

In the middle of the plantation is the *hacienda*, a residential farmhouse built in the old Spanish style. Surrounded by gardens and orchards, it may have been built a century ago when Latin American settlers began to plant coffee on a commercial scale. If the estate is large—and there are some with up to one million trees—it may include as many as a hundred cottages and dwellings for the workers and tenants. These form a small village enclosing the sheds and courtyards where the green coffee beans are washed, dried and graded.

NURSERY FOR YOUNG PLANTS

Not far away there will be a well-sheltered spot, where young plants are grown from selected seed. These are used to replace old trees. The most widely cultivated species is called *coffea arabica*, and its healthiest seedlings are bedded out when they are about six months old. On reaching a height of eighteen inches or so they are moved into the plantation. At this stage they are perhaps eighteen months old. After another two years, the first berries begin to appear. At the age of seven or eight years, the tree attains maturity and produces a full crop. It will continue to provide a good crop for another fifteen to twenty years, but reaches the end of its useful life when about forty years old.

PICKING THE " CHERRIES "

The picking season is the busiest time of the year on a *hacienda*. Everyone—men, women and children—works tirelessly to bring in the crop. One hundredweight of coffee cherries—enough to yield 25 pounds of beans—is a good day's picking for one person. The beans have to be extracted within four or five hours of picking, or they will acquire a bitter taste due to fermentation. There are two ways of doing this: by the " dry " or " natural " method, which is the most common, and by the " wash " method, which costs more but leaves the coffee with a better taste.

Directly they have been picked, the coffee cherries are brought to the yards, washed and spread on a cement base to dry. They are then taken into the sheds, where they pass through a series of machines which remove the shells and skin and clean the beans. Almost four-fifths of the total

The Coffea arabica *is the best of the twenty-five species of coffee tree. Ten to fifteen feet tall (a) with white, star-shaped flowers (b) and clusters of red fruit (c), each tree produces about two pounds of coffee beans.*

78

weight consists of pulp, jelly and a kind of parchment layer, all of which has to be removed; there is thus a large amount of waste.

PREPARING THE " BERRIES "

If the " wash " method is used the cherries are put straight into a machine which separates the green beans from the skin. A lot of pulp remains, so the fruit is soaked in troughs for at least a day, the object being to wash out the pulp it contains. After this treatment, the beans take a long time to dry and must be turned over and over in the sun before they are brittle enough to go through the hulling machines.

Hulling is necessary, no matter which method of extraction has been used. In this process, the beans are stripped of a fine silver skin which forms a protective covering on the kernel of the fruit. They are then polished, automatically graded and packed in bags which weigh 132 pounds each when full. At this stage, the coffee beans do not look like those we see in a shop. They are light green in colour and must be well and truly roasted before acquiring the rich brown hue and the fragrant smell so familiar to everyone who enjoys a cup of coffee.

THE FIRST COFFEE DRINKERS

Most of us like the flavour of a good cup of coffee, but few of us in English-speaking countries know how to make one. We are much more expert at making tea. The reason for this is probably that tea became an established drink in most English-speaking countries before coffee. Coffee grew originally in regions which were almost inaccessible, and the inhabitants were very reluctant to let the world know the secrets of their delightful drink.

According to legend no one took any notice of the coffee tree, which grows in stunted form in the Yemen, until one day an Arab goat-herd noticed his animals became frisky after eating its berries. So he picked some and took them to the wise man of the tribe, who found that when crushed and boiled they produced a bitter but quite palatable drink. What was more, this drink had the effect of waking you up and sharpening your wits. It seemed to put new life into you.

Partly because they wanted to hold on to the secrets of their plant, and partly because strict Moslems considered it a drug—the Koran prohibits the consumption of intoxicants and stimulating drinks—the Arabs were reluctant to pass on their knowledge of coffee. For several centuries it was either drunk in secret or prescribed by doctors as a medicine. Gradually it was realised that coffee was a harmless, pleasant drink, and cafés began to open in Mecca, the capital of the Moslem world.

THE HABIT SPREADS

From Mecca the coffee-drinking habit spread to Cairo, then on to Syria and Turkey. Here, it became the custom to boil water with sugar in it, and add the ground coffee afterwards. The Turks called it *kahveh*, a word which filtered through into many languages—into Chinese as *kai-fey*, into Russian as *kophe* and so on. The Venetian merchants, who must have enjoyed drinking coffee while trading in Constantinople, introduced it to the West.

The first public coffee house in Europe was opened in Venice in 1640. Several English coffee houses were destroyed by the Great Fire of London, the original City house having been opened in Cornhill in 1652. Meanwhile, the coffee habit was spreading to other countries: France, Holland,

Coffee cherries can be hand-picked or left on the tree to ripen and then be shaken off on to sheets placed beneath the trees. The principal coffee-producing countries are those of the continent of South America, with Brazil the largest single producer.

Austria, Italy and Spain. It was a habit that stuck, for coffee and wine go well together, and tea, its chief rival, was a product mainly of British-owned territories. This explains why Continental Europeans are more expert at making coffee than the British.

WHY " MOKA " IS THE BEST

Coffee grew well in the old Dutch and French colonies, and this was another reason for its great popularity on the Continent. Plantations were started in Java at the end of the 17th century. In about 1720 a French naval officer named de Clieu took a coffee plant from Paris to Martinique. Fifty years later, there were 19 million coffee trees growing on the island. From that single plant, which had once flourished in a hothouse belonging to King Louis XV of France, came all the hundreds of millions of coffee trees of Latin America.

Martinique still gives its name to some blends of coffee. So, too, do Puerto Rico and Colombia. Java has the reputation for producing the largest coffee beans. But the best and most famous coffee of all is " Moka " which comes from the mysterious country of the Yemen, where the Arab goat-herd discovered the original coffee plant. Only one of the two beans which normally develop in the coffee cherry survives in the " Moka " species. It kills off the other bean, growing larger, richer and rounder, and when roasted it acquires a special fragrance and flavour.

COFFEE ROASTING

Roasting is a most important operation in the preparation of coffee. The action of heat on the green beans removes all traces of moisture, brings out the aroma and fixes the flavour. It turns the beans a beautiful brown colour and reduces the amount of caffeine in them. Some blends are deprived of all their caffeine content in this way and sold to people who enjoy coffee but consider it harmful to the health. Roasting coffee is a process requiring great skill. There are now machines which do this job automatically, just as there are machines that make your coffee for you.

THE STORY OF THE NEEDLE

Ever since man began weaving textile fabrics, he has been badgering his womenfolk to make all manner of garments and furnishings from them. Over the centuries, wives and sweethearts have been acquiring and polishing the skills with which they create a great variety of textile products. And they have been able to do this by making use of one of the simplest and most efficient devices ever to be invented by man, the needle.

In Homer's legendary works, the *Iliad* and the *Odyssey*, we read of charming girls dressed in coloured gowns, who spent their days embroidering precious fabrics with deft and skilful hands. Even then, metal needles were in common use.

CHANGED INTO A SPIDER

According to one Greek legend, Arachne, the daughter of a dyer, learned the art of needlework from the goddess Athena. This young and beautiful seamstress was bold enough to challenge her divine teacher to a trial of skill. Judges were appointed, and the form the competition should take was decided. Arachne set about her task with eager fingers and produced a truly magnificent piece representing the loves of the gods.

Meanwhile Athena—the goddess who had taught Pandora's daughters to make tapestry—chose a subject showing a majestic group of Olympian gods. But the judges favoured Arachne's design, for the subject was perfectly portrayed and the colours were delightful. Athena was so enraged that she tore her rival's embroidery to shreds and struck her with the frame in which she had made it.

Deeply hurt by this insult, Arachne decided to take her own life. She knotted a rope around her neck and was on the point of jumping when Athena changed the girl

Exchanging light gossip and stories, the ladies of medieval England whiled away their time at their embroidery. Some of it, quite remarkable in its beauty, has been preserved to this day.

into a spider and the rope into a spider's web. This is the origin of the word *arachnid*, which zoologists use to-day for the group of animals which includes spiders.

A FEMININE ART

The homely art of needlework began long before the days of Ancient Greek civilisation. Egyptian, Hebrew and Phoenician women used their needles with great skill. So too did the matrons of ancient Rome, and the Etruscan women who lived in central Italy before the Christian era. In the Far East, the patient Chinese excelled in embroidery work, and the Japanese, who have a rich imagination, favoured subjects adapted from Nature. It may well be that many Eastern peoples owe something of their powers of application and their ability to learn quickly to the traditional needle.

At the time of the Crusades, some of the eastern arts spread to Europe. Among these was the technique of making fine brocades woven with the figures of animals, birds, trees and horsemen. Crusaders who brought home samples of these materials encouraged their wives and daughters to copy them as a pastime when their menfolk were away. Thus it became the fashion for the ladies of Norman England to spend long hours doing decorative needlework behind the studded doors of medieval castles. They were the originators of the "sewing bee".

THE FIRST NEEDLE FACTORIES

A great deal of modern embroidery work is done by machine. This is really a form of weaving, and tends to follow a uniform pattern. It has great charm and beauty, but machine-made work cannot match the character of a

In the Iliad *and the* Odyssey, *Homer tells us of Greek girls spending their days embroidering. Specimens of early embroideries of the 3rd and 4th centuries B.C. were found in Greek graves in the Crimea.*

hand-made article that has been produced, stitch by stitch, by a skilled needlewoman. To attain such skill requires a lifetime of patience and application. Embroidery is a craft that begins in childhood when hands are trained to produce works of art that reflect the taste and imagination of the young needlewoman. In the past there was plenty of time for learning such artistic skills, and a travelling packman would always be asked for needles when he called at the housewife's door.

In the old days, needles were treasured objects which were not always easy to come by. They were made by hand in small workshops, of which few records exist. There was, for instance, a needle works in Nuremburg in 1370. Another, belonging to a Mr. Mackenzie of Whitechapel, made very fine needles in the reign of Queen Elizabeth I. By then a Guild of Needlemakers, recognised by King Henry VIII, had been established, and small factories were meeting the growing demand brought about by elaborate fashions in dress.

The manufacture of good quality needles in many shapes and sizes created a revolution in dress styles. The flowing robes of the Middle Ages gave way to close-fitting tunics, breeches, collars, cuffs and gowns, which would have been impossible to make without this simple instrument. In due course, the invention of machinery for the manufacture of ready-made garments brought further changes to our style of dress. But the needle remained at the bottom of every woman's work basket, and it is still there to-day.

Meanwhile, the needle had found other uses. It became, for example, an essential piece of surgical equipment, being used for stitching wounds.

FOR SEWING AND SURGERY

To-day, needles are made from drawn steel wire by a process which is almost entirely automatic. The finest of all are pearl-threading needles with a diameter of about one-quarter of a millimetre. Ordinary needles, known as *Sharps*, *Blunts*, and *Betweens* are very much thicker. If intended for sewing, they are made from hard-tempered Sheffield cast steel. If they are to be used for hosiery work, a milder, softer steel is used. The elasticity of the needle depends upon the quality of the steel, which should have a high carbon content. This ensures that the needle will spring back to its original shape when it is flexed.

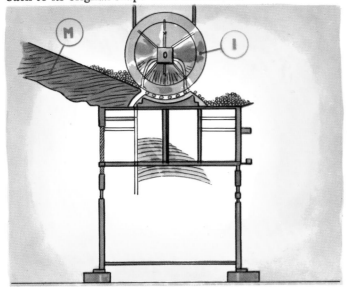

The needle is given its point. The lengths of steel are fed into the grinding wheel (I) from a sloping board (M).

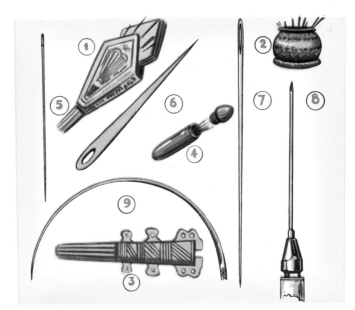

1 and 2. Medieval needle cases; 3. needle case from Pompeii; 4. modern needle case; 5. sewing needle; 6. bodkin; 7. mattress maker's needle; 8. hypodermic needle; 9. surgical needle.

The quality of steel is of great importance in making needles for surgical use, for example in suturing the wound resulting from an operation. These curved needles are made from the best alloy steels, so that they will penetrate the body tissues with a minimum of resistance. The same is true of the hollow hypodermic needles with which doctors give injections. Needles of this type come into the category of surgical instruments, and immense care must be taken in their preparation. They are commonly hand-made in moulds of accurate design and dimensions.

NEEDLES BY THE MILLION

When you examine a needle, it seems a simple object, and you would hardly imagine that fifteen different stages are needed for its manufacture. Let us look at some of them.

First, the steel wire is cut to the length of two needles. This single piece is straightened, tempered and then sharpened at both ends on a carborundum stone which is almost as hard as a diamond. Two operations are required to make the eyes: the impress of a stamping machine, followed by the sharp blow of a punch.

The twin eyes are pierced at the centre, forming two needles joined end to end which must now be broken. Only the finer qualities are broken by hand, but needles are made in such vast quantities that a team of operatives think nothing of breaking a million needles a week.

Next, the needles must be machine-ground to remove the rough edges from around the eyelet. The needles are then heated in a small furnace called a muffle, and plunged red-hot into a cold oil bath. Reheating to a blue heat, chilling, and repeated reheating serve both to harden the needles and give them elasticity. Washing, rolling, polishing and sometimes electro-plating follow, after which the needles are made up in graded packets for the trade.

It seems extraordinary that so small and commonplace an object should have to go through all these production phases before it is ready for use. But this is true of many manufactured products, and the technicians of modern industry take pride in ensuring that everything is done to make sure that the final product is as perfect as can be.

THE USES OF SULPHUR

The modern chemical industry uses all manner of substances as raw material. Some of these, like coal or salt, are commonplace substances that are familiar to all of us; others, however, are minerals and rocks that we seldom come across in everyday life. One of these is sulphur.

Sulphur, which has been known since very ancient times, is now one of the most important of all industrial raw materials. It occurs in many mineral ores in combination with metals such as iron and zinc. Sulphur itself is a non-metallic element, and was first defined as such by the great French chemist Lavoisier in 1777.

Sulphur used to be called brimstone, and was at one time widely used as a medicine. Brimstone and treacle was a favourite remedy of Victorian times. Pure sulphur is pale yellow, but the colour changes as it is heated. It is a poor conductor of heat or electricity.

Much of the sulphur used industrially is made into sulphuric acid, one of the most important chemical raw materials; modern industry uses tens of millions of tons of it every year. Sulphuric acid, also know as oil of vitriol, is a compound containing hydrogen, sulphur and oxygen; its formula is H_2SO_4.

WHERE SULPHUR COMES FROM

Small amounts of sulphur are present in human hair, in sheep's wool and in many vegetables, including cabbage. Larger quantities occur in most types of rock; iron pyrites, which is approximately half iron and half sulphur, is a commercially important source of sulphur, which is extracted by a roasting process; Spain and Portugal obtain sulphur from this source. Most of the world's sulphur comes, however, from deposits of the element itself, of which there are vast quantities in the United States, Mexico and Japan. There are also rich deposits in Sicily and in places on the Italian mainland.

Sulphur is a non-metallic element which occurs in pure, crystallised form or in combination with other elements.

One of the most interesting of the European sulphur deposits is the volcanic one at Pozzuoli a little to the west of Naples. Here, there is a volcano which stopped erupting about 750 years ago, but has been giving off noxious fumes of hydrogen sulphide ever since. Oxidation by the air releases sulphur from the gas. These semi-extinct volcanoes, still actively building up deposits of sulphur, are found only in a few places in the world.

EXTRACTION IN KILNS

Sulphur is mixed with chalk and limestone in many of the most important deposits. The rock is heated until the sulphur runs out as a liquid, leaving behind a slag called *gangue*. Two simple methods are used for doing this, one of which has been practised in Sicily since Roman times.

Round kilns sloping inwards towards the top are built near the sulphur quarries. The ore is piled in and covered with a layer of burnt-out material. The material at the bottom of the kiln is then lit, and the heat melts sulphur from the ore in the centre of the kiln. As the sulphur burns, it produces sulphur dioxide gas. Some of the sulphur is lost, as the gas escapes into the air. In effect, part of the sulphur is being used as fuel to provide heat which releases the rest of the sulphur.

A modification of this process is commonly used. The hot gases, instead of being allowed to escape, are passed from one kiln to another. Thus the ore, which in this case is packed into closed brick chambers, is preheated and less of the heat produced by the burning sulphur is wasted. The result is a better yield of sulphur.

Neither of these processes is very efficient, and most of the sulphur produced to-day is " mined " from underground deposits in the United States, Canada and Mexico, using a technique called the *Frasch Process*. This now provides about seven-eighths of the world's sulphur output of more than 10 million tons a year.

THE FRASCH PROCESS

The Frasch technique makes use of the fact that sulphur melts at about 113 °C. Boreholes are drilled into the underground deposits, which usually lie at depths of 200 to 2,000 feet, and a system of concentric pipes is installed. Operating from a base very like an oil derrick, the drill carries down with it a pipe consisting of three tubes. The outer one supplies superheated steam or water, the middle one is to carry the sulphur and the inner one is for compressed air.

When the sulphur deposit has been reached superheated water or steam is pumped in; the sulphur crystals in the area of the drill-head melt and trickle down into the borehole. The pipe is fitted with inlets which admit the liquid sulphur into the middle tube. Hot compressed air is forced down the inner tube and the molten sulphur is driven up the middle tube to the surface where it solidifies. Huge stacks of raw sulphur covering several thousand square yards are built up in this way. In America and Canada the reserve of sulphur in these stacks may amount to half a million tons or more.

About seven-eighths of the world's sulphur supply is now obtained by the Frasch process (above). The sulphur is melted by forcing super-heated steam underground through the sulphur deposits. The liquid is brought to the surface by compressed air.

In crystals, the atoms and molecules are arranged in well-defined patterns. Some substances crystallise in two or more geometric forms, a phenomenon known as *polymorphism*, which was first studied in the case of sulphur. Changes of pressure and temperature often result in the production of different forms of polymorphous substances in the form of minerals of varying crystalline structure.

Sulphur unites with most metals to form compounds which are called sulphides. When oxygen is also present, the substance will commonly be a sulphate. The following are commercially important sulphide ores: *lead sulphide*, or galena, used as a source of lead; *zinc sulphide*, or blende, used as a zinc ore, and in making paint; chalcopyrite, an ore containing *sulphide of copper and iron*; and cinnabar, or *mercuric sulphide*.

Two little-known *arsenic sulphides* are realgar and orpiment. The name realgar comes from an Arabic word meaning " powder of the cave ". It is used in fireworks, in which it produces a brilliant white light. Orpiment goes into yellow paints, one of which is called " King's Yellow ".

A common example of a sulphate is the calcium sulphate made by burning gypsum in a kiln. The product is made into plaster of Paris. Copper sulphate is a highly effective fungicide.

Pyrites is widely used as a source of the sulphur needed for making sulphuric acid. The pyrites is burned, when the sulphur in the ore combines with oxygen from the air to form sulphur dioxide. This must then be combined with more oxygen to form sulphur trioxide, which produces sulphuric acid when combined with water.

The combination of sulphur dioxide with oxygen, however, does not take place by a simple process such as that which produces the sulphur dioxide. In industry, two techniques are used, one of which is the old *Lead Chamber Process*, and the other the more modern *Contact Process*.

TWO COMPLICATED PROCESSES

The chemistry of sulphur trioxide production is quite complicated, and beyond the scope of this article. In the Lead Chamber Process, the sulphur dioxide passes through a series of lead chambers and towers where oxidation takes place, turning the sulphur dioxide into sulphur trioxide. The gases are sprayed with water from atomisers, and the sulphur trioxide dissolves to form sulphuric acid which falls to the bottom of the chamber like rain. Oxides of nitrogen are used in the oxidation process, most of them being recovered and used over and over again.

In the Contact Process, sulphur dioxide is oxidised to sulphur trioxide with the help of a metal catalyst. The ideal catalyst is platinum, but owing to its cost certain alloys of iron and vanadium are used. In the steel converter vessels, the catalysts help to bring about the transformation of the sulphur dioxide into sulphur trioxide. This is then absorbed in a solution of acid.

INDUSTRY'S " MAID-OF-ALL-WORK "

Sulphuric acid is a highly-corrosive, colourless liquid. It rapidly absorbs moisture from anything with which it comes into contact, including the human skin on which it leaves angry burns.

Sulphuric acid is used in one way or another by almost every important industry. It is used in making steel and fertilisers and in refining petrol; it is found in every car battery. Almost all manufactured products have required the use of sulphuric acid at some stage in their production. It is industry's " maid-of-all-work ". Fifteen million tons of sulphuric acid are used annually in the United States alone.

The most concentrated form of sulphuric acid is known as oleum, which is made by dissolving sulphur trioxide in 100 per cent. sulphuric acid. Oleum has a pungent smell, which contrasts strongly with the " bad-egg " smell of hydrogen sulphide.

FOR GUNPOWDER AND OINTMENT

On its way through the complex industrial maze of our modern world, sulphur may follow many different paths. It may end up in the vulcanising department of a rubber factory or in the bleaching room of a dyer's works. It may help to make gunpowder for the sportsman's cartridges or ointment and lotions for hair or skin diseases. But there is one traditional use of sulphur that has now died away without a murmur of regret. The schoolboy is no longer dosed with the brimstone and treacle that was a familiar cure-all in Dickens's day.

THE THIMBLE

The most brilliant inventions are usually the simplest, providing us with everyday gadgets so commonplace that we never give them a second thought. Imagine what a nuisance life would be without paper clips, or screws, or drawing pins, or combs. Or even the ordinary thimble!

Think how women and girls would have suffered over their sewing if, long ago in the distant past, someone had not had the idea of using an acorn shell to protect her fingertip.

Think how many jobs would have been left in the work basket if there had been no thimbles. For centuries, the thimble has been as much a part of woman's life as the sheath knife once was of man's. It has been a faithful companion during all those hours of needlework that mothers and daughters have devoted to the menfolk of the family.

Look back into the history of the thimble, and you will soon see how the importance of the thimble is much greater than its size might suggest. Egyptian mummies have been found with leather thimbles placed within easy reach, so that they might continue their embroidery work in eternity. Roman matrons used thimbles made of bone, horn and ivory to work gold thread into the purple cloth that was worn at Caesar's court.

In the Middle Ages, the Minnesingers of Germany paid homage to ladies in sentimental songs and verses that frequently referred to the thimble. On the tapering finger of a Nordic maiden the thimble was a symbol of patience and hope. In the past, it was often the custom to adorn thimbles with precious stones and enamel work. Men would give thimbles to their sweethearts on becoming engaged, and famous artists would decorate them. Members of the Rembrandt school in Amsterdam were fond of painting on thimbles in this way.

The Dutch claim that Amsterdam is the home town of thimbles in their present shape and form. Nicolas van Benschooten, a jeweller, made a thimble as a birthday present for a lady named von Reusselar. In the letter that he sent with the thimble on 19th October, 1648, he claimed to be its inventor. Thimbles have been playing their humble role in the domestic scene ever since.

Old books describing traditional arts and crafts refer to thimbles of a much earlier date than this. One of these books, which was published before Shakespeare's time, contains a sketch of a thimble-maker and his apprentice at work. In another published in 1628, a German craftsman is shown making a *fingerlin* on a hand lathe.

The most we can say for the Dutch jeweller, therefore, is that he started a fashion for giving precious thimbles on birthdays, engagements and similar occasions. Some of these old thimbles still exist, and any family possessing an old gold or ivory thimble should treasure it. For the time has gone when a girl would welcome a thimble as a gift, or as an alternative to an engagement ring. Sewing machines and ready-made clothes have done away with much of the drudgery of which the thimble was a symbol.

FOR PRACTICAL FINGERS

The thimble is no longer the romantic object that it was, but is simply a practical device that serves a very useful purpose. The modern thimble—still essential when sewing has to be done—is generally made of brass or steel. These metals are strong enough to prevent penetration by the needle.

Unless it is to be used for special types of needlework, the thimble is usually dotted over with tiny depressions, or it may have a saucer-shaped top to catch the needle if it slips. It must fit closely without pinching, and must cover the whole of the top joint of the finger.

For everyday sewing and mending, the thimble is worn on the middle finger. The little finger carries the thimble when embroidery is being done with a sharp, cutting thread. The index finger is protected by an open-topped thimble, as in the illustration. This is worn by weavers using special looms, where part of the work must be done by hand. With its open top, the thimble can be slipped over any of the other fingers if the index finger should become tired.

Although the thimble has lost some of its old meaning in the Western world, Oriental women still treasure it as much as they do their brooches and earrings. In Japan, it is not uncommon for a young woman to have two or three thimbles made from scooped-out pearls which have been finely worked over with gold thread. She keeps them, with other little gifts from her admirers, in a box made of mother-of-pearl.

Most of us have played " Hunt the Thimble " in the past, and it is a strange fact that thimbles show an unusual tendency to get lost. Cats have a liking for them, and will dribble them until they disappear under a cupboard; babies swallow them; girls at school leave a trail of lost thimbles behind them wherever they go.

1. Ordinary thimble; 2. Chinese thimble; 3. seventeenth-century German thimble; 4. steel thimble for leather workers.

COTTON
From Plant to Fabric

On a summer's day, you will often see little wisps of white fluff floating gently through the air. Caught by the breeze, these downy " snowflakes " may be wafted for many miles before settling on to the fields and hedgerows. If you pick one up and examine it, you will find it is a mass of slender fibres enclosing the seeds of poplar, willow, lime or other trees.

These fibres are, in fact, a form of cotton, similar to the cotton that we know as the most important textile fibre in the world. And the only reason we cannot spin them into useful yarns is that the fibres are too short.

The longer fibres that form the fluffy bolls of cotton plants are the basic material of all cotton fabrics. Soil conditions, temperature and rainfall, or irrigation, must all be right for the cotton plant to produce fibres of suitable *staple*, or length, for commercial purposes. One inch is the average staple of some three-quarters of the world's cotton crop. Certain varieties, like " sea-island ", have a $1\frac{1}{2}$ to $2\frac{1}{2}$ inch staple, but they are difficult to grow, and output does not exceed 500 bales a year.

Inside the fluffy bolls nestle the seeds of the cotton plant. From these comes the cotton-seed oil which is used in cooking and as a salad oil; the seeds are a source of meal for live-stock. The weight of seeds amounts to about twice the weight of the fibre that surrounds them. If the bolls were not har-vested, the seeds would be carried away by the wind, the fibres acting as streamers to catch the moving air.

Cotton-seed has become a commercially valuable raw material only in recent times, but the cotton plant has been cultivated for its fluffy fibre for several thousand years. It is a strange fact that the primitive peoples of Asia, Africa and America learned how to use cotton independently of one another. One reason for this was that cotton does not require any drastic preparation before spinning.

Herodotus tells us that by 500 B.C., women in parts of India were picking the bolls from this plant, spinning yarn and weaving it into fabric on their hand looms. There could hardly have been any connection between these people and the Indians of Peru, yet cotton burial cloths have been found

Cotton pickers in Pakistan and India spend long, hot days gathering the cotton bolls by hand.

which came from a Peruvian civilisation that flourished even before the time of the Incas.

It was probably in the Indus Valley of north-west India that systematic cultivation of the cotton plant began. Frag-ments of cloth found there were woven in about 3000 B.C. From the region that is now Pakistan, cotton growing spread in ancient times to almost all parts of the Far East which had a hot, damp climate. The Greeks and Romans who made journeys to the East, noted the existence of these fabrics, but never learned to grow the plant or to spin and weave cotton. Their clothes were made of wool and some-times of linen. Curiously enough, the Chinese, too, showed little interest in cotton until about the thirteenth century A.D., clothing themselves mainly in silk.

A LEGENDARY FABRIC

Climatic conditions were largely responsible for the slow development of cotton-growing in the Western world. Cotton needs a hot, moist climate, and Europe did not provide this. So we hear of cotton only spasmodically in early European history. Pliny, for example, saw it growing in Spain in the first century A.D. As the Arabs invaded the Mediterranean countries, they passed on their knowledge of cotton culti-vation, which they had learned in Persia. Only then was any real attempt made to cultivate cotton in these regions. But the climate of southern Spain and Sicily did not really suit it and cultivation died out.

In medieval Europe, cotton was even rarer than silk. Few people had seen a cotton fabric. Stories circulated of the woven cotton cloth that was produced in Abyssinia, Persia and India, and these reports—many of them coming from Marco Polo—inspired travellers to seek these fabrics and the raw materials from which they were made. Vasco da Gama, for example, brought a cargo of calicoes from Cal-cutta to Lisbon in 1497. Even more significant to the future

Left: *cotton plant;* Right: *flower, which may be yellow or pink according to variety, and the cotton boll.*

Several types of mechanical pickers are now used in the American cotton belt. The one shown detaches the ripe bolls by suction.

of the cotton trade was Christopher Columbus's voyage to the West Indies in 1492. Among the goods that the islanders offered him were some skeins of cotton yarn. This in itself was enough to interest early explorers in the New World.

Gradually, as the American and Caribbean shores were opened up by explorers from Europe, it became obvious that the climate suited cotton, and that the plant would grow well in this region of the world. The Mississippi basin was a particularly favourable area, and before long both British and French settlers began to establish plantations in the southern states of North America. Land was to be had for next to nothing, and the main problem was to find labour to cultivate and harvest the crop. So slaves were brought in from West Africa, a few at first, but in growing numbers throughout the 17th and 18th centuries. By 1790, Africa was being bled of about 75,000 negroes every year, who were sold into slavery on the plantations stretching east and west of the States of Alabama and Mississippi.

The time came—and it was only a century ago—when the industrial north of the United States of America decided to put an end to slavery in the cotton fields of the south. This led to the American Civil War of 1861-65, which ended in victory

for the north. The slaves were set free and the big plantations were split up. Many liberated slaves became tenant farmers. Meanwhile other countries were to fill the gap left by the United States.

As the southern states settled down, American production rose steadily, and for many years now America has been producing more than half of the world's annual crop of about thirty-five million bales. Each bale weighs four-and-a-quarter hundredweights. The next largest producers after the United States are Russia, India, Egypt, Brazil and Pakistan. These and many other countries turn out over seven million tons of fleecy " snowflakes " between them every year. Each individual cotton fibre in this enormous output is, on average, only an inch long and no thicker than the downy hair of a small child.

The cotton plant belongs to a *genus*, or class, which botanists call *Gossypium*. This class consists of eight *species*, of which only two, *herbacea* and *hirsuta*, produce cotton lint. Both species have several varieties, the most important being *hirsutum linnaeus* from which three-quarters of the world's cotton is obtained.

Sowing times differ in different countries; in the United States, plantations are ploughed and harrowed during the winter in readiness for sowing in early spring. This is done by mechanical drills which plant up to four rows at a time. Many weeds appear with the young shoots, and the ground must be weeded thoroughly if the cotton plants are not to be choked. This is done by multiple hoes called cultivators.

At this stage, there is a danger that weevils, bollworms, thrips and other insects may start laying their eggs on the plant's tender shoots. The cotton boll makes a perfect nest for these pests which, in the past, have destroyed many hundreds of millions of pounds worth of cotton. They are now attacked by spraying them with insecticides. Tractor-drawn sprayers sprinkle many rows of plants at a time with a mixture of DDT, sulphur or other chemical pesticides.

The really hard work begins when the seed is ripening inside the fleecy white boll. In countries like India, where picking is done by hand, the cotton harvest brings thousands of families to the plantations, The pickers move slowly between the rows of plants, stripping off the bolls and stuffing them into sacks.

In modern cotton gins, the cotton is blown through heated air and cleaned of unwanted debris before being pressed into 500-pound bales.

A more up-to-date method is to use a mechanical cotton picker, whose rotating spindles clear the crop and pass it on via an air conveyor into a container. Another type of machine collects the cotton by suction. These machines are widely used in the American cotton belt. They are very expensive, and it is common practice for the small farmer to hire one.

The next stage is known as ginning, a mechanised operation carried out in the factory sheds near the plantations. The object of ginning is to separate the cotton lint from the seed, and to clean it of leaves, burrs and other debris. The cotton is then conveyed to a press box where it is squeezed into a 500 pound bale, wrapped in sacking and bound with metal bands ready for shipment to the processing factory. Seed extracted during the ginning process totals twenty million tons per year, and it is now one of the world's most important sources of edible oils and livestock fodder.

" WEBS OF WOVEN WIND "

People sometimes say that the cotton industry is doomed and that man-made fibres will take the place of natural ones. But this is not likely to happen for many generations yet. Cotton is an inexpensive and versatile fibre, and is still used more than any other fibre in the modern world. Every day we talk about *poplin* shirts, *dimity* blouses, *cambric* underwear, *lisle* socks, *organdie* dresses, *corduroy* trousers, *gaberdine* breeches, *gingham* aprons, *denim* overalls, *chintz* curtains, *cretonne* chair covers and *huckaback* towels. These are all cotton fabrics, ranging from delicate " webs of woven wind " as they have been called, to tough, hard-wearing materials that seem to last almost for ever.

Left: *Bales of cotton arriving for processing at the factory.* Right: *Layers of the cotton bale are fed into a blender, where the fibre is opened out, cleaned and blended.*

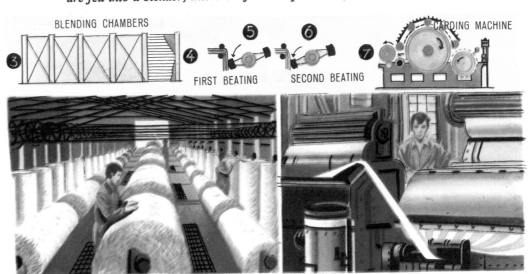

The cotton is then passed to the carding machine where revolving cylinders, covered with tiny steel teeth, clean and sort the fibres into a parallel direction before emerging as a soft, untwisted strand.

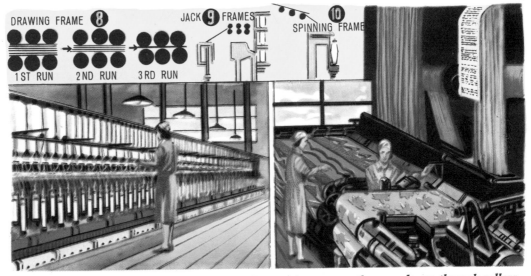

The drawing frame unites several slivers of cotton into one as they are drawn through rollers on to the roving frame which twists and winds the yarn on to bobbins. The yarn is further drawn and twisted on the spinning frame before being dyed and woven into cloth.

87

THE SEWING MACHINE

At one time or another, every one of us dreams of making a great invention that will bring us fame and fortune. Yet, when we learn what some inventors have gone through in their efforts to market their gadgets, the life of the inventor does not seem so glamorous after all. The story of the sewing-machine is a good example.

Sewing is a repetitive operation that has long attracted the attention of inventors. An attempt to ease the lot of tailors and dressmakers was made by Charles Weisenthal, a German, who invented the double-pointed needle in 1755. But no designs exist of the machine with which he is supposed to have used it.

The first real landmark in the development of the sewing-machine was the invention of a machine by Thomas Saint, a Middlesex man, in 1790. Saint's machine, which could stitch, sew and quilt, included some of the features of the modern sewing-machine. But Saint, like other inventors in those early days, thought that the answer lay in reproducing the actual movements used in hand-sewing. This was a fundamental error, and it persisted until 1830 when the first sewing-machine that really worked was constructed by a poor French tailor. His name was Barthélemy Thimmonier, and the story of his life is a tragic example of the trials and hardships that inventors often have to go through.

FRENCH INVENTOR

Thimmonier, who was about twenty at the time that the Luddites were smashing up textile machinery in Nottingham, worked at St. Etienne, an industrial town in the Loire province of France. The tedious work of stitching and sewing was not at all to his liking, and his thoughts turned often to the idea of inventing a machine that would do it for him. He marvelled at the patience of women, tatting away all day with crochet hooks. And it was while watching their swiftly-

In 1830, Barthélemy Thimmonier invented the sewing machine for the manufacture of ready-made clothing. It was a complete success. Made chiefly of wood, this first machine was subsequently replaced by metal machines.

moving hands, and their feet beating time on the floor, that inspiration came to him. He would build a machine that would do the work for them.

From that time on, all Thimmonier's spare hours were devoted to the development of a sewing-machine. And by 1830, he had something to show for his labours. The essential feature of his invention was the needle which curved upwards at the point. A foot pedal kept it in motion, each up and down motion inserting a stitch in the fabric. The machine was crude, but Thimmonier was on the right lines, as was shown by the application of his principle to later models. People who had thought he was mad now treated him with shy respect. With the help of an engineer in St. Etienne, he took out a patent covering his invention.

PARISIAN MOB WRECKS WORKSHOP

Thimmonier's next move was to go to Paris. Here he took some premises in the rue Sèvres, where he set up a workshop to build his machines and to take in sewing. Business began to grow, and there were soon twenty operators pedalling away in the small factory. Success was within his grasp, but this proved to be his undoing. The Parisian tailors did not relish the idea of serious competition. At first, they had regarded Thimmonier's sewing machine as a joke, but they soon realised that it was a real threat to their livelihood. One day, they stormed through the streets of Paris and burst into the Thimmonier workshop, where eighty machines were ticking their way steadily through an army clothing contract. This was too much for the enraged tailors. They picked up the machines, one after another, and dashed them to the floor, leaving the factory a complete wreck, and its owner badly injured.

RUIN AND POVERTY

Thimmonier's business was ruined, and he had to accept defeat at the hands of the mob who resented his invention. With one of his machines tucked under his arm, Thimmonier wearily tramped the streets of Paris seeking a job as a tailor. But the Parisian firms wanted no dealings with this man who wished to change the traditional pattern of their craft. So he had no alternative but to return to St. Etienne.

At home, Thimmonier did not waste his time. He soon perfected a new machine which was capable of doing 300 stitches a minute. Hoping that English manufacturers would be interested in it, he crossed the Channel, and sold the patent rights in Britain. The money he made was not enough to live on, however, and Thimmonier decided that he preferred to struggle on in France than in Britain. So back he went to France, where he spent his last years in poverty. Barthélemy Thimmonier died in 1857, a terrible example of the fate that can befall an inventor whose discoveries are seen as a threat to the established traditions of a trade or industry.

AMERICAN INVENTORS

Meanwhile, as Thimmonier was struggling to persuade his countrymen to accept his invention, two American

By 1841, Thimmonier had set up 80 machines in his Paris workshop and was busy on an army clothing contract when a mob descended on his establishment, wrecked the place and threatened to kill him if he continued to use his sewing machine.

inventors were racking their brains to build a practical sewing machine. One of them was Walter Hunt of New York—the inventor of the safety pin. The other was Elias Howe from Massachusetts.

Hunt's machine, like Thimmonier's, was fitted with a curved needle attached to a vertical arm that moved up and down. But he had given the needle an eye near the point. This meant that when the material was pierced, a loop was formed underneath. A small horizontal shuttle, moving backwards and forwards, passed another thread through this loop, thus forming what is now known as a lock-stitch. Unfortunately, Hunt did not attempt to patent this device until it was too late, and he was not directly involved in the great legal struggle over the patent and manufacturing rights on sewing-machines which took place in America during the 1850s.

ADDITIONAL IMPROVEMENTS

Meanwhile, Elias Howe had been making experiments and had reached virtually the same solution as Hunt. He, too, equipped his machine with a curved needle which had an eye in the point, and used a shuttle to make the lock-stitch underneath. His design included two new features: the needle moved horizontally instead of vertically, and the shuttle ran in a special groove. After patenting the machine in America in 1846, Howe came to London and sold the British rights to William Thomas, a corset manufacturer with a business in Cheapside. Here he stayed for some years, but the machine had only a small success and by 1850 he was back again in New York.

PATENT RIGHTS

Howe discovered on returning to America that several new patents had been registered during his absence. One of these had been taken out by Allen Wilson, whose machine differed from Howe's in several ways. With a rotary hook and bobbin, it was simpler and more practical. Isaac Merritt Singer, whose name was to become world famous, had obtained a patent for a machine essentially similar to Howe's, but more practical and much improved in detail. Whereas Howe's machine kept stopping, Singer's worked continuously,

operating at a rate of about 300 stitches a minute (which was the maximum speed at that time), producing a neat, regular stitch. The names of Seymour and of William Grover who had developed the double chain-stitch, also figured among the applications for American patents in 1851.

Elias Howe realised that his invention—which he knew owed much to the earlier work of Hunt—was big business, and he worked hard to produce a more efficient model. While Singer, Grover and Wilson had certainly been inspired by Howe's invention, it was Howe who now began to copy and modify the improvements of the others. Despite this, there was no doubt that Elias Howe was the first man to patent a sewing-machine with the curved needle and eye in its point, using the lock-stitch shuttle. He had had to pawn his American patent rights in London to raise his return fare to New York. Now he had bought them back, and they were dated 1846, which was several years before Singer,

In the United States, a number of inventors were working independently of each other to perfect the sewing machine. Elias Howe was the first to take out a patent on his lock-stitch machine, incorporating the under-thread shuttle and curved needle.

89

Wilson and Grover obtained the patents for their machines.

THE SEWING-MACHINE " WAR "

Howe became involved with his rivals in a Boston law case in 1854. He had some points in his favour. But the argument was that even if Singer had used Howe's idea—his machine could stitch only a few inches at a time—sewing-machines would have had no chance of getting on to the market at all without Singer's improvements. This sparked off a terrific row with other hopeful manufacturers, and everyone connected with this early sewing-machine was soon involved in the legal tussle. It was a war of inventors and manufacturers, and it was waged with violence and bitterness in the courts and press of America. In the end, an agreement was reached which satisfied all parties.

The sewing-machine " war " ended with the setting-up of the first American industrial cartel, or combine. It was called the " Sewing Machine Corporation ", and its associates agreed to pay into a central fund fifteen dollars for every machine they sold. This sum was to be split in five, one-fifth to each of the four manufacturers in the combine, and one-fifth to Elias Howe. He and his heirs were to receive these royalties until 1877, which was the year the patent rights lapsed. By that time, Singer sewing-machines were being used everywhere; but Howe was not to know it. He had died in Paris in 1867, after being awarded the medal of the Legion of Honour. This was only ten years after poor Thimmonier's life of poverty had come to an end.

HIRE-PURCHASE

To-day, the " war " of the sewing-machines seems no more than a fascinating episode in the history of industry. How strange, we reflect, that so homely and familiar an object as a sewing-machine should have created such a storm. But it was, of course, a machine that could be used in every home, and was therefore a splendid commercial proposition. For this same reason, the sewing-machine started off a new era in sales technique. It was the first household appliance to be sold in large numbers on the instalment system. The salesman got his foot in the door and convinced the housewife of the benefits of hire-purchase.

2,000 DIFFERENT MODELS

Modern sewing-machines are not restricted to the light and handy models that we see in the home. Specialised machines are now constructed for all kinds of work. They are essential in the tailoring and hosiery industries, and in every branch of the industry concerned with the manufacture of garments. Hats, boots, shoes, gloves, handbags and umbrellas are all produced with the help of different types of sewing-machines. Upholstery, curtains, linen, camping equipment, sails, parachutes and scores of other products flow in an unending stream from beneath the clicking needles. In all, over 2,000 different models are now being used throughout the world. Among the largest is a seven-needle sewing-machine which runs out seven rows of double chain-stitching at the rate of 20,000 stitches per minute.

TON-WEIGHT

Poor Thimmonier! Did he foresee the future that lay before his humble machine? Elias Howe and Isaac Singer certainly realised its immense commercial possibilities. But even they could not have imagined that the machines they constructed would be prototypes of hundreds of different

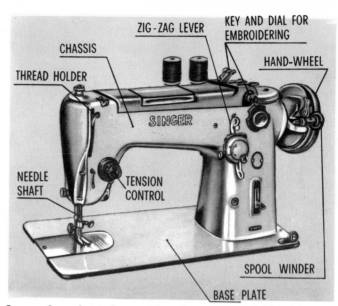

In use throughout the world to-day are over 2,000 different varieties of sewing machines, most of them specially designed for special purposes. Above is a sewing machine, typical of the electric models found in many homes.

models ranging from toy machines for children to ton-weight monsters that stitch the edges of the endless driving belts which turn the wheels of modern machinery. There is even a machine designed to sew and seal a zig-zag line of stitches in special materials used in oil refining. Another type of machine has sewn together the pages of this book.

5,000 STITCHES IN A MINUTE

All these developments have been possible because the sewing-machine " war " ended in peace. The inventor with his patents and the manufacturer with his commercial ambitions resolved their differences. So one new invention after another was patented and used for improving the sewing-machine. There were patents which showed how electricity could replace the foot pedal and provide the motive power of the sewing-machine. There were patents for automatic lubrication and for cooling the racing needles with jets of compressed air, and patents for muffling the noisy clatter that is a characteristic of the machine. The mind of man seeks always to improve on existing methods and machines. Thimmonier's 300 stitches a minute have increased to 1,500 stitches a minute on domestic sewing machines, and in hosiery factories the invisible needles of a good machine insert as many as 5,000 stitches per minute. They bob up and down more than eighty times a second!

ELECTRONIC FUTURE

What new miracles lie ahead as inventors seek to adapt the sewing-machine to modern needs? Judging by the recent invention of a sewing-machine without a needle, anything may happen. This amazing device makes use of heat generated by a high-frequency electric current to pierce as perfect a hole as any needle. Machines equipped in this way are particularly well suited to sewing plastic materials. Already, too, electronic engineers are adapting the sewing-machine to play its part in automation.

The time may not be distant when girls will operate their sewing-machines from control panels, and will watch on a television screen as clothes are sewn together automatically.

SILK AND ITS SECRETS

For thousands of years, silk fabrics have been regarded as the most beautiful and most comfortable textiles made by man. Silk itself is accepted as " Queen " of natural fibres. How strange it is, therefore, to find that this wonderful material is produced by a bloated caterpillar—the silkworm— as it spins a cocoon in which it plans to settle down and turn into a moth.

The silk we weave into textile fabrics is made by unwinding the silkworm's cocoon, which is constructed from a filament so fine as to be almost invisible. Each cocoon may contain as much as a mile or more of silk.

An old Chinese book, said to have been written by Confucius, tells us that it was the wife of the Emperor Huang-ti who discovered how to make fabrics of silk. The Empress, it is related, began to raise silkworms and to weave the filaments of their cocoons in about 2600 B.C. So successful was this lady of Si-ling, as she was known in her day, that she was regarded as a divine being. The Chinese came to regard her as " the goddess of silk ".

For many centuries, the Chinese kept their knowledge of silk production to themselves. Information was handed down from one generation to another and death was the penalty for anyone who gave away any of the secrets of producing silk. But even the best-kept secrets have a way of leaking out, and this one was given away eventually by a Chinese princess. According to legend, the princess was engaged to the King of Turkestan, and wished to provide herself with silk from which she could continue to make clothes after leaving China. So she took some silkworm eggs, and some seeds of the mulberry tree on which the insect feeds, hiding them inside her head-dress.

Although the Chinese remained extremely secretive about the methods of producing silk, they began to sell their silk yarns and fabrics abroad. The Roman legions obtained silk during their expeditions to the East. Trading contacts were

Hiding the silkworm eggs in hollow bamboo, two Persian monks brought the beginning of the silk industry to the West.

established, and by the time of Augustus, who reigned during the life of Christ, silk was being worn by the smart ladies of Rome. It was a very precious material, worth its weight in gold. It came, as everyone knew, from fabulous China by way of the markets of the Middle East. But nobody in the Western World knew how the Chinese produced it although some writers recorded that it came from the fibre of a plant cultivated in the Far East.

Gradually, the secrets of silk-production spread from one country to another. India had already been making silk for many years; the soil and climate of the Brahmaputra Valley suited the cultivation of the mulberry tree on which the silkworms feed, and the techniques of rearing the cater-

The silk industry originated in China over 4,500 years ago and its origin is credited to the wife of Emperor Huang-ti.

In medieval times, Florence, Genoa, Venice and Milan were famous for their silk merchants and trade.

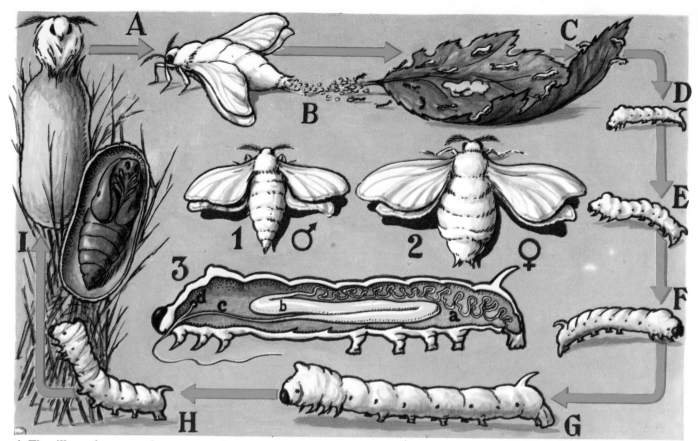

A. The silk-moth emerges from cocoon; B. egg-laying; C. hatching of grubs; D. E. F. and G. growing to full size of 3-3½ inches; H. feeding before wrapping itself in cocoon; I. cross-section of cocoon. 1. Male silk-moth; 2. female silk-moth; 3. cross-section showing one of the two thick-walled sacs which produces the silk fluid. (a) Silk secreting gland; (b) reservoir of silk fluid; (c) emission tube to under lip; (d) glands which secrete substance to make the two spun filaments into one strand.

pillars had been acquired from China or from Turkestan.

In about A.D. 300 a party of Koreans landed in Japan, bringing with them four Chinese girls who had been trained in the arts of silk production. The Japanese soon learned from them all there was to know about silk, and they were duly grateful to their instructors. A temple was erected to them in the Province of Settsu, in recognition of the fact that they had laid the foundations of an industry which was of great importance to Japan. In the 1920s, silk accounted for about one-third of the Japanese export trade, and in 1936 Japan produced over 48,000 of the world's total output of 65,000 tons of silk. Competition from artificial fibres has since hit the silk trade hard.

The secrets of silk production made their way into Europe at the time of the Byzantine Emperor Justinian the Great, who was ruling in Constantinople in A.D. 550. In that year, two monks whom Justinian had sent to China returned from a successful mission. Hidden inside hollow bamboo canes they brought back the eggs of the silk-moth, *Bombyx mori.* From this stock sprang all the silkworms that were bred in western countries up to the time of James I, who tried to establish silk-production in England and ordered mulberry trees to be grown as food for the silkworms.

More than a thousand years earlier, Justinian had planted mulberries in the imperial gardens that sloped down to the Bosporus, and reared silkworms for the production of silk. Soon, Byzantine silks became famous and the courtiers of Constantinople gained a great reputation for the elegance of their clothes. The secret of silk production was a secret no longer, and it was not long before the Moslem Arabs knew the techniques of this strange industry. They passed

on their knowledge as they moved westwards to conquer Spain. Sicily, which had already fallen to them, became a centre of silk production. Fabrics exist to this day which were worked by Sicilians to patterns designed by the Saracens.

In northern Italy, the countryside around Venice and Milan was now planted with mulberry trees, and silkworms were reared on their leaves. In Dante's day, a Guild of Silk Weavers already existed in Florence to supervise the trade. Then the French became interested, and Louis XI set up a factory at Tours. Demand grew, but the manufacturers, who had developed methods for combining several filaments into thread to make a stronger yarn (by the process known as " throwing "), were almost as secretive about their techniques as the Chinese had been before them. England, for example, depended on imported " thrown " silk until well into the 18th century, when a Derbyshire man obtained the secret of this process from Italy and opened the first British throwing mills, which were on the River Derwent.

Partly for climatic reasons and partly because of the tedious processes involved in producing silk, highly industrialised countries have not taken to silk production as readily as those in which there is plenty of cheap labour available. Silk production has made little headway, for example, in the United States, or in Britain and other industrial countries of the Western World. In recent years, these countries have made tremendous progress in the development of synthetic fibres such as nylon and " Terylene ", which have taken over many of the markets that were previously held by silk. Synthetic fibres have many advantages over the natural products. Their production can be controlled with scientific precision and fibres can be made for particular needs.

BRASS AND BRONZE

Bronze is a hard and durable alloy whose strength and useful properties are often superior to those of the individual metals of which it is composed. Confusion often arises over the meaning of the terms bronze and brass. Both are, in fact, alloys of copper with other metals, the difference arising from the nature and proportions of the alloying metals used.

The early forms of bronze were made from copper and tin, and the properties of the alloy would vary according to the proportions in which these two metals were mixed. Eighty-five to ninety per cent. of copper and ten to fifteen per cent. of tin would produce an ordinary bronze which was fairly malleable. When the percentage of tin is increased, the alloy becomes harder and rather more brittle, and its colour lightens to a golden yellow. In its liquid state, this tin-rich bronze is more mobile and easier to work.

For many purposes the basic mixture of copper and tin is modified by adding small quantities of such metals as zinc, lead and nickel; when the bronze is to be used in artistic applications, antimony and arsenic may be added. The first three give the alloy a bold and shiny appearance which we associate with brass—hence the expression " bold as brass". They may improve the strength, but do not always do so. In mechanical engineering, for instance, a type of brass is used that contains up to fifteen per cent. of lead. The other metals mentioned above are added to a copper and tin mixture in Japan and other eastern countries, where artistic bronzes are given their burnished colours by using a sprinkling of gold or silver, and perhaps a touch of arsenic.

THE BRONZE AGE BEGINS

The discovery of bronze, that is to say, of the process for alloying copper and tin, marks an important stage in the development in civilisation. Bronze has, in fact, lent its name to that long period of history between the Stone Age and the Iron Age. It was in the Bronze Age that man really learned the craft of making household and decorative articles in durable metal. Copper and some of its applications were already known, but the discovery of the new alloy brought two great advantages: first, while copper melts at 1,083°C., copper and tin together require a temperature of only 900°C.; second, the greater strength of bronze led to its being used for making arms and weapons.

The primitive people who first used bronze almost certainly knew how to build simple furnaces which could reach a temperature of 1,100-1,200°C. In one of these furnaces some ancient metal worker probably found a piece of fused copper and tin. Some archaeologists believe that this chance discovery may have been made by the Sumerians who lived along the banks of the Tigris and the Euphrates. In any event, its origin goes back at least to 3500 B.C., and can be placed with certainty in that part of the Middle East we now call Iraq. Spreading first to Egypt, the use of bronze was taken up in countries of the eastern Mediterranean region during the third millennium before the birth of Christ. By 2000 B.C., the secret of making bronze was known in Europe.

TIN FROM MYSTERIOUS SOURCES

The source of the tin from which the ancients made their bronze has never been identified with certainty. Copper was readily available, but tin was comparatively rare in the ancient world; also, it occurs in forms that are not easy to recognise. The richest deposits of tin are a long way from the old Middle East and Mediterranean centres of civilisation: Malaya, Thailand, Indo-China, the Congo, Nigeria and Bolivia. The Mediterranean metal-workers could not have imported it from countries so far away. The most probable sources of tin in ancient times were Britain and Portugal. From the Atlantic shores of these countries, tin was carried to the Mediterranean by Phoenician traders. The tin was no doubt bartered for bronze ornaments and weapons which the people of Western Europe had not yet learned to make for themselves.

The use of bronze gave a new stimulus to the development of arts and crafts in Egypt, Greece and Italy. Countless articles of bronze have been found in the tombs of the Pharaohs. The island of Samos is regarded by many historians as the home of skilled bronze-makers whose beautiful work the Greeks so highly appreciated. After establishing itself in Sicily and Sardinia, the production of bronze soon spread through Italy as far as Venice. Metal slag, moulds into which the molten metal was poured, old furnace sites and bronze articles are frequently unearthed near the prehistoric towers of Sardinia and the Greek settlements in the Po Valley around Padua.

ARMOUR AND CANNON

During the first millennium before Christ a new epoch in the history of mankind opened with the discovery of iron. But bronze continued to hold its own and, even when most common household utensils were being made of iron, bronze

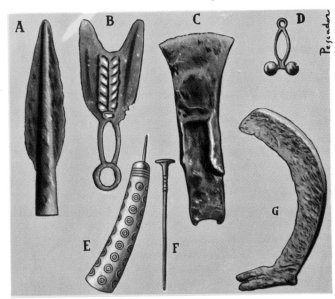

Some Bronze Age objects found in the Mediterranean area: A. spearhead; B. double-headed razor; C. axe-head; D. earring; E. sewing awl; F. long pin; G. sickle.

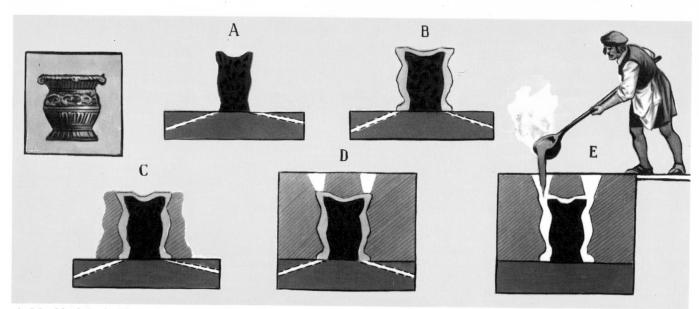

A. Mould of the inside of the vessel (left) is made in fireproof material. On this core a layer of casting wax (B) was moulded. More fireproof material (C) was packed round the wax, which was melted (D), leaving cavity into which bronze was poured (E).

was still favoured for the manufacture of weapons. The quality of the bronze was high, by comparison with the poorly smelted iron of those early days.

When bronze is heated until red-hot and then cooled in water, it can be hammered readily into a desired shape. If it is then re-heated, it becomes harder, stronger and more flexible; these characteristics are all essential in material used for making weapons. The sword, for example, owes its origin to the discovery of bronze; the weaker metal, copper, was suitable only for making shorter weapons such as knives and daggers. At the height of their power, the ancient Greeks made weapons from bronze, and agricultural implements from iron. In ancient Rome, bronze was used for the shields, armour and headpieces of the gladiators who fought in the Colosseum.

Bronze, which was in less general use during the Middle Ages, reappeared on the field of battle with the discovery of gunpowder in the fourteenth century. For the next five hundred years, cannons were cast in bronze. Then, with the outbreak of the Franco-Prussian War, steel guns were used for the first time; this was in 1870, an important landmark in the history of warfare.

STATUES AND BELLS

Bronze soon became a serious rival to stone and baked clay in sculpture and related arts. At first, it was worked hot at the forge; beaten out, rolled, engraved, embossed. In the course of time the process of casting was developed. One of the earliest examples of this technique was found near Baghdad: a bronze statue cast about two thousand years before the Christian era.

The art of bronze casting spread westwards and fine specimens are to be seen to-day in most large museums. Some have been unearthed in Crete, others come from the old Mycenaean kingdom of southern Greece. Before the Romans subdued them, the Etruscans were making bronzes so lively and expressive in their form that they are a source of inspiration to modern artists. Life-size figures came a little later: the bronze charioteer which is preserved at Delphi in Greece, and the statue, now in Rome, of Marcus Aurelius on horseback, are two famous examples, remarkable for their technical perfection.

In medieval times, the art of casting bronze statues fell into disuse, and those who know something of the life of Benvenuto Cellini will remember the difficulties he had to overcome in making his statue of Perseus. The artistic use of bronze revived, however, with the Renaissance. Among Italian artists, Lorenzo Ghiberti, Donatello, Sansovino, Verrocchio and the great Luca della Robbia, whose majolica is to-day so precious, all worked in bronze.

It has been said that the Middle Ages was the period when bronze really discovered its voice. Something in the sound of a bronze bell had caught man's imagination. Soon its notes were heard, gentle and penetrating, in mountainous regions where the cattle wore bells as they wandered on the hillsides; and deep and resonant in churches where bells weighing half-a-ton were hung in carillons that pealed on Sunday mornings. There is a commanding, almost compelling note in a bronze bell; but it must be cast without flaw or defect. To be " as sound as a bell " means just what it says: to be perfectly fit and healthy.

WHEN BRONZE BECOMES BRASS

Steel is the most important metal in our modern world. The alloys of iron, including steel, have ousted bronze from many of its engineering applications. And many of the things that were previously made from bronze are now made from brass. This, too, is an alloy of copper which differs from bronze in the percentage of the tin, nickel, zinc and other metals it contains.

Brass is still widely used in industry. Tubes and rods, bearings, die moulds, gear cogs, valves and many household fittings are made of brass. It is used for instruments which must withstand gas or water pressure. Metallurgical research has given modern industry a wide range of new copper alloys, many of which have special uses. Propellers, for instance, are made from an alloy of copper and aluminium called aluminium bronze. There are also silicon bronzes and phosphor bronzes.

Finally, there are those alloys from which we make our low-value coins; the good old " copper ", which is in fact made of bronze, and the brass farthing that no one ever cared about. It may not be long before even " brass " is replaced by alloys of lighter and cheaper metals.

THE CONQUEST OF THE SOUTH POLE

If you look at a map of the world, you will see that most of the great land masses lie in the Northern Hemisphere. Much of the " bottom half " of the world—the Southern Hemisphere—is covered by vast oceans that increase in extent the farther south we go. It isn't surprising, therefore, that early explorers believed the Antarctic and South Pole to be a landless wilderness of snow and ice.

The story of Antarctic exploration is very different from that of man's conquest of the Arctic. Little interest was shown in the the South Pole region until the exploration and surveying of South America and Australia was well advanced. There was no reason to believe that large land areas existed south of Cape Horn, and explorers were not interested in venturing into the frozen seas of the Antarctic.

The first hint of the existence of a continent to the south of the 65th parallel of latitude came from the survivors of Magellan's voyage round the southern tip of South America into the Pacific in 1520. Some months before being killed in the Philippines during this historic voyage—the first to encircle the globe—Ferdinand Magellan had sighted land far to the south. But no explorer ventured into those forbidding regions until Captain Cook crossed the Antarctic Circle in 1773. At latitude 67°S, Cook's two vessels were blocked by floating ice, and the British explorer reported that it was most improbable that land existed farther south. Half a century later, whalers began to penetrate into Antarctic water, and land was discovered where people had long believed there was none to be found.

In 1819, William Smith, captain of an English whaling vessel, found himself in the midst of a group of islands which was later to be called the South Shetlands. At this time, some species of whales were becoming hard to find in northern waters, where many had been hunted almost out of existence. Whalers were turning their attention to the Antarctic, where whales were still to be found in great numbers. In 1821, two Russian fishery vessels under the command of Fabian von Bellingshausen found two islands within the Antarctic Circle, which they named after Peter I and Alexander I of Russia. On landing, they were met by swarms of elegant penguins strutting over the ice to meet them; these friendly birds appeared to be the sole inhabitants of the remote islands.

EREBUS AND TERROR

Many expeditions were made into the Antarctic in the years that followed. To include in these chapters all the explorers, scientists and whalers who took part would be impossible. We shall confine our attention to those whose expeditions made a real contribution towards the eventual conquest of the South Pole. The first of these was James Ross, who commanded a British expedition consisting of two small ships. Sailing from Hobart, Tasmania, in November, 1840, Ross penetrated the pack ice and surveyed a great expanse of sea along the shores of what is now known as Victoria Land. Nor was Ross, who gave his name to this sea, stopped by the next great ice barrier. He pressed on until, between latitudes 78° and 79°, a barrier of solid ice

In 1819, William Smith of the brig Williams *landed on the South Shetland Islands.*

blocked his way. The zone beyond is now known as the Ross Ice Shelf.

Among the peaks that rose above this barrier were two volcanoes, which Ross named after the ships *Erebus* and *Terror*. So Magellan's story that land might lie to the far south was proved true. But there was still no way of deciding whether these volcanoes were part of a large land mass or of a chain of scattered islands projecting above the ice fields.

In 1897 a Belgian expedition organised by Adrien de Gerlache reached Graham Land in the *Belgica*; the ship became locked in the ice for nearly a year. Among the crew—the first men to winter inside the Antarctic Circle—was the young Roald Amundsen, whose experience was to serve him well on future voyages of discovery. When the ship escaped in due course from the ice, de Gerlache and his crew returned home with a great deal of geological and other scientific information. Meanwhile, interest in the race to the South Pole was mounting. The success of Arctic expeditions had encouraged explorers to turn their attention to the Antarctic too.

SCOTT AND THE DISCOVERY

The famous Captain Scott, in command of the 700-ton ship *Discovery*, set out in 1901 for the Ross Sea, which was regarded as one of the best approaches to the South Pole. With him was E. A. Wilson, and Ernest Shackleton, who was to make such a name for himself in the history of Antarctic exploration. Reaching the great barrier, which had held up Ross, the *Discovery* became locked in the ice, and it was soon obvious that the party would not be able to move again that winter. Nearby was the towering volcano, Erebus, which Ross had mapped as part of the Antarctic continent, but which Scott discovered to be an island.

Scott had no intention of spending the winter in the ice-

In 1902, Robert Scott made a journey which gave him valuable experience for his later expedition to the South Pole.

locked *Discovery* and he took a small party on the first real trek towards the South Pole that had ever been undertaken. With Shackleton and Wilson he advanced across the white desert of snow and ice, until he reached the foothills of a high mountain in latitude 82° 17′S. But the cold was becoming ever more intense, and provisions were running short. One by one, the dogs succumbed to the bitter weather. The explorers decided to return by the same route, and their journey back became a race with death. Had it not been for a favourable wind which filled the sails attached to the sledges, the party might never have got back to their ship.

Here, a bitter disappointment awaited them. The summer came, and with it hopes of refloating the *Discovery*. But the thaw did not come, the ship remained imprisoned in pack ice and the expedition was forced to spend another winter in polar waters. Scott and his men made good use of their time. Hauling their own sledges, they spent several months of 1903 surveying the country to a point 300 miles west of the ice-bound *Discovery*. They returned to base on

Christmas Day of that year and sailed back to England where they were given a great welcome.

It was now generally accepted that much of Antarctica was really a huge land mass, a white continent larger in area than Australia. And it offered a new challenge to European explorers who had proven themselves in the Arctic. One of them, Nils Nordenskjöld, took an expedition to Graham Land, the long tongue of Antarctica which lies opposite to South America. This region, also known as the Palmer Peninsula, was shown by Nordenskjöld to be, in fact, a number of islands.

Nordenskjöld was followed by a French expedition led by Jean Charcot, and a Scottish expedition under W. S. Bruce. A German party led by Erich von Drygalski surveyed another region of Antarctica, but the greatest exploration in the first decade of the present century was made by Scott's old companion, Ernest Shackleton, now a lieutenant in the Royal Navy.

SHACKLETON'S PONY SLEDGES

Shackleton and his party sailed from New Zealand on 1st January, 1908, taking with them a herd of Manchurian ponies to pull the sledges. After steering a course up the Ross Sea, Shackleton landed in the vicinity of Mount Erebus and sent a party of mountaineers to explore the volcano. Under the leadership of T. W. E. David, they reached the top at 13,202 feet. Shackleton's next objective was the magnetic pole which is situated at latitude 72°25′S and, as Shackleton found, at a height of 7,000 feet. But the epic feat of this expedition was a long trek which took its leader and three others—J. B. Adams, E. Marshall and F. Wild— to within ninety-seven miles of the South Pole.

Starting from their winter base at the head of the Ross Sea, the party pushed inland for 435 miles before coming up against a gigantic glacier 120 miles long and of immense width. In this area, the temperature drops to minus 70°F. and the snow is whipped by blizzards that sweep across a blinding white landscape, ten thousand feet above the level of the sea. These conditions slowed down their progress, but the four men struggled on till they reached latitude 88°23′S. Realising that to continue would mean certain

In 1908, Ernest Shackleton left England on the Nimrod. *Disembarking at the head of the Ross Sea, he sent a party to the top of Mount Erebus. On this expedition Manchurian ponies were used to draw the sledges.*

96

On 14th December, 1911, Roald Amundsen and his party hoisted the Norwegian flag at the South Pole.

death, Shackleton ordered his men to turn back. Food was running short and some of the ponies had to be killed to provide meat. This meant lightening the sledges and leaving behind everything that was not absolutely necessary. Once again the wind came to the rescue, helping the explorers forward over the last few hundred miles. But it was a very exhausted party that clambered aboard the *Nimrod*, which was waiting to take Shackleton and his men back to England. On reaching home, he was knighted in recognition of his work in pioneering the route to the South Pole.

THE NORWEGIANS REACH THE POLE

The invasion of Antarctica was now intensified. Roald Amundsen, who had been a member of de Gerlache's expedition in 1897, set out with a Norwegian expedition in 1910. While preparing for the trek to the Pole, he met Captain Scott with the *Terra Nova;* the two expeditions almost bumped into each other in the southern waters of the Ross Sea. Obviously, there was going to be a race—and a marathon one—between Scott and Amundsen, both of whom were eager to be first at the South Pole.

Amundsen had the advantage; he had spent the winter of 1910-11 in planning his route and building up storage depots at latitudes 80°, 81° and 82°. When he was ready—it was now 20th October, 1911—he set off with four companions, moving steadily over the ice with fully-loaded sledges at about four miles an hour. Having crossed the Ross Ice Shelf, he reached the mountain barrier and found a small glacier giving access to the high uplands. Here Amundsen and his men were held up by a snowstorm that raged for four days. The dogs—there were fifty-two of them —were becoming restive for lack of food, and some of them had to be abandoned to their fate. Eventually the storm abated, the party pressed on and reached its goal on 14th December, 1911. Amundsen raised the Norwegian flag over virgin snows that no man had ever trodden. Then he saluted the flag, and the party began the long homeward trek, covering the 840 miles between the South Pole and the Bay of Whales in thirty-eight days.

CAPTAIN SCOTT'S EPIC JOURNEY

A few days before Amundsen returned to his base, Captain Scott's expedition was slowly making its way across the centre of the Antarctic Continent. It had been a gruelling journey. The motor sledges had broken down, the ponies had had to be shot, the dog teams and several members of the party had fallen out. Almost ten weeks had gone by since Scott and his men had left their base at Cape Evans, and they were now in sight of the South Pole. There was no mistaking where it was. There, before their eyes, flew the Norwegian flag.

We can imagine the feelings of Scott and his four companions—Wilson, Bowers, Oates and Evans—as they stumbled towards Amundsen's flag. The Norwegian explorer had beaten them to the South Pole by a bare five weeks. But it was the luck of the game, and when luck turns against a man it often strikes a double blow. Returning in the foulest weather that even the Antarctic can muster, the explorers began to lose strength. Evans died on the Beardmore Glacier in mid-February of 1912. A month later Oates walked out into the blizzard to die, in the hope that his comrades might live. Supplies of food and fuel were almost exhausted, but there was a storage depot less than twenty miles away. Had it not been for the terrible weather, the three survivors would have reached it. But the nine-days' storm sealed their fate; first Bowers died, then Wilson and, last of all, Scott. After writing up his diary, Scott lay down beside his dead companions and fell into a coma from which he never awoke. The following November a search party found the bodies of these brave men, and noted that Scott's last entry had been made on 26th March, 1912. Just ten weeks out and ten weeks back . . .

LITTLE AMERICA

The South Pole had been reached by two expeditions in circumstances more dramatic than Peary's conquest of the North Pole in 1909. And it would not be long before airborne explorers were flying over the desolate regions of Antarctica just as they were planning to fly over the Arctic.

Hubert Wilkins was the first to pilot an aeroplane through these bleak skies, when he made a series of reconnaissance flights over the Palmer Peninsula in 1928-29. At about the

On the return journey from the South Pole, Captain Scott and his party were beset with shortage of stores and bad weather. At the height of a nine-day storm, Oates sacrificed his life in the hope that the others would survive.

R. E. Byrd, the American naval aviator, established a base, now known as Little America, in the Bay of Whales. From this base, he made a series of flights preparatory to the successful one he and his companions made over the South Pole and back.

same time, R. E. Byrd, the great American explorer, was getting ready to fly to the Pole from the same base that Amundsen had used. Here, within the icy frontiers of the Bay of Whales, he built a small village complete with its own airfield. It is now marked on the map as " Little America ". Huts were erected, a gymnasium was built, electric light and radio equipment were installed. Eighty people and many packs of dogs moved in. Never before had there been so much activity in Antarctica. Byrd's preparations were justified when, on 29th November, he and three of his fellow countrymen made a successful flight to the South Pole and back to " Little America " in nineteen hours.

During the ten years that preceded the Second World War, the explorers of many nations, mainly British, Americans, Australians and Germans, made a succession of expeditions to the far south. Their object was to gain further knowledge of the region and to undertake research programmes of scientific and geological importance. But none of them was organised on the scale of Rear-Admiral Byrd's second colossal expedition of 1946. Nothing like " Operation Highjump ", as the U.S. Navy called it, had ever before been seen in Antarctica. Thirteen ships, including an aircraft carrier, a fleet of planes and a vast number of caterpillar trucks, motor sledges and amphibious tractors invaded the white continent. This armada included 4,000 men whose job was to gain polar experience, test new equipment and photograph Antarctica from the air. Among the more spectacular achievements of the expedition was the discovery of an unknown mountain range rising in places to nearly 20,000 feet. Byrd made his second flight to the South Pole on 15th February, 1947.

By 1947, the days when Antarctic expeditions consisted of a schooner, a few dog sledges and a little party of men ready to risk their lives in the snow had gone for ever. In that year the first women to winter in the Antarctic mainland, Mrs. Ronne and Mrs. Darlington, accompanied their husbands on a scientific survey of the Palmer Peninsula. The same region claimed the attention of ten British scientists who were brought back in 1950 by the *John Biscoe*. It was during this period that a spate of expeditions—British, Australian, French and Scandinavian—went south in the

wake of American explorers and scientists who were now using helicopters to assist them in their work.

Between 1949 and 1952, Norwegians, Swedes and British co-operated in the investigation of Queen Maud Land from the ship *Norsel*, commanded by John Giaever. In the same years, the *Commandant Charcot* was exploring off the Adelie Coast under Captain Liotard, while *Discovery II*, commanded by F. Blackburn, was operating along another sector of the coast. In February 1954, an Australian party in the *Kista Dan* set up a scientific station at Mawson in the unexplored McRobertson territory. Since that time, many expeditions have co-operated in opening up the Antarctic continent, including joint expeditions starting from the shores of the Ross and Weddell Seas which were to meet at the South Pole. One of these was led by Dr. Vivian Fuchs of Cambridge and Sir Edmund Hillary of Everest fame. Other expeditions organised under the 1956-7 programme of the International Geophysical Year, made valuable meteorological studies of the region. Twice-daily weather maps of Antarctica were issued, with the object of showing the influence of Antarctic weather on climate in other parts of the world. Temperatures as low as minus 50°C. were recorded.

THE ANTARCTIC CHALLENGE

Despite all this activity in recent years, it would be wrong to think that man has really conquered the Antarctic. It has become more accessible, that is all. The same bitter winds blow there as Scott and his men had to face. In places, their velocity never drops below fifty miles an hour. The same raging blizzards and fierce frosts prevail. What progress has done is to make the crossing of this continent of five million square miles of snow and ice an easier undertaking. Tractors and jeeps fitted with caterpillar tracks can plough through polar snows much faster than the dogs and pony-teams of the pioneers. Mechanical vehicles can be re-fuelled from dumps laid down by aeroplanes and helicopters. But, for the men who go there to continue the work of scientific research and exploration, the Antarctic offers the same challenge as before: the challenge of loneliness and isolation in a continent that might well belong to another world.

GRAPES AND WINE

If you have motored through almost any part of central or southern Europe, you must have marvelled at the huge vineyards through which you passed. In France and Italy, in Germany and Greece, in Spain and Portugal, you would see millions of vines, often covering the entire floor of a valley and reaching up the gentle hillsides as far as the eye can see. From each vine there hang bunches of luscious grapes—some small, some large, some green and some purple. These grapes are the raw material from which Europe makes the bulk of the world's wine.

Europe is the greatest wine-producing region on earth. Between them, France and Italy account for almost half of the world's total production of 6,000 million gallons per year. Spain and Portugal contribute 750 million gallons, and Germany 70 million gallons. The Greeks, who have been drinking wine since Homer's time, produce 100 million gallons; this alone is enough to provide everyone in Britain with one hundred glasses each a year!

TYPES OF VINEYARD

The vines from which wine is made are grown out-of-doors; hothouse grapes are much too precious. The vineyards are to be seen at their best throughout Italy and in the famous Rhineland of Germany.

One of the first things we notice on a trip through the vineyards is that there are several ways of growing vines. In some districts, the vines look like upturned tree trunks, with gnarled roots clutching at the air. This type, known as the *headed vine*, is grown mainly for wine and raisin production—raisins are sun-dried grapes. In other districts, the vine is trained along wires tight-stretched between strong stakes. This is the *bilateral cordon* method, and grapes are grown in this way either for wine-making or for the table, according to variety. Around Bologna, in Italy, the supporting wires are attached to the trunks of pruned mulberry trees. The vineyards in this district are a truly beautiful sight. So, too, are those vineyards in which the grapes are grown on pergolas. They hang in clusters from the green canopy of trellises forming long shady tunnels across the sunny hillside.

Most of the crop from these beautiful vineyards is used for making wine. The remainder provides grapes for the table, for canning and crushing into juice, and for conversion into raisins. At a glance, the grapes might appear to be of only two varieties—purple or green. But, in fact, there are many varieties, as you can tell quite easily when you sample them. Table grapes are deliciously sweet, and have a high sugar content; wine grapes, on the other hand, may be rather bitter due to their high acidity. Nor should we think that green grapes are necessarily used for making white wine. Red wine, it is true, can be made only with purple grapes, but white wine can be made with either.

For many people, the attraction of vineyards, whether set in terraces or in open fields, is linked with the warmth of southern summers. For climate is the main factor in cultivating grapes; the type of soil on which they grow is much less important than the weather. Vines flourish in a climate that provides a cool, moist winter, followed by a frostless spring and a summer which gradually heats up to a steady 27°-32°C. in July and August, with just a touch of rain to swell the fruit before the September harvest. Wherever these conditions are combined with a suitable soil, we find the highest-quality grapes. Just as there may be one corner of the garden where sweet-peas grow better than anywhere else, so there are corners of France and Italy and other wine-growing regions where the delicate vine yields its best fruit. That is why such famous French wines as *Château d' Yquem* and *Clos de Vougeot* are rare and expensive. They come from small areas of perhaps only a few square miles, where grape vines are grown in perfect conditions and under the constant supervision of French wine experts.

FIGHTING PLANT DISEASES

When a new vineyard is to be laid out, the plants are usually raised from shoots and cuttings in a nursery. It is strange to think that none of the vines now grown in Europe has descended from plants that produced wine for our ancestors. The reason is that a pest, called *phylloxera*, swept the Continent in the 1860s, destroying two and a half million acres of vineyards in France alone. This insect, which attacks the root of the vine, brought wine production almost to a standstill. And there it would have remained but for the fact that American vines are resistant to phylloxera and were transplanted in great numbers.

Vines suffer from other diseases, including mildew, black rot and black measles. These can be prevented by spraying with fungicides; the most common treatment makes use of a copper compound. This checks mildew, turning the plants a familiar blue colour that lies like a haze over vines caught in the early morning sun.

When the grapes are ripe—in Europe, during the second half of September and early October—the pickers swarm

In late September, or early October, the grapes are gathered and taken in large baskets to the wine presses.

into the vineyards and gather the bunches in large " chips " which they empty into tall wicker baskets. These are collected up and the fruit is taken to be crushed. At one time this was done by treading on the grapes with the feet. This rather unhygienic practice now has been largely abandoned; the grapes are now unloaded into crushing machines, where rollers squeeze them quickly and thoroughly. The raw grape juice is called *must*: this is the unfermented juice from which wine is made.

Fermentation is caused by moulds that come from the outer surface of the grape skins; it begins as soon as the must is poured into the vats. These moulds, which are microscopic living organisms, feed on the sugar in the juice, producing alcohol. When white wine is being made, the skins are removed; if red wine is being made, the skins are left in, to give the wine its ruby colour. The main fermentation process is complete in a matter of weeks. Then the fermented must is drawn off, filtered and refiltered to remove as much as possible of the sediment and lees that may sometimes be seen at the bottom of a bottle of wine. The clear liquid is then stored in large vats, where it slowly matures; the vats are usually made of wood, which allows a small amount of oxygen to reach the wine, to assist the ageing process. If the wine is to mature properly, it is left " in the wood " for about three years; it is then bottled.

FROM BURGUNDY AND BORDEAUX

Wine was made at Glastonbury in Somerset until late in the last century, but there is little wine produced from British-grown grapes to-day. This does not mean to say that wine is not made in the United Kingdom. Very large quantities of grape juice, or must, are imported into Britain from France and other countries, and then fermented and bottled by British wine merchants. Many of the cheaper brands are marketed in this way. Medium-priced wines are commonly imported in barrels and then bottled. The most expensive wines come in labelled bottles from the estate, or *château*, on the Continent where they were matured.

Even in Britain, where wine has only recently become a really popular drink, the names of different types are familiar to many: Bordeaux, Burgundy and Champagne from France;

To-day grapes are crushed and the juice extracted, not by treading them with the feet, but by machines like these.

After pressing, the wine ferments and is then matured in these huge vats until it is ready for bottling.

port wine from Portugal, sherry from Spain, hock from Germany and chianti from Italy. But few people appreciate the finer points of wine-drinking. To an Englishman, *chablis* may mean little; but a Frenchman would recognise it as one of the greatest dry Burgundy wines and would drink it with oysters or other shellfish. Everyone has heard of champagne, the fizzy wine drunk at weddings and other celebrations. Some champagne is made from green grapes, but most is made from purple grapes. The wine is bottled before fermentation is complete, giving it the familiar bubbly effect. It is then " nursed " to maturity in vaults deep in the chalk hills south of Epernay.

SHERRY, HOCK AND CLARET

It is not surprising that most people are puzzled when it comes to choosing a wine. There are so many names, so many vintages, each bearing the year when the grapes were gathered. An expert on wines is called an oenologist, and in wine-producing countries, oenology is a branch of agricultural science. To complicate matters further, the United States, Australia and South Africa all make excellent wines which are sold as hock, sherry, claret and Burgundy. These are names that originated in Europe, where wine production has flourished for a thousand years and more.

English people were first encouraged to drink Bordeaux wines when Eleanor of Aquitaine married Henry II, bringing this region under English rule in 1152. From that time on, these wines were called claret after the French *clairette*. Hock, which first came from the Rhineland town of Hochheim, was being made in that district in the days of Charlemagne. Sherry, known in Shakespeare's time as *sherris*, takes its name from the southern Spanish town of Jerez de la Frontera. Port, which is made by adding brandy to the grape must, was concocted by English wine merchants who settled at Oporto after a trade treaty in 1703 provided for the exchange of English woollens against Portuguese wines.

IN VINO VERITAS

In vino veritas: " truth in wine ". Wine is an alcoholic drink, and the familiar saying refers to its habit of loosening men's tongues. People in wine-growing countries drink wine at mealtimes, and it is traditional in many districts for children to drink water coloured by adding a dash of wine.

ALABASTER

Although rather similar to marble, alabaster can be distinguished easily as it is slightly transparent. There are two varieties of the stone. *Yellow Oriental Alabaster* is of fibrous structure with fine spiral and concentric veins of a darker and sometimes greenish colour. This variety has a sheen like polished fingernails; it contains lime, and for this reason is also called *Calcareous Alabaster*. The other variety, known as *Gypseous Alabaster*, is a gypsum of fine granular texture with the colour evenly distributed in shades of white and flesh-pink.

Oriental alabaster is found in various parts of Europe, but the best qualities, with superior colour, shine and hardness, come from the mountains that lie between Cairo and Assiut in Egypt. Gypseous alabaster occurs in Egypt, Greece, England and Italy. Some of the finest deposits lie along the Tyrrhenian coast of Italy, particularly around Volterra. Because of its beauty and the ease with which it can be worked, alabaster is frequently used for making decorative architectural features and objects d'art. Unfortunately, the stone weathers badly and is usually reserved for indoor work.

AN ANCIENT ART MATERIAL

There is evidence that alabaster was excavated and worked by man as long ago as the Stone Age. Later, the Cretan and Mycenean civilisations of the eastern Mediterranean made fairly wide use of it. In the ruins of Knossos and other Cretan cities alabaster slabs have been found which were used for covering floors, ceilings and columns. The Assyrians and Phoenicians, too, used alabaster in a similar way. In Egypt, where rich deposits lay at hand not far from Cairo, alabaster was associated with funeral rites. Tombstones and urns for preserving ashes of the dead were made of the stone.

Alabaster won immense popularity during the flourishing Cretan and Mycenean epochs. Sculptors found that it provided an easily-worked material for statuettes and wall friezes. The custom of making alabaster vases for precious ointments spread north from Egypt, and the Greek and Latin peoples in due course used the term " an alabaster " for all fine types of vase in which oil or ointment was kept. These vases were cylindrical, ending in a short neck and a broad flat top with a narrow duct through which the liquid could be passed in a fine, thin stream. Ever since then high-quality ointment jars and ointment pots have been made of alabaster.

Because of its poor resistance to long exposure, alabaster was seldom used by the artists of ancient Greece and Italy for statues to be displayed outdoors. Marble, such as that found at Carrara in Italy, was a more durable material in which to commemorate the immortals. Nor did the Romans attach great importance to the alabaster quarries of the Etruscans at Volterra. They preferred the grained oriental stone to the cloudy-white variety, and imported it from the Near East.

PROFANE AND SACRED USES

The alabaster of east Mediterranean countries reached Rome, at first, in small quantities—sufficient to make drinking vessels and ornamental fittings for chairs and beds. Later, consignments were shipped in the form of huge blocks, and in the first century A.D. these were being made into large jars and even baths. In A.D. 64, the Consul Lentulus Spinther returned to Rome with a collection of alabaster jars as big as barrels. A few years later thirty-foot columns of solid alabaster were being erected in the city. We are told by the historian Pliny that some of them went into the theatre of Cornelius Balbus; others, even more magnificent, adorned the banqueting hall of Callistus, a former slave whom the Emperor Claudius had liberated.

Alabaster containers: A and B. vases and measure found in Tutankhamen's tomb; C. ornamental cup; D. perfume bottle.

Alabaster is quarried like marble. Sawing and cutting are used in preference to blasting, to avoid damaging the material.

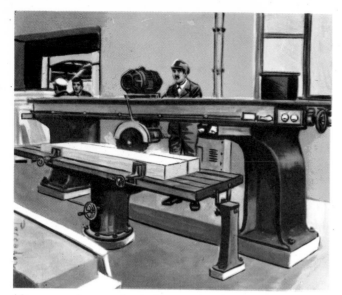

After quarrying, mechanical saws trim the alabaster to blocks of convenient size. Here a steel disc edged with carborundum is being used to cut a length of alabaster.

After the fall of the Roman Empire alabaster was almost completely neglected for many centuries. The Chellaston deposits in England were quarried at intervals between 1350 and 1600, providing a variety of alabaster which was much admired for its transparency and fine dark veins. Little was then heard of the stone until the nineteenth century, when it came into use again for bas-relief sculpture. Sacred subjects were treated in this way, the bas-relief being framed in wood and erected on church altars. A growing demand brought the old Italian quarries at Volterra back to life. But the art of working alabaster has declined during the present century, resulting in a fall in world output.

IN THE ALABASTER QUARRIES

Alabaster is extracted and worked in a similar manner to marble. When a large deposit is found, the rock and surrounding soil are cleared away, thus laying bare the seams of alabaster. The stone is then prepared in large blocks.

The old method was to drive wedges and crowbars deep into natural fissures and crevices, and split the material into pieces of convenient size. With the invention of dynamite, blasting was used, but this had the disadvantage of splintering the alabaster into small fragments due to the force of the explosion.

A more up-to-date method, which is now in general use, is to cut the alabaster from its seams with wire saws. These saws have blades like screw-shaped cables; they are immersed in hard sand, wetted and drawn backwards and forwards by electric motors. Pneumatic rock drills and compressed-air equipment complete the modern quarryman's outfit. With their help he cuts the alabaster into blocks which are taken down to the loading yard to be shaped and trimmed by pneumatic chisels.

From the rough pieces skilled workmen cut and polish slabs and panels for the interior decoration of churches and fine buildings. Selected specimens go to the few remaining craftsmen who know know to make artistic use of alabaster, producing a range of products, from ointment jars and boudoir sets to statuettes and busts: a bust " like his grandsire cut in alabaster," as Shakespeare has it in line eighty-four of the first scene of the *Merchant of Venice*.

TIN

Tin has been mined since ancient times and it is believed that at least one reference is made in the Bible to this metal.

The Chinese were making bronze vessels during the early years of their civilisation, and must have known a great deal about the tin which was alloyed with copper in making bronze. They obtained their tin probably from India, which was also a source of supply to the Greeks of Homer's day.

At that time, as we learn from the historian Herodotus, the British Isles were known as the Cassiterides, a name which has survived in the word cassiterite, or tinstone. Britain was rich in this metal and many Etruscan and Roman relics now seen in museums contain tin that came from Cornwall. For centuries, Britain was one of the main tin-producing countries, but much richer sources have since been discovered, notably in Malaya and its archipelago, and in some South American countries such as Bolivia.

FROM ORE TO INGOT

Tin is one of those metals that rarely exist in a pure state. It is extracted from cassiterite, or tinstone, which is an oxide of tin. Tinstone is dark in colour, due to the iron that is present; the ore is found in layers between rock strata or as alluvial deposits.

An alluvial deposit results from a flow of rain or river water, which forms a drift of mineral-bearing particles. When tin ore accumulates in this way it means that it has been washed from the crumbling seams of hills and mountains and carried by a river which may have changed its course thousands of years ago. The deposit consists mainly of sand in which the tin ore is mixed with other minerals.

This raw material is first heated to remove sulphur and arsenic which, at this stage, are always present. It is then burnt in coal furnaces where carbon combines with oxygen from the oxide to form carbon dioxide. The tin is set free as

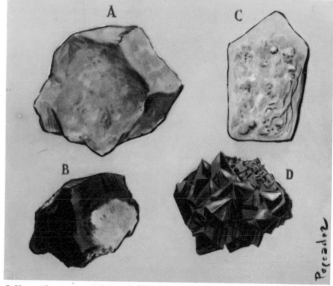

Mineral ores which yield tin: A. Cassiterite from Italy; B. Dioxide of tin; C. Stannite; D. Cassiterite from Bohemia.

102

molten metal, which trickles through the furnace. This process of heating with carbon is widely used in metallurgy to extract metals from ores in which they are present as an oxide. When used for producing tin, special types of furnace are necessary and the process is completed in two or more stages.

Tin extracted in this way is drawn from the furnaces as molten metal, which is poured into brick-shaped moulds. It is then refined to a high state of purity and cast, like gold, into ingots.

THE CHEMISTRY OF TIN

Tin is silvery-white in colour, and it melts at quite a low temperature: 232°C. It is easy to work and can be rolled into extremely fine sheets. Tinfoil is a familiar product, with innumerable uses.

It is a peculiarity of tin that if we bend a thin bar of the metal it makes a creaking noise. This is due to the crystalline structure of the metal, the noise being produced by tiny crystals rubbing and pulling against each other when the metal is distorted. Another strange characteristic of tin is that at temperatures lower than 13°C., it disintegrates into powder, known as " grey tin ". This condition is sometimes called " tin sickness".

When tin solidifies its atoms automatically fall into a geometrical pattern which governs the internal structure of each tiny crystal. When white tin turns into grey tin, the change is brought about by the atoms altering their position and assuming a different pattern. Transformations of this sort occur quite frequently in minerals and are the basis of polymorphism; this is the capacity of a chemical compound to crystallise in two or more forms. In the case of tin, we are dealing with an element and not a chemical compound, and the correct chemical term for this property is *allotropy*.

Unlike certain other metals, tin undergoes no change in contact with air. For this reason it is used as a coating to cover metals which are attacked and corroded by air and by other substances. The familiar thin sheet metal we call tinplate is made by covering iron, which would otherwise go rusty, with a thin layer of tin. The sheet iron is first washed with acid and then immersed in a bath of molten

From the mines of the Malay Archipelago come ores which yield tin of the highest quality.

Pure tin has few uses as an engineering material, but much is used as a protective coating on iron to produce tinplate. Its other major use is in alloys such as bronze and pewter.
Above: *a man is soldering, using an alloy of tin and lead.*

tin. Tin in this form is entirely harmless, and tinplate is used throughout the canning industry for the safe distribution of every kind of foodstuff from the proverbial sardine to the exotic shark's fin soup.

This protective property of tin has long been known, and at one time copper pots and pans were given an internal coating of tin. Unfortunately, it was not understood how dangerous this practice could be if the plating was not well done. In tin there are always traces—usually very slight—of lead, and lead is most poisonous to man. If the tin plating on a copper pot is defective, contact may be made between the lead and the copper; an electrolytic cell is created in the presence of food acids, and the lead in the tinplate may be released to pass into the food. Until this fact was recognised, many people must have suffered from lead poisoning after eating food cooked in badly-made copper pots and pans.

SOME LITTLE-KNOWN USES

Many compounds of tin are essential to various branches of industry. In dyeing, for instance, colours may wash out of a fabric unless treated with a *mordant*. Tin compounds are used as mordants, fixing colouring matter firmly to the fabric. Tin is also used in medicine, for example in the destruction of parasites such as tapeworms.

Tin has another interesting use which people seldom know about. Clocks, decorative vases and high quality picture frames and furnishings are sometimes finished in *ormolu* which, in old French, means " ground gold ". A gilded effect of this type may be obtained by mixing tin with copper and zinc, and this is the basis of modern ormolu. Gilding of this kind is also called " mosaic gold "; this has no connection with real gold—it is nothing more than disulphide of tin.

The bulk of the world's tin production reaches the consumer in a disguised form. It is mixed with various metals, notably copper, in making brass and bronze and other alloys which have properties more useful than those of the pure metals. The scrap merchant who collects " any old iron " is well aware of the value of tin, and he is just as interested in bronze and tinplate. From these sources tin can be extracted and used over and over again.

CABLE RAILWAYS

In 1644, a Dutch engineer named Adam Wybe was in charge of building a new fortress in Danzig. In order to speed up the conveyance of building materials to the building site, he conceived the novel idea of aerial transport.

Wybe got his men to erect two stout poles opposite each other on each side of the valley, one on the road and the other on a building site. Poles were fitted at the top with wheels, similar to those used for pulleys and winches, and round them an endless rope was passed to operate like a driving belt. A small truck was slung over the rope above the road and another at the building-site end, so that when the rope was set in motion, a load of stone could be hauled to the site while an empty truck was brought back to the road. Adam Wybe could hardly have foreseen that his primitive ropeway was to be the forerunner of those cable-railways that carry us up to the mountain-tops to-day.

"AERIAL ROPEWAY"

No substantial improvement was made on Wybe's invention until well into the last century. Major developments in this form of transport had to wait until trains, motor-cars and even aeroplanes were coming into use. Only then was it realised that "aerial ropeways" could be of immense value in mountainous regions. Their possibilities were investigated, and the success of a "ropeway" erected in the Harz Mountains of Germany in about 1860, encouraged engineers to experiment with new systems.

Broadly speaking, there are two classes of aerial ropeways; those which are used for transporting materials and those which carry passengers. The first of these are called cable-ways, more particularly in America; the second are known as cable-railways. The term chair-lift or ski-lift is used when the cab is replaced by individual open seats.

The cable-railway is not to be confused with the funicular, which runs on ordinary rails and is hauled uphill by a cable.

The ascending car of the funicular is often pulled up by the weight of the car going down. Another type of transport used on steep gradients is the cog-wheel or rack railway, well-known to tourists who have travelled by rail to the summit of Snowdon, the highest peak in Wales.

CABLEWAY SYSTEMS

Cableways and cable-railways are used for the transport of heavy materials in skips and buckets, and of passengers in cabin cars and chairs, suspended from overhead cables supported at intervals by pylons. There are five main parts to the cableway systems: the terminal stations, the pylons, the cables, the electric plant which supplies motive power, and the vehicle itself.

Cableways and cable-railways are operated by two distinct systems: the *continuous movement system* and the *two-way system*. The continuous movement system was that developed by Wybe in the seventeenth century. It now has two variations: the *single cableway* and the *double cableway*. The first is the simplest and consists of a single endless cable running on pulley wheels. Buckets and skips are attached to this cable which is kept moving in the same direction, thus carrying the loaded vehicles to their destination and back again as empties. A speed of about 6 m.p.h. is commonly attained, which is not too fast for automatic loading and unloading. It is not possible, however, to carry really heavy weights in this way as the single cable has to do the double job of supporting and hauling the load.

The *double cableway* is a safer but more complicated version of the continuous movement system. A separate cable running parallel to the fixed carrier cable is employed for hauling. In this case, vehicles are not attached to the overhead cable, as on single cableways, but run freely along it on grooved wheels at a speed of up to 12 m.p.h. The hauling rope, which is also an endless one, is powered by an electric

For travelling short distances up mountains, for instance to the ski slopes, the chair lift is used. The chair, with a bar to stop the passenger falling out, hangs from a suspension arm which runs on trolley wheels along a cable.

A skip for carrying minerals. Working on an endless belt system, the skips are fitted with an automatic unloading device.

motor installed at the head of the line. Double-cableway skips often carry loads of a ton or more and can be unhooked from the hauling line when they reach their destination.

PASSENGER TRANSPORT

A single line is not usually considered suitable for passenger-carrying cableways; double lines are preferred. Anyone who has visited Switzerland and Northern Italy will have seen these cable-railways moving easily from peak to peak across the Alps, neat little cars that look like brightly-coloured insects against the snow-clad mountains. These cableway cars have three main parts: trolley wheels, suspension arm and passenger cabin. They are all strongly made, especially the suspension arm and trolley wheels, which, to give maximum balance and support, are shaped in the form of the letter C.

Inside, the passenger cabins resemble the interior of a tram or a lift, their windows giving magnificent views of valleys, gorges, trees and rivers. Between ten and twenty persons may be carried at a time. Sometimes, particularly

in ski resorts, chairs for one or two persons are used instead of cabins.

The double cableway is the most widely used of the two continuous-movement systems. And it is much the safer. The other system, the *two-way* method, requires three cables. In this case an endless cable is not employed for hauling the cabins; instead, a single cable is used to pull the vehicle up, the descent being controlled by the same cable which uncoils from a drum at the top of the run.

HIGH ABOVE THE ALPS

At a time when the development of railway systems has been checked in many countries by the greater use of motor-cars and aeroplanes, it is surprising to learn that the use of cableways is on the increase. This is because they operate over territory where no other form of transport can compete. In the Alps, for example, cable-railways alone can traverse the valleys and mountains. Their great value was first realised during World War I, when single cableways were erected to supply mountain troops fighting along the Italian, Austrian and Yugoslav frontiers. Cable trucks and skips

Cable cars were introduced about a hundred years ago and are now a very popular way of travelling in the Alps.

did the work of the hardiest mules in a fraction of the time. After the war, these installations were adapted and used to carry tourists to peaks that had previously been visited only by mountaineers. Cable-railways are now to be found in all the main holiday centres of the Alps. In Scotland's ski-ing centres there are chair-lifts for skiers and tourists.

ASCENT OF MONT BLANC

Mont Blanc, 15,781 feet high, is the most famous of several Alpine peaks to be approached by cable-railway. It may be reached from both France and Italy by a system of cable-ways rising thousands of feet at a time in a single span, carrying passengers to snowy slopes 12,000 feet above sea level. This spectacular method of transport is also used in countries like Switzerland to keep remote villages in touch with the world. Children living high in the mountains travel to their school in the valley by cable-railway.

Besides being exciting tourist attractions, these little cable-railways are very much more to the inhabitants of mountain districts. They are an efficient and practical means of carrying goods and passengers in mountainous regions.

In mountainous districts, the cableway is the best way of transporting heavy loads. This type can carry half a ton.

THE STORY OF THE GLOVE

No one can say when or by whom the first glove was made. But there is an old legend that the beautiful Venus, while searching for handsome Adonis, scratched her hands on some thorn bushes. On hearing her cries, three lovely hand-maidens came to her help. They swathed her hands in band-ages so light and perfect in their fit that when the wounds were healed the bandages came off in the form of a pair of gloves.

GLOVES FOR THE PHARAOHS

This is little more than a delightful legend. Turning to history, Xenophon, the Greek writer, tells us that the ancient Persians wore gloves. Certainly they were known at an early date over a wide area of the Near East. The Egyptian Pharaohs wore them: they were regarded by the Pharaoh's subjects as a token of his divine power.

It is reasonable to suppose that the custom of wearing gloves originated in the cold climes of northern Europe. Perhaps it did, but it is more likely that the Etruscans and the Romans learned of their use from the East. At meal-times the Romans would often wear a form of finger glove for greater cleanliness when eating. Thus the glove had already become a symbol of delicacy and refinement.

THE GLOVE IN CHIVALRY

In medieval times the status of the glove reached new heights. Kings and emperors used it in the exercise of their authority. When feudal rights or noble titles were awarded, the glove, which was to become the symbol of a challenge, was conferred upon the subject. For the king to give a glove to someone meant to entrust him with a mission, to give him power to act on the royal behalf. The importance of this honour is demonstrated by ballads like the *Chanson*

de Roland, which was sung of Charlemagne's legendary nephew in the Romanic language of old Provence.

Thus the glove became associated with feudal rule, with loyalty and chivalry. Feudal overlords used it to symbolise the protection they offered to their vassals. By the same token, an heir received title to his inheritance. Despite the legen-dary origin of the glove on the hand of Venus, women were not permitted to wear it. This was essentially a man's privilege, for the glove formed part of a knight's uniform and served to protect his hands in duel or on the field of battle.

The glove, together with a chain that secured the bird to the hand, became associated with medieval falconry. The falconer, who trained and carried his birds to the hunt,

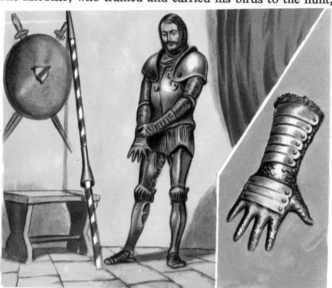

In the Middle Ages, the gauntlet was an important part of a knight's armour. Throughout the period, improvements were made and the simple chain-mail glove developed into the carefully jointed plate gauntlet used in the fine suits of armour which were made in the early sixteenth century.

wore a *single glove* as a necessary part of his equipment and as a badge of office. This glove, to which the falcon returned, was made of deer or buffalo skin and was sometimes decorated with gold buttons round its wide collar. The falconer's glove, like so many others, was still a ceremonial as well as a practical garment.

As the age of chivalry progressed, men bowed to the wishes of their ladies. The fair sex wanted gloves and they got them. Glovers increased in number and skill; soon they were offering the lady of the castle a selection of embroidered gloves in decorative designs and patterns. By the middle of the thirteenth century, France, Spain, and Italy were rival-ling one another in the production of elegant gloves of rare workmanship.

JEWELLED GLOVES

Some of the finest gloves of this period came from Venice, the famous port situated at the head of the Adriatic Sea.

In ancient Rome, people did not use knives and forks, but ate with their fingers. In the patrician families, small finger gloves were worn to keep the hands clean during the meal.

Venetian traders sent their vessels all round the eastern Mediterranean. They returned with pearls, rubies, sapphires, emeralds and semi-precious stones such as coral, all of which were used in glove adornment. Noble families wore velvet gloves with gems sewn on the back around a coat of arms woven in threads of gold and silver.

The designs most favoured by the Venetian glovemakers were those inspired by oriental tastes: the same delicate patterns are still used by Venetian embroiderers on the lace bought by modern tourists. An age-old practice was to soak the fabric in oriental scents and perfumes, which clung to a lady's glove and gave its wearer confidence when she raised her hand to be kissed. Hand-kissing may be seen in Italy to-day, though never with gloves on.

Once the custom of wearing gloves had caught on among women it was not long before every pattern and design had been tried out by the glovemakers of Europe. Succeeding centuries brought their variations, and there was no limit, other than cost, to the richness of the adornments that might be added to the glove. The most perfect specimens of the glove were generally to be found at court. The gloves of Queen Elizabeth I blazed with precious gems, an extravagance in which the French and Spanish royalty also indulged. But, during the eighteenth century, the fashion in gloves, at least among women, began to change. Long-sleeved gloves crept farther and farther up the arm, and with this development came a trend towards greater simplicity.

GLOVES FOR MEN

So far as men's gloves were concerned, changes had been few and far between. Some were made of leather, others of velvet; some had wide cuffs, others were trimmed round the wrist with lace. But, in general, the design of men's gloves was dictated by military and equestrian needs. The " mailed fist " retained its warlike significance; the glove that was thrown to the ground continued to be regarded as a challenge: " If the glove fits wear it." In time even these expressions of defiance began to lose their meaning. The

The pieces of the glove are sewn together on special machines, although the best gloves are sewn by hand. The sewn gloves are then ironed and polished.

glove was destined to become as ordinary a garment as a tie or a pair of socks.

MANUFACTURING LEATHER GLOVES

The everyday needs of modern life demand that gloves should be of a simple and dignified appearance. Some factories cater for outlandish modes, mainly in their seasonal supplies to shops fashionable among women. But most people are now content if their gloves are smart, warmly lined and suitable for all occasions. Our taste in gloves, as in so many other things, has turned against the showy extravagance of the past. We do not want frills and fancies; we prefer something comfortable and strong, made if possible with good quality leather.

The modern manufacture of leather gloves is carried out on a practical, business-like basis which is much the same all over the world. First, hair is removed from the skins by treatment with lime. This process is followed by seasoning, after which the skins are sorted and the best ones chosen for high quality products. These are then dyed, trimmed and cut into sections according to the size required. The shape of a glove is so complex that it is impossible to cut or stamp it out in one piece. Each section must be cut separately and hemmed or pleated, the parts then being assembled and sewn together, occasionally by hand, more often by machinery.

Two processes remain: buffing and ironing. The first of these is carried out by fast-moving wooden rollers covered with a special kind of felt. Its effect is to bring out or imitate the dull brownish-yellow of good buffalo leather: from this animal comes the name of the colour buff, and of the Buffs, a famous regiment. Ironing is done either by the older method of pressing with a revolving wooden spindle, or by the modern method, using electrically-heated irons corresponding in shape and size to the glove.

A good pair of leather gloves made in this way is a popular gift at all times. Except in the hottest climates, gloves are in universal demand, and the glove-making industry is now to be found throughout the world. As in the days when gloves were a luxury, top-quality gloves are still made in Europe, especially in England, France, Italy and Belgium.

Numerous processes go into making a pair of leather gloves. First, the skins have to be dressed and treated to produce the right finish, for instance, smooth or suede. The leather is then put in a mechanical press and the pieces which make up a glove are stamped out. The gloves are then ready for sewing.

FLAX
The raw material of Linen

Ever since we human beings began wearing clothes, textiles of one sort or another have been of great importance to us. We make these textiles from the fibres that are produced for us by nature, or which we make synthetically for ourselves. And since the very earliest times, the fibre we call flax has been used for making the fabric we know as linen.

Flax has been grown by man for almost as long as wheat. One supplied the fibre for making cloth, and the other provided bread. As time went on, cotton supplanted flax to a large degree, and synthetic fibres have affected the importance of flax in more recent times. But flax and the linen that we make from it remain among the most valuable textile materials to-day.

Common flax belongs to the genus *Linum* of the Linaceas family; it includes about ninety species. Only one species, *Linum usitatissimum*, produces good linen yarn, and there are two others with which it should not be confused. These are the parent plant, *Linum angustifolium*, which grows wild and crosses easily with the cultivated variety, and *Linum catharticum* (often called purging flax) which is widely grown in Europe and Asia for medicinal purposes.

A DELICATE-LOOKING PLANT

To see a flax plant growing unobtrusively in a corner of the garden, one would not imagine that it is a source of two important industrial commodities: linen and linseed oil. Flax grows to a height of two or three feet, the main stem branching out near the top to produce lance-shaped leaves and small, attractive flowers. The leaves grow alternately up the stem and branches, and the blue, white or pink flowers, each on its own stalk, close their petals in the evening to bloom again next morning.

Several weeks after flowering, the plant produces the seed pods of the plant. The ripening of the seeds is observed closely by the flax-grower, as it is usual to harvest the crop when about half the seeds are ripe. This occurs three to five months after planting, according to the climate. The crop is pulled up, dried, and the stalks treated, to produce the fibre from which linen is made. This fibre comes from the inner core of the stem: 400 pounds of it per acre is a good average yield.

PRODUCING FLAX YARN

Flax grows best in a damp mild climate; Northern Ireland, for example, is well-known for the excellent quality of its linen. But flax is also grown as a winter crop in sub-tropical countries, and the seed of the plant is commonly being sown in some part of the world at all times throughout the year. When the crop is being grown for its fibre, seed is sown more thickly than when being grown for oil.

Harvesting is often done by hand, but pulling machines are used in the United States, Ireland and elsewhere. If the flax is grown both for the fibre and the seed, the sheaves are left outside to dry, and then threshed to release the seeds from the pods. Next comes a process known as *retting* (a word which really means *rotting*) in which the stalks are exposed to damp and moisture. Retting loosens the core of flax fibre from the outer layer of the stalk which encloses it. Different methods are used in different flax-growing districts: the straw may be placed in vats of water, in which chemicals are dissolved; it may, as in Russia, be left on the ground to rot in the dew; or it may be spread out in shallow ponds and streams. This last method is practised in many countries, including Belgium, where flax grown near the River Lys is used to make the famous Belgian lace.

Retting takes from one to three weeks, after which the crop must be dried until the stalks are brittle. The retted straw is then passed through a machine which breaks up the stalks, an operation known as *scutching*. This is followed by *hackling*, which separates the fibres from the unwanted material. The rough fibre is combed and re-combed, twisted

Left: *the flax plant in flower.* Right: *a magnified section of the stalk showing the polygonal fibres.*

A Flemish woman at her loom. Linen is now woven almost entirely on power looms.

Scutching and hackling, the processes by which the outer covering is broken and separated from the linen fibres.

and drawn to a slender strand, and finally passed through the spinning machines which produce a yarn. The best lace yarn is so fine that twenty miles of it will weigh only one pound. Even coarse grades, used in making rough fabrics and twine, run to two miles per pound.

Cultivated flax, or *Linum usitatissimum*, is among the oldest of man's crops. It was used for making linen cloth in ancient Egypt, and by most of the Mediterranean civilisations that followed the Pharaohs. It may have reached Northern Europe by this route, or it may have been brought by migrant tribes from the region of the Caspian Sea. There is evidence that the wild parent plant, *Linum angustifolium*, was grown by prehistoric lake-dwellers in Switzerland. It is possible that they grew the flax for its oil, rather than its fibre. The seeds also served as food, being eaten by both the Greeks and Romans. The seeds are still enjoyed in Eastern Europe.

From these beginnings, the cultivation of flax has spread throughout the world; millions of acres are now sown in Russia, Poland and Western Europe. The best qualities come from the Irish and the Belgian crops. In the United States, where flax was introduced in colonial days, it is grown mainly for the linseed oil and associated products. In Arizona, California and other States, the flax crop covers four million acres every year. America produces 40 million bushels of seed a year; this is an important contribution to the world output of 130 million bushels. (A bushel is 56 lb., and there are about 100,000 seeds to a pound.)

TWENTY MILLION ACRES OF FLAX

Linseed oil extracted from the seed of the flax plant is used in paints and varnishes. It undergoes chemical changes in contact with the air, forming a tough film on the painted or varnished surface. It is also used in the manufacture of linoleum and oilcloth, in the treatment of certain leathers, and as an essential ingredient in printer's ink.

The residue left when the seeds have been crushed and the oil extracted is pressed into cakes and fed to livestock.

Some twenty million acres of the world's surface are now sown with flax every year. When you think of the products we get from the crop, ranging from clothing to artists' " oils ", from cattle cake to linoleum, it is a useful reminder that the most worthy of Nature's creations are often hidden beneath an unassuming exterior.

THE COCONUT PALM

In every region of the world, nature has provided resources that people have learned to put to good use. In Britain, she has given us coal; in Canada, Scandinavia and Russia she covered millions of square miles with timber forests; in South America and New Zealand, in South Africa and Australia she has left huge tracts of grazing land. And in the tropical islands of the Pacific and the countries of the Far East she has provided that most versatile of all trees, the coconut-palm, which has as many uses as there are days in the year.

WHIPPED BY HURRICANES

When mature, the coconut palm stands anything from fifty to a hundred feet high. Its slender, graceful trunk is crowned by a feathery plume of immense leaves. In common with other palms, it has a fragile look, but like many apparently delicate creatures it is well equipped to withstand the force of Nature.

When hurricanes blow, the flexible trunk of the coconut-palm bows before the wind. As the wind drops, it straightens

The tall coconut is the most common palm in the tropics. It is an important crop tree.

itself up to tower proudly over the roofless houses and battered shrubs that the wind has left in its path. In the heat of the midday sun, the fronds of the tree droop limply, reminding us of *flabella*, the palm leaves that were used to fan the Pharaohs of Egypt.

FIFTY COCONUTS ON A TREE

High out of reach, in the middle of clusters of foliage, grow the coconuts, about fifty on each tree. They take a year to ripen, by which time they have reached the size of a small rugby football. Outside, there is a hard, fibrous shell which surrounds the kernel of the fruit. The white, fleshy core is the endosperm—the food which nourishes the plant germ when it starts to grow. The centre of the coconut is filled with " milk ", which also serves to nourish the germinating plant.

Coconuts are often blown from the trees, and washed out to sea. The nut floats easily on the water, and it is in this way that it has become so widely distributed among the islands of the Pacific. The agile natives of these regions are always ready to climb the trees when the crop is ripe, cutting away the nuts and letting them fall to the ground to be collected together.

COPRA AND COIR

The coconut tree has always grown fairly close to the sea, and the rough, brown fibre that covers the nuts has acquired a great resistance to salt water. This fibre, called coir, is used for making ropes, brushes and brooms, the waste being crushed and used for horticultural purposes. The hard part of the shell, which is smooth and watertight, makes excellent drinking vessels. The leaves are woven, while still green, into mats, screens and baskets, and in some Pacific islands are used for thatching the roofs of huts and houses.

By far the most valuable product of the tree is copra, the nutty part of the fruit, which is dried and squeezed for its high oil content. Copra may be dried in the sun, or in kilns—as in the Philippines—or it may be given a hot air treatment. It is then ground up and squeezed in a mechanical screw press, which extracts oil equivalent in weight to two-thirds of the amount of copra treated. One press is capable of handling as many as thirty tons a day. A very large quantity of coconut-oil is produced in the coastal regions of India, Malaya, Indonesia and the Pacific.

Every part of the coconut tree is used. The wood, the nuts, and the leaves have many uses. Here the leaves are being woven into baskets while they are still green. They can also be used to thatch houses and make mats for the floors.

COCONUT-OIL MAKES MARGARINE

Coconut-oil is an important raw material which is in great demand throughout the world. It provides us with soap, detergents, glycerine, synthetic rubber, and even brake fluids. In refined form it is extremely nourishing. Moreover, it contains an acid which resists the tendency of some foodstuffs to go rancid. For this reason confectioners use coconut-oil in cakes and confectionery which may be kept for some time before being eaten. But the greatest demand for coconut-oil comes from the manufacturers of margarine, who use it in large quantities, especially in Europe. In the United States the use of coconut-oil for this purpose is prohibited by law. This legislation was introduced to stimulate U.S. home production of cotton-seed and soya-bean oils, which Americans now use for the production of margarine.

In countries where the coconut grows, people make a drink called toddy from the sap or juice, which is obtained by cutting a slit in the flower stalk. This toddy may be drunk fresh—the tropical " toddy bird " does in fact live on the fresh juice—or it may be fermented into a highly alcoholic palm wine, which, if distilled, makes a very rough spirit.

SALAD AND PORCUPINE WOOD

What an extraordinary tree this is! The same buds that yield toddy develop into cabbage-like growths which are eaten as a salad. If the buds are left to ripen, they eventually form the coconut whose oils, extracted from copra, provide a livelihood for hundreds of thousands of people. When the tree has reached a ripe old age, it is felled and cut into lengths of " porcupine wood " which is widely used as an ornamental timber. The wood takes its name from the characteristic markings of the grain, which resemble a porcupine quill.

When next you are at the fair and see a row of coconuts at the shy, spare a thought for the wonderful tree from which they came. At home in the Pacific, the coconut-palm is a queen among trees. But she has become a maid-of-all-work to the people who live in her lands.

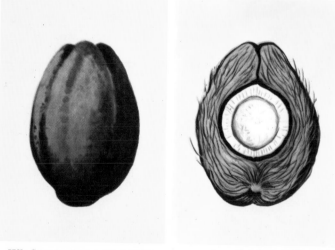

Whole coconut and (right) cross-section showing milk and edible flesh which feed the plant seed while it is germinating.

HEROES OF THE SPACE FRONTIER

On 12th April, 1961, Major Yuri Gagarin soared aloft in a rocket ship from a base in Russia, and made man's first journey into space. Before the year was out, he had been followed by Commander Alan Shepard in the U.S. space-craft *Freedom 7*, and by Major Gherman Titov in *Vostok II.*

The year 1961 will be remembered as marking the beginning of man's exploration of the Universe. At last, after thousands of years of earth-bound life, human beings had escaped into the vast territories of outer space. A new type of explorer had appeared—a space-explorer, to whom we have given the name astronaut.

The great explorers of old were tough, courageous men. They travelled the face of the earth, surmounting all manner of perils and hardships as they made their way to places that civilised man had never reached before. They hacked paths through jungles inhabited by wild animals and by savage tribes; they staggered forward against blizzards that raged across the frozen lands of polar regions. They endured stifling heat and bitter cold; they died of strange diseases and starved to death for lack of food.

The modern explorers in space, the astronauts, are facing hazards of a different kind. But the dangers they meet as they venture into space are just as real as any that were experienced by the explorers who made their way into the unknown regions of the earth.

The astronauts are men of immense courage and determination. Their lives are at stake every time they roar into space in the tiny craft perched on top of the huge rockets that carry them away from earth. They are venturing into the vast unexplored regions of emptiness that lie between the earth and other bodies of the universe.

Here, all manner of hazards must be faced. The astronauts are leaving their familiar world behind them, and with it all the material things that are needed to support life. In space, there is no air to breathe, no water to drink, and no food to eat; all these essentials must be taken with the astronaut in his space-craft if he is to survive. But there are also many difficulties and dangers which arise from the strange surroundings that the astronaut finds in space. And everything must be done to help the astronaut to overcome the hazards that he meets.

SCIENTISTS' CONTRIBUTIONS

Scientists were well aware of some of the dangers of space-travel long before man ventured away from earth. It was known, for example, that the astronaut would have to be protected from radiation that can damage and destroy the tissues of the body. It was realised that he would have to withstand the effects of intense acceleration as the rocket-ship carried him through the earth's atmosphere and into space. And, of course, it was understood that there is always the risk of mechanical failure of the rocket or the space-ship.

Despite these dangers, and others which will no doubt arise as man's experience of space-travel grows, there are always brave and resolute men who are prepared to risk their lives in space. They are determined to blaze the trail along which future generations will make their way to the moon and planets.

Selecting men to serve as astronauts is a difficult task. All sorts of physical and mental requirements must be met, and it is essential that the men must undergo a long and arduous period of training. We know little about the life of the Soviet astronauts, but it is probably very similar to that of the U.S. space-men, of which we know a great deal.

When we watch an astronaut being sent off into orbit round the earth or the moon, we are seeing the culmination of a long and complex effort on the part of thousands of men and women. Vast organisations are involved in the planning and carrying-out of space programmes such as those of the Soviet Union or the United States of America.

After World War II, the U.S. government made plans for a programme of research which would culminate in the sending of astronauts into space. But it was realised from the outset that an immense amount of preliminary work would have to be carried out before a human explorer could leave the earth with a reasonable prospect of survival. All sorts of questions must be answered, and innumerable technical problems solved by the small army of people involved in the huge space programme.

Thousands of scientists, engineers and technicians worked through the late 1940s and the 1950s, and one after another the technical problems were overcome. Rockets were built and tested. There were many failures, and every failure created new problems. But the lessons learned were useful, and helped to contribute to the eventual success.

As the reliability and power of the rocket vehicles increased, it became possible to take the first real step towards putting a man in space. Satellites were launched. As these bundles of instruments sped in orbit round the earth, they collected

Strapped into his space capsule, an astronaut prepares to explore the unknown world of space.

111

information about the strange environment of space. Information was radioed back to earth, and man began to gain his first real understanding of the conditions he would find outside the atmosphere of the earth.

The satellites were followed by space probes which set off on immense journeys of millions of miles into the unknown. These instrumented vehicles, in their turn, relayed information about the regions of space that lay far beyond the reach of orbiting satellites.

So, during the 1950s, the problems of building rockets and vehicles capable of escaping from earth were overcome, at least to the point at which it was considered possible to send an astronaut into space and bring him safely back to earth.

The U.S. project aimed at putting a man in space was carried through under the code-name Project Mercury. The space-craft was designed in the form of a bell-shaped capsule which would be carried aloft on the nose of a huge Redstone rocket.

By this time, a vast store of information had accumulated about the hazards that the astronaut himself would face as he made his journey into the unknown. And intensive research had been going on in an effort to ensure that every danger could be overcome.

ACCELERATION AND DECELERATION

Every material thing in our world—including man—is attracted towards the earth by gravitational forces. The pull of gravity holds us in a powerful grip, and it is only by overcoming these forces that we can escape into space. In order to do this, our rocket vehicles accelerate to tremendous speeds as they make their way through the earth's atmosphere. And this rapid acceleration exerts tremendous forces on the body of the astronaut in his space-ship in the rocket's nose.

By the time that man was preparing to hurl himself into space, experience with aircraft had shown how serious the effects of acceleration could be. Pilots making tight turns at high speed, for example, would " black out " owing to the acceleration developed by the turn.

Most of us have felt the effects of acceleration in one way or another. As a car gathers speed, for example, we can feel our bodies being pressed against the back of the seat. It

is easy to imagine how uncomfortable these forces could become if we were accelerating to a speed of several thousand miles per hour, instead of 50 or 60 miles an hour.

In the same way, we find our bodies subjected to tremendous forces as we slow down rapidly. These are the effects of deceleration, and they too are familiar enough to anyone who has ridden in a car. We can feel the body pressing against the safety-belt as the driver brakes hard. If we are not wearing a safety harness, we may find ourselves bumping against the windscreen.

Long before World War II, scientists were studying the effects of rapid acceleration and deceleration ; they wanted to find out, for example, how passengers in a plane could be protected from the rapid deceleration experienced in a crash.

This work was continued after the war, when the problem of acceleration and deceleration became important in the space programme. The inhabitants of a space-ship must be able to withstand not only the acceleration as the vehicle leaves the earth, but the deceleration as it enters the atmosphere again and loses speed.

SLED ON RAILS

One of the pioneers of these researches is Colonel John P. Stapp of the U.S. Air Force. In 1946, Colonel Stapp and his colleagues began a series of experiments designed to test the effects of acceleration and deceleration on human " guinea pigs ". A special sled was built, which ran on rails, and could be accelerated to high speeds by a rocket motor. As it reached the end of its short rail-trip, the sled was brought to a halt by a braking system. It could be stopped in less that 20 feet, from a speed of 180 miles per hour.

Between April, 1947 and June, 1951, the rocket-propelled sled made hundreds of runs at the Edwards Flight Test Center in the United States. Dummies were strapped into the sled during the early runs, being followed by chimpanzees and, later, human volunteers. Altogether, 73 people took part in these nerve-shattering tests, including Colonel Stapp himself. Among the volunteers were three flight surgeons, one pilot, two parachutists, two harness makers, a medical technician, a photographer, an air gunner and an ordnance specialist. Their ages ranged from 25 to 41 years.

Time and again, these volunteers were strapped into the

Colonel John Stapp of the U.S. Air Force, in a special sled built to run on rails, was one of the men who pioneered the effects of acceleration and deceleration on the human body.

The Americans launched this Ranger space-craft at the moon. Unfortunately, the instruments failed to function and no information was gained. However, a later launching, on 31st July, 1964, was completely successful and over 4,000 close-up pictures of the surface of the moon were televised back to earth.

rocket-propelled sled, accelerated to tremendous speeds and then brought suddenly to a stop. Ciné pictures taken on the sled show the flesh of the volunteer's face being distorted and his eyes pressed into their sockets under the effects of the tremendous forces.

These acceleration tests have continued and are still going on to-day. In many research centres, volunteers are subjecting themselves to acceleration in other types of equipment. There are pendulum devices, like large garden swings that come to a sudden halt as they reach the bottom of the swing. And there are centrifugal devices that whirl their victims round at terrific speed, pressing them against the outer wall of their " space-ship " by centrifugal force.

As a result of these researches, scientists now know a great deal about the effects of acceleration and deceleration, and the best way of protecting astronauts against them. When the rocket vehicle lifts the space-ship away from earth, the astronaut lies in a special couch, contoured in such a way as to give support to every part of his body. He lies across the direction in which the acceleration is taking place, minimising the effects of the forces exerted on him.

In this way, it is possible for the astronaut to withstand the acceleration and deceleration forces experienced in space-flight. Thanks to the courage of many " backroom " boys, willing to subject themselves to unpleasant and often dangerous experiments, he can be boosted into orbit without suffering any ill effects from acceleration forces.

RADIATION

The atmosphere that surrounds our earth acts as a shield, which protects us from much of the radiation which would otherwise reach us from space. The atmosphere absorbs part of the radiation from the sun, for example, including ultra-violet rays which would make life impossible here on earth.

It has long been known that anyone venturing outside the earth's atmosphere would be subjected to the effects of fierce radiation, and some form of protection would be necessary. The satellites and space-probes have shown that this radiation is more intense than had been supposed. Surrounding the earth, for example, there are two doughnut-

shaped bands of radiation which are now known as the Van Allen radiation. An astronaut passing through these bands in his space-ship would be subjected to concentrated radiation which could be dangerous if he were not protected.

In addition, cosmic rays will be encountered almost everywhere in space. And most important of all, there are the bursts of radiation resulting from solar flares, the great upheavals which take place intermittently on the sun.

The astronaut setting off on a prolonged journey into space will have to protect himself as best he can from radiation. He may be able to by-pass the bands of Van Allen radiation by taking his space-ship through the " hole " in the doughnut-shaped bands. Cosmic rays should not, as a rule, present a very great hazard. But the radiation from solar flares may be so intense that he will suffer serious effects.

Some protection against radiation is possible by using shields of metal, such as lead, to absorb the rays. But it would not be a practical proposition to surround a space-ship with sufficient shielding to give complete protection against the burst of radiation from a solar flare.

At present, this is probably the greatest hazard that the astronaut will have to face, and his best protection will be to try and make his journey at a time when the sun is going through a quiet period. This is why a great deal of research is now being carried out in the hope of predicting when a solar flare is going to appear.

Designed initially to carry a war-head, an Atlas ICBM was successfully orbited in 1958, by the United States, as a communications experiment.

113

Project Gemini*: This part of the American space programme put two men in orbit round the earth as a preliminary test for the* Apollo *project which put man on the moon.*

WEIGHTLESSNESS

The effects of acceleration, and the danger from radiation are hazards that can be studied by scientists here on earth. But there is another potential danger to our astronauts—the strange phenomenon of weightlessness that they experience when travelling in space. And it is not easy to simulate the condition of weightlessness for any length of time.

When the first astronauts made their journeys into space, they did not know what the effects of periods of weightlessness might be. It was a case of finding out the hard way.

Already, astronauts have experienced weightlessness for periods of a few days, and suffered no serious ill effects. Major Titov felt as though he was upside down when his weight deserted him. And he suffered from a form of space-sickness or nausea which was unpleasant without being harmful.

It may well be, however, that weightlessness could become more serious when the astronaut experiences it for long periods. Nobody knows yet what the psychological effects may be.

Russian biologists made the strange discovery that onion seeds sent up in a satellite were stimulated into growth. This was not due to any changes in the chromosomes of the cell, but was apparently caused by the condition of weightlessness. The cells were not subjected to the usual gravitational influence.

It might well be that the cells of higher animals, including man, will be affected in some such way after a prolonged experience of weightlessness. Also, it is possible that the removal of the normal gravitational forces may upset the balance of organs, such as the heart, which are used to operating in conditions including the pull of gravity.

SELECTION OF THE ASTRONAUTS

As scientists involved in the U.S. space programme struggled to find ways of protecting astronauts against these known hazards of life in space, the selection and training of the first U.S. astronauts began. Minimum requirements were laid down by the National Aeronautics and Space Administration. The men selected must be thoroughly experienced

and well-trained test pilots, with at least 1,500 hours flying time. They must be absolutely fit and healthy, and no more than 5 feet 11 inches in height. The maximum age was 40. In addition, each astronaut had to be highly intelligent, with a degree in science or engineering.

Sixty-nine pilots answering these requirements were selected and summoned to Washington to hear about the Project Mercury programme. They were invited to take part, and 80 per cent. of them volunteered to do so. The volunteers were then subjected to rigorous tests, and seven were chosen to undergo intensive training that lasted for more than two years.

During this period, three of the men, Shepard, Glenn and Grissom, were selected to become the first American astronauts. They continued with their training, which became more and more intensive to prepare them for space-flight conditions. They were spun in centrifuges to accustom them to acceleration and deceleration effects. They flew in aircraft which manoeuvred to produce the effect of weightlessness.

Protected by space-suits similar to those they would wear in the actual flight, they were subjected to extremes of heat and cold. They were bumped and spun and tumbled about to simulate conditions they would experience in launching, during their flight in space and on re-entry into the atmosphere and their return to earth.

The astronauts had to learn how to manipulate the controls of the space-craft under every conceivable difficulty. They were even catapulted into the sea and into the desert, so that they would learn to cope with any eventuality on landing.

By early 1961, the Redstone rocket was ready. The chimpanzee Ham was sent on a test flight, making a successful trip to a height of 155 miles, landing 420 miles out in the Atlantic.

RUSSIAN SUCCESS

On 12th April, 1961, at 9.07 Moscow time, the Russians launched the space-craft *Vostok* with Major Yuri Gagarin on board. At 10.55, *Vostok* landed safely in Russia, and Major Gagarin stepped out after spending 108 minutes circling the earth. Man had made his first successful journey into space.

In May, 1961, Commander Alan Shepard became the first American astronaut to travel in space, when he made his 115-mile-high trip in *Freedom 7*. In August, Major Titov remained in orbit for a day in *Vostok II*, and on 20th February, 1962, Lieutenant-Colonel John Glenn became the first American astronaut to encircle the earth in his space-ship *Friendship 7*.

MEN ON THE MOON

Since 1961 the Americans and Russians have been aiming for the moon with unmanned spacecraft, capable latterly of making soft landings. This culminated, on 20th July, 1969, in the first moon landing of a manned craft and, for the first time ever, men walked on the moon. They were Neil Armstrong and Edwin Aldrin, crew members of America's Apollo 11 craft, and they returned safely to earth after spending several hours on the moon. The second successful moon landing took place in November, 1969.

There will be many more moon landings in the future but this is only the beginning of man's quest into the unknown and mysterious universe of which our earth is so small a part.

MARBLE ~ THE SHINING STONE

Many of our most beautiful and useful materials come to us in the strangest ways. The stone we know as marble, for example, from which many of the world's grandest buildings have been made, was formed from the remains of countless tiny sea creatures that lived and died millions of years ago.

Marble has been used in building and sculpture since the earliest times. A form of limestone, it is so hard that it resists the wear and tear of centuries. Civilisations of the past have left evidence of their greatness in marble buildings and works of art that survive to this day.

In their marble quarries, the Pharaohs of Egypt, the Greeks of Hellas and the Romans maintained armies of slaves who spent their lives cutting out large blocks of stone. Tall columns of black and rose-coloured marble adorned the palaces of the Nile, and of the Babylonian and Assyrian kings who ruled the lands of the Tigris and the Euphrates. The columns were shaped and polished by thousands of slaves and captured prisoners.

FOR KING ARTAXERXES' PALACE

Two famous sources of the " shining stone ", as the Greeks called marble, are Mount Pentelicus in Attica and the Aegean island of Paros. Pentelic and Parian marble were used by Praxiteles and other Greek sculptors. During one of his voyages, King Artaxerxes of Persia called at Paros, and was so struck by the beauty of its emerald marble that he gave orders for his palace to be paved with it.

Fulfilling these orders was no easy task. At that time marble was cut by means of a thin blade, moved by hand in a groove filled with hard sand mixed with water. Hundreds of slaves worked for ten years to quarry the slabs and cut them to proper thickness. But Artaxerxes' marble floor was a great success and the potentates of the Middle East were

Marble, throughout the centuries, has been the stone in which great works of sculpture were created. Michelangelo, greatest of the Florentine Renaissance sculptors, chose white marble from the Apuan alps of Liguria.

soon trying to keep up with him. In due course, the famous Temple of Jerusalem was paved with the same emerald marble; light entering the temple made the floor shimmer like green silk in the evening sun. (This lustrous effect of marble is caused by reflection of light from crystals beneath the surface of the stone.)

FOR ROMAN PILLARS AND PORTICOES

The early Romans led a hard, military life, and were not greatly interested in luxury or art. But as their power increased and trade expanded, they built new temples of increasing splendour. One of the finest is the Temple of Fortuna Virilis, built under the Republic in the third century B.C. and still standing. It is constructed of tufa stone and travertine marble from the Lazio quarries near Rome, and is a rare gem of the Greco-Roman style of architecture.

The first Roman house to be adorned with marble belonged to Quintus Metellus who, in 146 B.C., defeated the Achaeans and made a Roman province of Macedonia. To commemorate this victory the praetor erected a sumptuous villa with marble columns and a marble bath supplied with rainwater. The villa brought general scorn on Quintus Metellus' head, and he was described by one Roman historian as " a purveyor of luxury and softness". Fifty-two years later, Lucius Crassus had six columns of green marble set up at the entrance to his villa. The envy of other patricians was aroused and Crassus was called before Marcus Brutus who reproved him, saying:

" Your love of luxury is equalled only by that of the Palatine Venus." These were harsh words, which in effect accused Lucius Crassus of being vulgarly effeminate.

But Roman austerity was already on the wane. A desire for beauty in the home was encouraging many rich citizens

King Artaxerxes was so struck with the beauty of the emerald marble found on the Greek island of Paros that he ordered his palace floor to be paved with it.

to turn their houses into villas of great splendour. Public buildings, too, were becoming less austere. According to Pliny, Marcus Scaurus the Younger, who lived at the time of Julius Caesar, built a theatre for 80,000 persons which contained 360 forty-foot marble columns and a forest of marble statues. Such magnificence was possible only in a civilisation making use of slaves who were worked to death in the most miserable of conditions.

MICHELANGELO'S STATUES

Marble had now become famous throughout the ancient world. Rulers sent their agents into the hills and mountains to seek fresh sources of marble, porphyry and granite in new and richer hues. The skill of the stone cutters won recognition; they were highly paid, and there was great competition for their services.

Some of the finest deposits of marble were to be found around Massa Carrara on the Ligurian coasts, and Italy soon acquired a tradition for the excellence of her marble. In the Middle Ages, Carrara marble was to achieve an international reputation; and artists and dealers went there, as they still do, to buy and ship the stone. Michelangelo, for instance, paid frequent visits to the Apuan Alps behind Carrara, selecting stone which was then transported to his studio in Florence. Canova was another great sculptor whose genius is said to have been discovered when, as a boy, he modelled a lion in butter: he used the white marble of Carrara for the statues that made him famous.

GEOLOGICAL ORIGINS OF MARBLE

Much of the earth's crust is formed of rock which geologists divide into three main groups: igneous, sedimentary and metamorphic rock. Igneous rocks such as basalt, have solidified during the past 2000 million years from great masses of molten matter called magma. They are closely associated with volcanic activity. Sedimentary rocks, of which limestone is a good example, have been formed largely by the accumulation of the remains of living organisms and suspended materials. Metamorphic rocks, including marble, are rocks which have undergone a subsequent change

Because of the danger of shattering the rock, explosives are rarely used in marble quarrying. Nowadays, special machines such as saws with special cutting edges are used and the blocks of marble are then shaped and squared by hand.

(metamorphosis is a Greek word meaning " change " or " transformation "). Marble is a recrystallised limestone, formed originally from fossilised organisms that once lived in the sea. Since Palaeozoic and pre-Cambrian times, the limestone has been undergoing changes which have transformed it into the stone we now recognise as marble.

HOW MARBLE IS QUARRIED

There are two ways of quarrying marble: by blasting, and by cutting. Blasting, the more spectacular method, has been largely abandoned for the safer and more economic one of cutting the rock with special wire saws.

When a bed of marble suitable for quarrying has been selected and stripped clean, it is examined to determine its structure and the orientation of the rock. This is a highly skilled job requiring great experience, especially when a blast is to be made. Pneumatic drills are used to drill holes about one and half inches in diameter to a depth of as much as thirty-five feet. The charges are then laid, the warning siren is blown and the hill quivers under the force of the blast.

Blasting is a wasteful process, as much of the marble is broken into useless fragments. It is more usual nowadays to use an electrically-operated wire saw, which has a cutting edge consisting of two strong steel wires. Held taut between two wheels, the wire rubs against the stone, moving at great speed. The deep groove in which the wire moves is flushed with water and an abrasive sand, harder than the marble itself. Large blocks of marble are cut in this way and deposited in a clearing where they are roughly squared by machines. They are then held for inspection by architects and other buyers, or else transported down the mountain to be cut into smaller blocks.

The large blocks are cut by a saw consisting of one or more bands of extremely hard steel. The bands move backwards and forwards against the stone, the cutting edges being treated as before with water and abrasive sand. A second cutting reduces the blocks to slabs and panels of a size and thickness required by the trade, using a large emery wheel that revolves at 2,000 revolutions per minute. The surface is polished, using a series of fine-grained grinding wheels, and if the marble is to have a really fine finish, it is finally polished with lead blocks damped in oxalic acid. These processes are wholly or partly mechanised, and it is only in making columns, pillar heads, tombstones, and sculpture that skilled hand-work may be employed.

THE TAJ MAHAL

Marble is found in many parts of the world, including France, Germany, Holland, Sweden, Roumania, Egypt and Tunisia. In the United States there are quarries in Colorado, Vermont and Tennessee. Britain has few large deposits, but several cathedrals and abbeys, including Westminster, contain specimens of workmanship in Purbeck marble from South Dorset.

The finest marble still comes from those countries where it was first used. Greece and Italy are the principal producers of those attractive shades of creamy white and emerald green marble used for decorative and ornamental work. But they do not hold a monopoly of this beautiful stone. The Taj Mahal at Agra, which is perhaps the finest piece of architecture in the world, owes much of its glory to the use of white marble from Makrana, India. In the moonlight, this mausoleum built by Shah Jahan in memory of his wife, has shone resplendent for over 300 years.

MIRRORS

The earliest mirrors were made by polishing bronze and other metals. The surface was often slightly convex, or curved outwards, making the user's face look smaller than it really was. The secret of making glass mirrors was discovered in Roman times, the methods used being primitive by comparison with later techniques. Glass was coated with a mixture of molten lead, tin and antimony. The mirrors made in this way were not completely smooth, and the alloy forming the reflecting surface produced a greenish-blue reflection. In spite of their shortcomings, these early mirrors were greatly appreciated by women, and it is recorded that in A.D. 625 Pope Boniface IV sent one as a present to Queen Aethelberga of Northumbria.

The manufacture of mirrors on an industrial scale did not begin until late in the Middle Ages. One of the earliest mirror-making centres was Murano, an island near Venice; the Doge's government had given the island to the glass-makers because their furnaces had caused many fires in the city. By the middle of the sixteenth century, the Venetian mirror-makers had formed themselves into a guild similar to one already existing in Nürnburg.

A new process, still in use in places to-day, had been developed by the Venetians. A thin layer of pure mercury was poured over a very fine sheet of tinfoil, and a piece of glass, polished bright and cut to the required size, was then laid over the amalgam of mercury and tin. Pressure was exerted on the glass by means of heavy weights; the excess mercury was squeezed out, leaving a layer of amalgam adhering to the glass. This formed a perfect surface for the reflection of light. It was customary to varnish the amalgam to prevent deterioration by the air.

It was a short step from this process to the more modern technique of silvering mirrors, which was discovered by the

In the electrolytic bath, mirrors are given a coating of copper to protect the delicate under-surface from oxidation.

German chemist, Baron von Liebig, about 130 years ago. Liebig used a chemical process by which a layer of silver was formed on the glass, providing an excellent reflecting surface. Silvering gradually replaced the use of tin amalgam, and in the meantime glass manufacturers were finding new ways of producing large sheets of glass of sparkling clarity. In the latter half of the last century, mirror-making ceased to be a craft and became an industry; factories began producing fine plate-glass mirrors at prices everyone could afford.

The glass of a mirror must be perfectly smooth, and both sides should be exactly parallel, or the glass will distort the image. It is essential too that the back of the mirror should be silvered evenly with a coating that does not discolour or flake off.

Sheets of glass to be used in making mirrors are checked to make sure they are not defective, and are then washed in a solution of tin chloride. This is done to eliminate every trace of grease or other substance that might prevent the silvering from sticking to the back of the mirror. The glass is then rinsed in distilled water to wash off the tin chloride; if this were not done, the mirror would appear streaky with bluish-grey blotches. Silver is now deposited on the surface of the glass, forming a hard, uniform layer, and the back of the mirror looks as if it had been pasted over with a thin sheet of foil. This process takes about ten minutes.

Other types of coatings consist of chromium and aluminium, which are commonly used in cheaper mirrors. Lead nitrate or gold chloride may also be used, providing mirrors giving a darker reflection; these reflecting layers absorb more of the light than does a silver layer. No matter what type of reflecting layer is used, it is protected from deterioration by some form of sealing coat; this may consist of shellac, followed by a varnish made from kauri-gum and oil of turpentine, which leaves a smooth, hard surface.

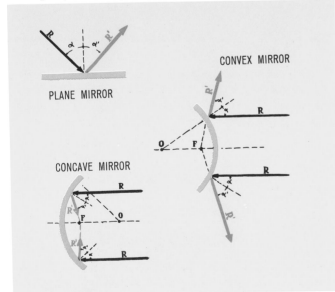

The illustration shows how plane, convex and concave mirrors reflect light. R = incident ray; R′ = reflected ray; α = angle of incidence; α′ = angle of reflection; F = focal point.

THE EVOLUTION OF THE TRAIN

The popular notion that George Stephenson invented the railway engine is a highly misleading one. Stephenson and his son, Robert, were certainly the co-authors of the railway revolution that swept Britain during the early years of the nineteenth century, but others long before them had recognised the potential power of steam. Indeed, legend has it that the Greek philosopher, Hero of Alexandria, was experimenting with steam over a century before the birth of Christ. But Hero and other sages of the day looked upon their inventions as little more than playthings and it was not until the Renaissance, the great intellectual movement that roused Europe seventeen centuries later, that man made his first serious attempts to harness the power of steam.

The first distinct step forward was probably that made in 1601 by the Naples philosopher, Giovanni Battista della Porta, who published a commentary on Hero's work. Della Porta perfected an apparatus for raising water from a low to a higher level by steam power. This apparatus was a forerunner of the pumping engine which a century later, in the hands of Cornish mine-owner, Thomas Savery, became the earliest commercially successful steam invention. A contemporary of della Porta, the Italian engineer, Giovanni Branca, designed an engine shaped like a water-wheel and driven by the impact of a jet of steam on its vanes. Unfortunately, most people regarded the "steam wheel" as nothing more than a practical joke.

Edward Somerset, Second Marquis of Worcester, is often credited with having devised the first useful steam-engine. We are told that he first recognised the power of steam while watching an iron cooking pot on the fire in his cell in the Tower of London where he was a prisoner of Oliver Cromwell. While watching the lid moving on the boiling pot, Somerset is said to have realised there was a great force at work. Although there are no drawings in existence, it appears that the pumping engine he designed included a pair of displacement chambers, from each of which alternately water was forced by steam from an independent boiler.

Many and varied were the fanciful schemes suggested by would-be inventors at this time. Dr. John Wilkins, Bishop of Chester, went so far as to suggest it was possible to travel to the moon in a steam-driven flying chariot.

The next important figure in the long line of steam pioneers is Denis Papin, the French physicist, who died in London in 1712. Dr. Papin is best remembered for his steam "digester", which was designed for cookery and did in fact embody the principles of the modern pressure cooker. Dr. Papin also invented the safety-valve and suggested that the condensation of steam should be employed to make a vacuum under a piston previously raised by the expansion of steam. Papin's was the earliest cylinder-and-piston steam-engine.

In 1698, Savery designed his famous "fire engine". This engine was constructed on the principle that steam, once it is cooled, condenses (becomes water). The water occupies considerably less space than the steam. Savery's engine admitted steam into an egg-shaped vessel which was subsequently cooled by spraying its exterior with cold water.

This resulted in condensation of the steam inside and the creation of a partial vacuum. The atmospheric pressure outside was therefore able to force water into the vessel through a pipe from beneath.

Savery's engine was inefficient and wasted large quantities of steam but it was widely used for pumping operations in flooded mine-workings. Scarcely more efficient was Thomas Newcomen's "atmospheric engine" which had a piston and cylinder, but was slow-moving and wasteful.

In 1769, a French military engineer, Nicolas Cugnot, constructed a steam wagon in which he is said to have reached a speed of 25 miles an hour over a short distance. But five years later a much more significant event took place—the invention by a Glasgow instrument-maker, James Watt, of the first really efficient and powerful steam-engine.

JAMES WATT

Watt was engaged at Glasgow University in repairing a model of Newcomen's engine when he was struck by its inefficiency. His remedy lay in keeping the cylinder as hot as the steam that entered it. Watt provided the cylinder with a steam jacket, and added to the engine an entirely new organ—an empty vessel, separate from the cylinder, into which the steam could be allowed to escape and be condensed by the application of cold water.

A small pump, called the air pump, was fitted to extract the water from the condenser together with air that leaked in. In 1782, Watt invented the double-acting steam-engine, and other refinements patented by him included valve-gear to shut off steam after the piston had travelled for part of its stroke, permitting the expansion of the steam to push the piston through the rest of its stroke.

The most significant and far-reaching of all Watt's inven-

Denis Papin (1647-c.1712), invented a "steam digester", a closed vessel in which high pressure was generated.

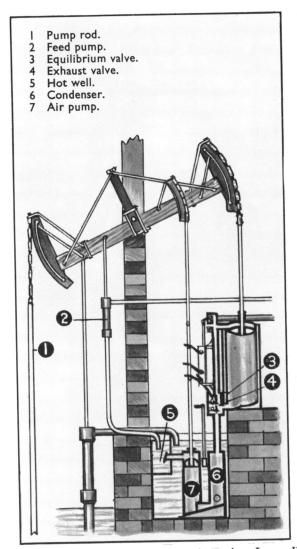

1 Pump rod.
2 Feed pump.
3 Equilibrium valve.
4 Exhaust valve.
5 Hot well.
6 Condenser.
7 Air pump.

While repairing a model of Newcomen's engine, James Watt saw that a separate steam condenser would improve the efficiency of the engine by cutting the consumption of steam.

tions was the number of methods he introduced to change the push-and-pull action of the piston into the rotary movement needed for most machinery. Although Watt did not actually invent the steam-engine, he improved it so much that it played a vital role in the Industrial Revolution of the nineteenth century. The way was now open for the pioneers of the railway engine.

Railways existed long before there were railway engines. Railways had their origin in the wagonways which, as early as the sixteenth century, were used in the mineral districts around Newcastle for the conveyance of coal from the pits to the River Tyne for shipment. It was found that horses could pull heavier loads along a smooth track than on a rough road, and flat wooden rails were laid down for the purpose.

With the great upsurge in industrial activity that came in the wake of the Industrial Revolution, the roads and canals of Britain could no longer cope with the traffic, and an alternative had to be found. Necessity was the mother of invention, and the outcome was the railway.

RICHARD TREVITHICK

The distinction of building the first real locomotive to run on rails belongs to the Cornish mining engineer, Richard Trevithick. He saw that high-pressure steam must be used instead of the atmospheric pressure employed in previous designs. It was Trevithick, too, who realised that there must be a stronger boiler to contain the high-pressure steam.

Trevithick's locomotive had a cylindrical boiler, and the fire-box was built inside the water space of the boiler, increasing the heating area. It is noteworthy that the exhaust steam was conveyed from the cylinder to the chimney by a pipe to force the furnace draught, a device which twenty-five years later, in the hands of George Stephenson, went far towards making the locomotive what it is to-day.

Trevithick's was the earliest form of engine to achieve a standard of efficiency comparable with that of the modern locomotive.

HIGH-PRESSURE ENGINE

In 1802, Trevithick took out a patent for his high-pressure steam-engine which he built to work a hammer at the Penydarran iron works, in South Wales. Under the direction of Samuel Homfray, chief proprietor, Trevithick mounted the engine on a wagon chassis and turned it into a locomotive. The locomotive made its first journey on 24th February, 1804, on the Penydarran cast-iron plateway. It won a 500-guinea wager for Homfray by conveying five trucks containing ten tons of iron bars and 70 passengers over the nine miles to Merthyr Tydfil at an average speed of five miles an hour. Trevithick exhibited his invention at a small circular track in London, but eventually the show was a financial loss. The public were suspicious of the new contraption and did not show much interest. Trevithick, in disgust, went abroad.

Although Trevithick did not follow up the development of the locomotive, it is fortunate for progress that the engine aroused the interest of engineers and colliery owners, who saw in the invention the means to accelerate the transportation of coal wagons.

Mr. John Blenkinsop, proprietor of the Middleton Colliery, near Leeds, decided in 1811 to convey the coal to Leeds by locomotive instead of horses. The locomotive was constructed by the Leeds engineer Matthew Murray, and although it was a practical success its future was limited by its dependence for propulsion on a gear on the locomotive engaging with a toothed rack on one of the rails.

Other engineers like William Hedley and George

On Christmas Eve, 1801, the first steam-driven vehicle carried passengers part of the way up Beacon Hill in Cambourne.

When the directors of the Manchester-Liverpool railway held an open competition to find the best locomotive, George Stephenson and his Rocket *won the £500 prize.*

Stephenson were already working on the Trevithick principle that trucks could be hauled by reliance on the adhesion of a smooth wheel on a smooth rail. One of the most famous locomotives of all time was Hedley's " Puffing Billy " which began running on the rails of Wylam Colliery tramway in 1813, and was kept in constant use until 1862, when it was removed to the South Kensington Museum.

Progress was so rapid that Stephenson's " Blucher ", built in 1814, was the twentieth locomotive built since the first engine at Penydarran. It was Stephenson who, perhaps more than any other man of the day, foresaw the ultimate possibilities of the railway as a national transport system.

FIRST PASSENGER TRAIN

On the Stockton and Darlington railway, authorised by Parliament in 1821, the use of horse-power was at first proposed but on the advice of George Stephenson, its engineer, steam-engines were adopted. The principal business of the new railway was intended to be the conveyance of goods but, from the first, passengers insisted upon being carried.

And so, at nine o'clock on a fine September morning in 1825, the world's first passenger train, carrying 600 passengers in converted coal-wagons, steamed out of the little English mining town of Brussleton on its historic run through the Durham countryside. The 10-ton locomotive, named " Locomotion No. 1 ", was built by the firm of Robert Stephenson & Co., founded, in 1823, by George Stephenson and his son, Robert.

SCOTTISH RAILWAY

The example of the Stockton and Darlington line was followed by the Monklands Railway in Scotland, opened in 1826, and several other small lines including the Canterbury and Whitstable, worked partly by fixed engines and partly by locomotives.

The Liverpool and Manchester Railway, opened in 1830, first impressed the national mind with the fact that a revolution in the methods of travelling had burst upon the nation.

TRIALS AT RAINHILL

While Stephenson was building the railway and was advocating the use of steam traction, the directors of the company remained unconvinced. In order to settle the issue they decided to hold a trial, with a prize of £500 for the best locomotive which satisfied a basic set of conditions as to weight and performance drawn up by three eminent engineers.

The result of the trials held at Rainhill in October, 1829, is now a part of history, George Stephenson's " Rocket " running out an easy winner. This world-renowned locomotive weighed, with tender, just over seven tons and could haul on the level a load of 17 tons at a speed of 20 miles an hour.

" ROCKET "

It is easy to understand why the " Rocket " vanquished its rivals for it combined, for the first time in any locomotive, two principles which even to-day remain unchanged. The first was a multi-tubular boiler (previous locomotives had had only one or two flue tubes), and the second was an exhaust outlet pipe situated in the chimney. The blast from this created a vacuum, drawing the fire through the tubes. It was these two features which put the steaming capacity and potential development of the " Rocket " far ahead of other locomotives of the day.

The Liverpool and Manchester Railway achieved a success which outstripped the anticipations of even its promoters and, there followed a wild railway boom in Britain and overseas.

This was the period sometimes known as the age of the " railway mania ". Lines were laid down in all directions, often between the same places by rival companies, and an unnecessarily enormous amount of capital was sunk. Fortunes were made and fortunes were lost. By the middle of the nineteenth century the whole country was covered by a close network of railways.

VARIED GAUGES

At first, much variation existed in the methods adopted by the different lines. Even the gauges of the tracks differed widely. Gradually two gauges—4 feet 8½ inches and 7 feet—became common, the narrower one being all but universal in Britain except on the Great Western Railway which adhered to the wide gauge until near the end of the nineteenth century.

Other countries were quick to follow Britain's lead and the railway revolution swept the world in the middle years of the nineteenth century. British locomotive builders and engineers were in heavy demand as other nations strove to take advantage of the new form of transport.

WORLD-WIDE EXPANSION

The "Stourbridge Lion", built in Britain and exported to the United States, was the first locomotive to run on an American railway. In 1835, the Brussels-Malines railway was opened and operated by three British locomotives. The first Canadian railway, between Laprairie and St. John's, was operated by a Stephenson-designed locomotive, "The Dorchester".

Railway-builders bridged rivers and chasms, crossed lakes, marshes and the most arid of deserts, burrowed through the densest of tropical forests and scaled or tunnelled through the highest mountains to push the railway to its farthest limits.

The hazards of the terrain through which they pushed their lines were often aggravated by the wrangling of politicians, the onslaughts of the weather, and the incursions of marauding natives. Many lines were built on blood, sweat and tears.

The first French railway was opened near Lyons in 1830, and the first in Germany, between Nuremberg and Furth, five years later. Italy and Holland opened their first railways in 1839, Switzerland in 1847, and Spain in 1848. Belgium, with its dense population and high degree of industrial activity, was the first European state to achieve anything like a railway system and, by 1848, had nearly 500 miles in operation.

TRANS-CONTINENTALS

Railways joined the east and west coasts of America, and pushed into the heart of Africa, Australia, Asia and South America. Russia opened her first railway in 1837 with a line between St. Petersburg and Pavlovsk, and the first public railway in India—between Bombay and Thana—was opened in 1853.

George Stephenson's Rocket, *forerunner of all subsequent steam locomotives and winner of the famous Rainhill trials.*

A railway line across North America was first completed in 1869, when the Union Pacific, building westwards from the Missouri River at Omaha, met the Central Pacific, which built eastwards from San Francisco. This made a line 1,848 miles long through a country then for the most part uninhabited. The Canadian Pacific, a true trans-continental line, was built from Montreal to Vancouver—2,906 miles—and was opened in 1885. It has been said that Canada owes its very in-

The coming of the railway opened up vast areas of the west of America to settlers, and enabled trade to develop between settlements. The Indians of the plains saw the railway as a threat to their existence and waged war on the builders.

121

Work on the Trans-Siberian railway was started in 1891, and the link between Moscow and Vladivostok was completed in 1917. The snowbound steppes were traversed by 4,500 miles of track.

ception to the promise of railway construction; its continued existence was dependent on the realisation of the promise. Without the link of a trans-continental railway, the new country could not hope to remain united, and British Columbia extracted the promise of such a line before it would join the new Dominion.

TRANS-SIBERIAN

Even the trans-American railway routes were dwarfed, however, when, at the turn of the century, Russia embarked on building the trans-Siberian Railway across the entire continent of Asia from Chelyabinsk to Vladivostok, a distance of 4,073 miles. The main line was finished in 1902, except for 170 miles in very difficult country around the south end of Lake Baikal. This was constructed, by means of a magnificent series of rock tunnels and cuttings, in 1904. Communication in the interval was maintained by ferry-boats which conveyed entire trains 40 miles across the lake, except when the lake was ice-bound.

In Britain, rivalry between the various railway-owning concerns reached a peak in 1888 and 1895 in a series of exciting railway races between the East and West Coast companies running trains between London and Scotland. The rivalry was so intense that the companies posted " spies " at King's Cross and Euston stations to learn of their " enemy's " intentions. The races were terminated in August, 1895, in the interests of public safety, after the West Coast train covered the 541 miles between Euston and Aberdeen in 512 minutes. That record is unbroken to this day.

AMALGAMATIONS

The first step towards reducing the chaos which resulted from so many companies running railways in Britain was taken in 1873, when a Railway and Canal Commission was set up to regulate rates and to exercise general supervision over the workings of the railways. In 1921, an important move was made, in the interests of economy and to prevent overlapping, of services, by the amalgamation of all the existing companies into four. These were the L.M.S. (London Midland & Scottish), L.N.E.R. (London & North-Eastern), G.W.R. (Great Western) and S.R. (Southern).

It was in Britain that the railways began and it was in Britain, too, that the steam-engine reached the zenith of its success. The heyday of the steam-engine was in the first thirty years of this century before Britain, like some continental countries before her, recognised that the future of the railway engine lay in electrification and dieselisation.

" MALLARD "

The most glorious feat of all during the era of the steam-locomotive was probably that accomplished on 3rd July, 1938, when a streamlined Class A4 Pacific locomotive built by Sir Nigel Gresley and named " Mallard " established a world speed record for steam of 126 miles an hour, between Grantham and Peterborough.

One of the most famous British trains which ran in the 1930s, was the " Silver Jubilee " . This high-speed streamlined train of aluminium coaches and silver-painted engine, ran regularly between London and Newcastle in four hours, with a stop at Darlington.

THE " FLYING SCOTSMAN "

The most famous train of all is probably the " Flying Scotsman " which celebrated its centenary in June, 1962. When this train went over to non-stop running between London and Edinburgh in 1928, it became one of the most luxurious in the world. The coaches were furnished in the style of Louis XIV, but with concealed electric lighting. There were individual armchairs for each passenger in the first-class coaches. A news-vendor travelled with the train, selling papers and magazines. From May, 1929, the " Flying Scotsman " carried a hairdressing saloon, and in 1932, a cocktail bar was introduced, and later a cinema coach.

In 1948, the four British railway companies were merged and the British railway system was " nationalised "—taken over by the State. They are divided into six regions—Scottish, Western, Southern, Eastern, North Eastern and London Midland. In 1955, the British Government launched a 15-year modernisation plan for the railways costing £1,200 million. Two years later, this figure was upgraded to £1,600 million. This entailed the ultimate elimination of the steam locomotive and its replacement by diesel and electric trains.

GOLD
The King of Metals

Innumerable stories and legends have been woven around the fascinating metal we call gold. Men have sought gold since the earliest times, and it has always been a metal of great importance. Prospectors have struggled to find gold in every part of the world, and the desire for gold has caused untold misery and hardship. The legends about gold take us back into the earliest days of civilisation.

The tragic poem of the Nibelungen and the Rhineland treasure tells us the innocent story of the magic hen that kept laying eggs of gold. There is the tale of Jason who captured the Golden Fleece, and the story of Midas, the miser king, who turned everything into gold simply by touching it. These and other legends show how gold has always been associated in men's minds with struggle and disillusionment, with crime, punishment and sorrow. And, even though they are stories, we must accept that there is much truth in them, for the function of legend is to present reality in a form that can be easily understood and remembered.

HOW GOLD WON ITS CROWN

How did gold become the king of metals? The explanation is to be found in its unique combination of properties. The rich yellow colour of gold gives it great beauty. It is heavy, yet it can be worked into almost anything from thin sheets of gold leaf a millionth of an inch in thickness to magnificent jewels that last for ever. It never rusts as iron does when exposed to the air. It dissolves only in aqua regia, a mixture of hydrochloric and nitric acids. The rarity of gold has helped to place it on its pedestal as the most noble of metals. This scarcity, and the physical and chemical properties of gold, combine to make it a perfect metal for coins. No better standard than gold has ever been found as a basis for the world's monetary systems.

A VEIN THROUGH HISTORY

The importance of gold to ancient civilisations of the Mediterranean and the Near East is clearly seen in the coins and jewels found in tombs and buried cities. The writings of poets and historians have confirmed that gold was indeed held in the greatest esteem.

In ancient Egypt gold and money were one and the same thing. Precious objects made of gold abounded in the treasuries of the Pharaohs, and the coinage of successive dynasties demonstrates the skill of their designers and craftsmen. Writing of the Palace of Menelaus, Homer tells us that the walls were adorned with bas-reliefs worked in gold. According to Pliny and Herodotus, some of the temples of the ancient world contained huge statues, all in solid gold.

Before Rome became rich a certain austerity was observed under its republican government. Thus we read of a law that was made in 215 B.C., forbidding Roman women to wear gold ornaments weighing more than half an ounce. But as the spoils and plunder of the Empire accumulated, and mines came into their possession, the Roman rulers had a change of heart. Rich people rivalled one another, displaying their gold with an ostentation second only to that familiar in Eastern courts.

The Etruscans and the Romans exploited their own resources of gold, extracting the metal often with the help of slave labour. Pliny, the Latin historian, tells us that the number of men employed in sifting gold from river sands near Vercelli had to be limited to five thousand. The barbarian tribes to the north were no less interested in gold. Their warriors wore heavy necklets, armbands and buckles made of gold. But the cost of war, the exhaustion of natural deposits and their limited trade resources took their toll. North of the Alps, gold lost much of its prestige value and became rare during the early centuries of our present era.

Throughout the Middle Ages, gold production was at a low ebb. Mines had been abandoned and their location forgotten. The Arabs opened new ones in Spain, but the output was trivial compared to that of the ancient world. This did not mean that gold had lost its fascination. On the contrary, medieval alchemists held it in the greatest esteem, and sought in vain to find the *lapis philosophorum*: the philosopher's stone which, it was believed, had the power of changing all base metals into gold or silver. The alchemists failed in their search for gold, but the great navigators of the day succeeded in finding gold in newly-discovered lands.

Christopher Columbus had two main objects in mind when he made his famous voyages; he wanted to spread the Christian faith, and to find gold. Many of his companions joined him only because they were attracted by stories of a distant El Dorado; here, it was said, there was so much gold that temples and palaces were roofed with it. As

Evidence of the Aztec civilisation of South America is seen in these finely embossed gold objects, unearthed by archaeologists in Mexico, Columbia and Peru. Top: *Priest and animal figures of (right) Ancient Peru and (left) Columbia.* Bottom: *a gold jaguar and (right) a gold breast-plate of early Mexico.*

things turned out, expectations had run too high, but there was more than enough gold to satisfy the explorers. Huge quantities were brought back to Europe from the newly discovered America, mainly by the Spaniards, French and English during the seventeenth and eighteenth centuries. The middle of the nineteenth century—the 1850s—was to see the great gold rushes of more modern times.

As long ago as 1579, Sir Francis Drake had explored the coastline of California, reporting back to the Court of Queen Elizabeth that in certain places he had seen gold mixed with the river sands. About 270 years later two pioneers came across the precious metal almost in the very place where Drake had seen it. The first was a German immigrant named Sutter who had been attracted to the Pacific coast by the fertility of the Sacramento Valley; here, he established himself with the object of forming an agricultural settlement. The other was James Wilson Marshall, a young carpenter who was responsible for looking after the sluice gates of an irrigation canal. One morning, on his way to work, Marshall noticed some fine particles gleaming in the sand beneath the water. Gold dust!

Marshall went at once to Sutter, who was much respected in the district, and told him of his discovery. The two men agreed to keep their find a secret so as not to cause an up-heaval in the settlement. But the rumour spread that gold had been found in the Sacramento Valley, and following the rumour came an outbreak of " gold fever ". Soon, swarms of prospectors were heading west for California from all parts of America. For Sutter this was sheer disaster. The fertile lands on which he had planned to develop a model agricultural settlement were overrun. The gold of Sacramento brought wealth to many, but it robbed Sutter of his cherished hopes. He died in poverty in 1880.

The Californian Gold Rush started in 1849, and it triggered off an itch for gold that spread around the world. Throughout the second half of last century new gold fields were discovered; some of them were rich in gold, others had little or none. Prospectors flocked to America, Canada, Australia and South Africa. Their story is one of endless struggle and disappointment, of riches won at great cost only to be lost

One method of gold mining was by dredging. Gravel was broken up into fine sand and washed through sluice boxes. The gold sank to the bottom of the troughs and was caught by cross-bars.

in a fight or at the gaming tables. Some came home rich; many died disillusioned and in poverty. It is an epoch that has now gone for ever. The world's gold is now produced by controlled exploitation of the deposits, often deep underground, in regions where pioneers once searched the surface soil for nuggets.

GOLD IN ITS NATURAL STATE

Some metals exist in chemical combination with other elements from which they have to be released by a smelting process. Gold is *not* one of these. It is found in a pure state in deposits which are called primary or secondary, according to their nature. In some deposits the gold is mixed with silver.

Primary deposits are those where the gold occurs in various rock formations. It may be in the form of particles so fine as to be invisible to the naked eye, or it may have been laid down in past ages in veins of varying thicknesses. Secondary, or alluvial deposits are those which occur in the beds of rivers and streams in which the water has washed the gold from its primary location in the rock. In this case, fine particles of gold may be mixed with sand or clay or the metal may be found as small nuggets rounded and smoothed by long contact with the moving sand and water.

Almost every river contains gold-bearing sands, but seldom in sufficient quantity to make it worth while extracting the metal. These alluvial deposits form very slowly and, once they have been worked, it may be many thousands of years before the gold builds up into a worthwhile concentration again. Sea water also contains traces of gold, but it would be necessary to process about 550 cubic yards of salt water to produce one ounce of gold. No method has yet been developed which could extract the gold from such huge volumes of water. In the meantime, modern techniques have completely transformed the methods used for extracting gold from deposits on land.

MODERN EXTRACTION METHODS

Gold mining to-day is a highly organised industry, and has changed greatly during the last century. The old method of extraction was based on separation of the gold particles

The Californian gold rush of 1849 brought thousands of prospectors from every corner of the world to stake their claim in the Sacramento valley. It is estimated that 80,000 men arrived in California in search of gold.

from the much lighter sand by a washing process. The gold-bearing material was carried along wooden troughs by a slow-moving current of water, the heavy particles of gold being deposited on the bottom of the trough, whereas the lighter sand was carried along. Modern techniques are much more efficient than this old process, making it possible for gold to be extracted from deposits that were thought to have been worked out long ago.

In the Congo and in California, river beds are now dredged to a great depth by heavy machinery, and the gold is extracted from untapped alluvial deposits. If the gold is nearer the surface, the mixed shale and rock is loosened by directing high pressure jets of water at the deposits. The gold ore is taken to crushers which reduce it to a fine powder. The powder is then subjected to a complex treatment involving the use of mercury. The gold-bearing material is brought into contact with the mercury which amalgamates with the gold; the mercury is then removed from the gold by distillation. This is a costly process, and there is now a more widely-used process based on potassium cyanide.

In 1886, Macarthur and Forrest carried out many experiments in the hope of being able to find a chemical process for extracting gold from its ores. After a long series of tests they found what they were looking for in a process that made use of potassium cyanide. It was already known that cyanide would dissolve gold, but no way had been found of putting it to practical use. Credit goes to Macarthur and Forrest for showing that a very dilute solution of cyanide dissolves gold in the presence of atmospheric oxygen. Cyaniding, as it is called, has since come into widespread use. The gold ore is first crushed and roasted, then submitted to the cyanide process. The gold obtained is impure, and further purification is necessary; this is usually done in the big refineries of America and Europe. Finally, the molten gold is poured into moulds which shape it into bars and ingots. Each piece has to be stamped with the name of the refinery before being put on the market.

Incredible as it may seem, the world's present annual gold output amounts to about two and one third million pounds (pounds avoirdupois) This comes mostly from four or five

Working deep in the bowels of the earth, these men are drilling through the rock strata of a South African gold mine. The mines of the Transvaal are the world's richest source of gold.

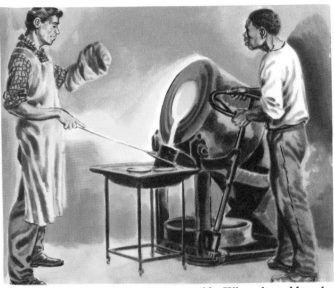

Molten gold being poured into a mould. When the gold cools, it is in the familiar form of bars or ingots. At this stage the gold still contains many impurities.

states, the most important producer being South Africa. The other great gold-producing countries are America, Russia, Canada and Australia.

COINS AND JEWELS

Pure gold is very soft, and is seldom used in practice. It is commonly mixed with other metals such as copper which gives it a slightly reddish tinge. Silver produces a greenish hue. Jewellers use these and other alloys, including white gold, which is the result of mixing " aurum "—here we have the Latin origin of its chemical formula *Au*—with chromium, nickel or palladium. The latter is a hard white metal of the platinum group.

Only a minute part of the world's gold production goes to the jewellery trade. The makers of fine porcelain and certain instruments also use gold. So do dentists, chemists and, to a lesser extent, photographers. But the amount taken up for these purposes is very small indeed. Much gold is hoarded by merchants and private individuals, especially in Eastern countries, as a safeguard against economic disaster. But, in proportion to the total, even hoarded gold is relatively unimportant. What, then, happens to the world's gold?

Its great function remains, as always, to serve as money. This does not mean that people still go around with gold coins jingling in the pocket; all that ended with the First World War. Paper money has taken the place of the old coinage everywhere and, except for special issues, gold coins are a thing of the past. Yet gold is such a convenient measure of values, so durable and so universally respected that the country without gold reserves to support its banknotes would soon go bankrupt. The bulk of the gold produced to-day, therefore, goes into the state coffers of a hundred different nations and is used for paying international credits when these cannot be written off in their trade balances.

Essential to trade and financial stability, gold has thus retained its title as a noble metal. And if it has sometimes brought misfortune, the jewellers of to-day no longer think of it as a metal of ill-omen. Gold is made into a wide variety of objects, many of great beauty, ranging from the lucky charms of women's bracelets to works of art that may be worth a fortune.

DEVELOPMENT OF THE TRAIN

For well over a century the steam-locomotive, relatively simple to maintain and low in initial cost, dominated the railways of the world. But even before the steam-locomotive had reached the peak of its powers, its successors had already been born. The advantages of electrification on underground and on city and suburban systems were quickly realised, particularly in Europe, and the diesel-engine was not slow to follow in popularity. The first electric railway in the world to carry the public as passengers was laid at the Berlin Exhibition in 1879. In 1833, electric power was first used for public transport in Britain, for two small tramways at Brighton and in Northern Ireland; but it was not until 1890 that the first full-scale railway installation was made. This was the City and South London Railway, which was the first underground electric railway in the world, and it marked the beginning of the vast " tube " system of present-day London.

DIESEL

The application of the internal-combustion engine to rail traction first took place at Munich, in 1898, when a German engineer, Dr. Rudolph Diesel, demonstrated an engine operating on a mixture of low-grade fuel oil and coal dust injected into the cylinders by an air blast. Widespread use of diesel traction on railways can be dated back to the 1930s. The German State Railway introduced its " Flying Hamburger " diesel-electric express between Berlin and Hamburg in 1932. This train was the first of numerous high-speed diesel trains between important business centres in Germany, and averaged nearly 75 miles an hour.

The United States railways were also quick to recognise the advantages of diesel power, and the Union Pacific demonstrated a three-car aluminium diesel train to the nation in 1934. In the same year, the Burlington Railroad launched its " Pioneer Zephyr " with a non-stop 1,000-mile run at an average speed of 78 miles an hour.

By the late 1930s, electric and diesel traction were fully established as rivals to steam, although it is only now that electric- and diesel-locomotives are supplanting the steam-locomotive.

QUICKER JOURNEYS

The principal advantages of the new forms of traction are their cleanliness, smart acceleration and high availability for work. Diesel- and electric-locomotives need less time out for servicing and enjoy the benefit of quick turnrounds at terminals. On busy suburban routes with numerous stops, rapid acceleration allows journeys to be made in times that steam cannot approach. It also enables trains to follow each other at shorter intervals. Electric- and diesel-locomotives consume no fuel while standing idle but are instantly ready for service when needed.

MOVEMENT AND CONTROL

Adoption of these new forms of traction throughout the world has radically altered the appearance of the train and has caused a revolution in the methods of moving and controlling the train.

The most striking developments in railway construction are to be found to-day in the long-distance trains which have to meet severe competition from the car and the airliner. The furnishings and décor in many of these trains are reminiscent of a hotel lounge rather than a railway train. They are distinctive in style and colour and employ the latest techniques to make journeys comfortable and attractive.

LUXURY AND SPEED

High-speed trans-Continental trains are designed with smooth, flowing lines to minimise wind resistance and so encourage speed. There are few projections or recesses, and doors are fitted with automatically-controlled steps that can be moved in and out when at stations. Windows are flushed, and coachwork all but obscures the wheels from view.

Some of the most modern advances in train development are to be seen on the Italian State Railways, where high-speed streamlined four- and seven-car electric sets have observation compartments in the rounded " nose " at each end, and driving compartments which extend into glazed "cupolas" above the roof. One of the best-known of these is the " Settabello " which is in daily service between Rome and Milan, and does the run of 380 miles at an average speed of about 65 miles an hour.

Among the most luxurious trains in the world are those on the network of international services between major European cities, known as " Trans-Europ Expresses ".

These " multi-system " electric trains can, at the push of a button, switch from one electric system to another, and it is now possible to travel by them from the Channel coast to the " toe " of Italy. All vehicles are air-conditioned and sound-proofed. Windows are fitted with Venetian blinds

The Condor *freight train, which runs nightly between Glasgow and London.*

The idea of using pallets has greatly facilitated the loading and unloading of goods trains by fork-lift trucks.

which can be raised or lowered at the touch of a button. Two of the four-car sets can be coupled to form an eight-coach train.

JAPANESE EXPRESSES

In Japan there are plans to run electric multiple-unit trains at speeds of up to 125 miles an hour on the Tokyo-Osaka main line. The Russians have been experimenting for a number of years with "driverless" electric trains, in which computers control the electric motors in the engine. The computer keeps the train running exactly to the time-table and the driver's only task is to start and stop the train at stations and to take over in an emergency. Experiments have also been carried out with an entirely automatic train on the New York underground railway, and the British Post Office has its own system of driverless trains for the carriage of mails and parcels under London's streets.

PULLMAN TRAINS

The latest advance in train development in Great Britain is the series of luxury diesel Pullman trains running between London and Manchester, London and Birmingham, and London and South Wales. These blue-and-white-liveried trains were introduced in an attempt to win the businessman over from the aeroplane or his car. They consist of six coaches and are exclusively first-class. Facilities include individually-adjustable armchairs, individual buttons to summon waiter-service, full air-conditioning, double-glazed windows with Venetian blinds, sound-insulation and modern décor.

OBSERVATION COACHES

The use of parlour coaches, with observation platforms to enable passengers to view the passing scene, has long been commonplace in America. America was also the first country to introduce a double-decker coach. It was called a "dome" car and passengers on the upper deck have a completely uninterrupted view of the countryside.

Great steps forward have also been made in the transport of freight, with high-powered diesel or electrically-hauled freight expresses running to passenger timings between major industrial centres and extending door-to-door services to trade and industry. Fast services are backed up by wagon

development aimed at ensuring safe carriage and a speeding up of loading and unloading times.

TRAFFIC-CONTROL AND SAFETY

The dramatic developments in the evolution of the train have had to be accompanied by a revolution in the methods of traffic-control. Old signalling systems were inadequate for the new era of faster trains running at more frequent intervals. Old signal-boxes were replaced by modern fully-automatic installations covering longer stretches of line and giving the advantages of increased line capacity, more trains per hour, faster trains and reduced operating costs.

In the early days of the railways it was possible to achieve the safe running of trains by operating them at well-spaced intervals; but, with the greater volume of faster-moving traffic, more intricate methods of control became necessary.

COLOUR-LIGHT SIGNALLING

The old semaphore arm has been replaced by colour-light signalling, which has the advantage of telling the driver the position of trains for several sections ahead. This is achieved by incorporating not only the red and green but also two amber aspects representing two stages of distant or caution signals. Colour-light signalling is particularly valuable in areas of heavy traffic density, and in fog and other bad weather conditions when it remains clearly visible to the train driver.

In the new signal-boxes it is possible to do in a matter of seconds, with one or two fingertip movements over a series of switches, what previously might have required the movement of half a dozen full-size levers. The signalman can also see, on an illuminated track diagram in his cabin, the exact location of each train in his area. This is accomplished by track circuiting. The two rails of the track are made into electrical conductors between a battery and a relay, and stretches of line are insulated into track-circuited sections. The wheels and axles of a passing train form a short-circuit, and the change in current flow is utilised for many modern signalling purposes, from the automatic operation of the signals in the rear of the train, to describing the train's progress on the illuminated lay-out in the signal-box.

Colour-light signalling is accompanied by automatic

The Blue train represents a big advance in the modernisation of the railways in Britain.

train-control. This reminds the driver, by sight and sound in his cab, of the position of the distant signal. It works on electro-magnetic principles. It does not relieve the driver of the responsibility for watching the signals and obeying them, but it cautions him that he must be ready to stop at the next signal.

If the distant signal is at clear, a bell rings in the driver's cab and a circular disc in an indicator shows all black. If the signal is at caution, a horn sounds. The brakes are also automatically applied unless the driver operates a re-setting handle on the indicator. When this is done, the circular disc in the indicator changes from black to show alternate black and yellow spokes.

FREIGHT TRAFFIC

The advent of automation has been particularly useful in the movement and control of railway freight traffic. The automatic marshalling of wagons, first introduced in America, is now commonplace in most of the world's modern marshalling installations. A shunter walks along the train when it arrives in the yard and divides it into " cuts ". Simultaneously he passes to the traffic office in the control tower, by means of a lightweight portable radio transmitter, information concerning the siding destination of each " cut " and the number of wagons in the " cut ". This information is put on punched tape in the traffic office. The method of sorting consists of propelling wagons to the top of a hump and then allowing them to run down by gravity into one of a number of tracks.

When a train is about to be humped the appropriate punched tape is fed into the control, which then moves the points automatically in the correct sequence so that as the wagons come down each is directed to its correct line in the sorting sidings. As each wagon or group of wagons rolls down from the hump it is weighed and its speed assessed by radar. Its progress is regulated accordingly by electronically-controlled pneumatic retarders on the track. By this means any excess momentum is removed and the wagon comes to rest at the point required in the chosen siding.

Automatic signalling under the control of programme machines is another interesting example of automation on

The interior of a modern signal box with push-button controls.

the railways. On the London Underground, there is a system of complete automatic operation of junctions by means of a progressive punched tape which contains codes of train destinations and which arranges for the correct route to be set in a safe manner as a train approaches a junction. These routes were previously controlled by signalmen located at junction signal cabins.

The faster and heavier trains of to-day have also demanded widespread modernisation of track involving deep ballasting, improvements in track alignment, the provision of additional tracks, and changes in track design. More and more railway systems are laying long-welded rails for smoother riding.

CONTAINERS, ROADRAILERS AND PALLETS

A modern method of reducing delay and avoiding damage to goods is by the use of containers. The goods are packed into the containers at the factory and then lifted on to lorries which take them to the goods station. The process is reversed at the other end of the journey. The best-known of the high-speed freight trains in Great Britain, devoted exclusively to the conveyance of container traffic, is the " Condor ", which runs nightly between London and Glasgow. This train halves the time taken by door-to-door road transport between London and Glasgow.

An interesting development during 1960 was the appearance of the Roadrailer. Produced by the Pressed Steel Co. in conjunction with British Railways and British Road Services, this is an experimental dual-purpose vehicle which can travel equally well on rail or road. On rails, Roadrailers are designed to run at speed in train formation. At their destination they can be transformed in a few minutes into conventional semi-trailers, ready to be hauled away by ordinary articulated road tractors. The vehicle has been demonstrated to transport users and operators in various parts of Britain and may soon be widely applied on British Railways. The Roadrailer is a version of a vehicle patented by the Chesapeake & Ohio Railroad in the United States.

America and a number of European countries have made great strides forward in " piggyback " methods of freight transport, by which road trailers are loaded bodily on to railway flat trucks for long-distance haulage from railhead to railhead.

More than a million freight wagons carry the million tons of goods that are handled by British Railways every working day of the week. The most-used coal wagons carry 16 tons, but there are even larger wagons carrying up to 33 tons. There are many kinds of special wagons. Lots of things like cement, chalk and grain need to be carried in big quantities, and there are bulk wagons for this. Glass is easily broken, but great quantities of it travel by train, in wagons that hold it firm and safe. There are other wagons for timber, sheets of steel, coils of steel strips, steel girders, iron-ore, motor-cars, and even elephants.

Tank wagons are used to carry liquids in bulk—chemicals, oils of all kinds, petrol and tar are some of them. Milk comes up from the country to the cities in glass-lined tanks. Large consignments of goods are also carried on pallets—platforms on which a number of packages can be stacked. The platform is raised slightly off the floor so that it, and its contents, can be lifted bodily by a mechanical handling machine, such as a fork-lift truck, direct from and to railway vans. Much time and money is saved by this method, as otherwise the packages would each have to be loaded or unloaded by hand.

THE CHALLENGE OF MOUNTAINS

" *Everest has been climbed.* " Millions felt a thrill on hearing these words that echoed round the world in 1953. On the 29th of May, two men had at last done the impossible; they had reached the highest point on the surface of the earth, 29,030 feet above sea level. The men who made this historic climb were Edmund Hillary, a New Zealander, and Sherpa Tenzing of Nepal. As they stood on the summit of Mount Everest they looked for all the world like men from another planet. Their faces were hidden by oxygen masks, and their bodies were encased in special clothing to protect them from the intense cold.

The two men had climbed from a camp perched at 28,000 feet on a ridge dividing Nepal from Tibet, reaching the summit at 11.30 in the morning. Their route followed the crest of the mountain, where the mighty walls which guard the peak come together to form a pyramid shaped like a giant ice-cream cone. Let us accompany them in imagination as they make their journey to the summit.

Chipping footsteps with their ice-axes, they move a rope-length at a time, one climber safeguarding the other in case of a slip. The most frightening place is where the " ice-cream " has slipped away from the mountain, leaving a gap between the rocks and the snow overhanging a 10,000-foot drop.

Hillary understands full well the risk he is taking as he jams his body into this cleft, and presses with his knees against the crumbling mass of snow. If the snow breaks away, then he may fall to his doom. But he must take the risk. Tenzing plays out the rope to him as he wriggles upward, using the spikes on his boots, his knees, his elbows and the friction of his clothing. The struggle continues for half an hour, then his hand thrusts clear of the fissure. He is up. Tenzing quickly follows, helped by a taut rope.

The climbers rest for a little, knowing that they are reaching the end of their tether. They see that the thin ridge of snow continues ahead of them; then without thinking they hack their way onward, each taking his turn at cutting a line of steps. Obsessed with the climb, their minds are closed to everything but the job in hand; they force their bodies to do their bidding, like men in a nightmare. Nothing is easy. Every step demands several breaths, every movement is in slow motion. The world goes up and up, without end.

THE SUMMIT

Then suddenly they halt. They cannot realise for a moment what has happened. The mountain no longer rises before them. It slopes *down!* They are on the summit. Beneath them is the North Col and beyond it the wild Highlands of Tibet; the route over which other climbers had previously tried to climb the mountain.

Gradually, the truth dawns, and they begin thumping each other on the back. They have done it at last; they have climbed EVEREST. Hillary looks at his watch and finds they have been climbing for only five hours. Now he tries an experiment, taking off his oxygen mask to breathe the rarefied air. He finds that his breathing is only slightly affected, provided he keeps still. The two climbers are actually enjoying themselves up here. For once, nature seems

to have relented. The terrible winds that have so often drained the life from climbers on Everest have died away. The whole Roof of the World lies beneath their feet. What a moment that must have been for Hillary and Tenzing!

One question they must try to settle immediately. " Had Everest been climbed before? " Two men, Mallory and Irvine, had made a tremendous bid for the summit in 1924. They had never been seen again. Hillary searched the summit, digging with his ice axe, but he could find no trace of anyone ever having been there. Mallory and Irvine must have perished without reaching their goal; they were two of the fifteen men who died trying to climb Everest before success was achieved.

Hillary inspected the route which Mallory and Irvine must have followed, but they left no trace. On the day of their climb, the mountain had been lashed by a blizzard. They were last seen alive at 12.50 p.m. and in good weather they might have reached the summit by darkness, for they had only 800 feet to go. But eight hundred feet is a very long way on Everest, and the climbers could not have reached the summit in a blizzard. It seems certain that Mallory and Irvine were killed while trying to return from the highest point that men had ever reached on the mountain.

PREVIOUS EXPLORATIONS

Looking back, it is astonishing to remember how much these earlier explorers achieved. Without the help of oxygen, they reached over 28,000 feet on two occasions. They did this at a time when little was known about the effects of high altitude on the human body.

Mallory, more than anyone, knew how lack of oxygen could sap the strength. He was on the mountain from the very first expedition in 1921, and three times had walked the 300 miles from Darjeeling to the bleak Tibetan Plateau. He had trudged up every glacier, climbing many high points to map the mountain in every detail. Mallory realised that the key to the summit, rearing above them a further two miles into the sky, was a high saddle known as the North Col. He was certain Everest could be climbed, but 29 years were to pass before his dream came true.

Other expeditions came, only to fail when success seemed within their grasp. Shipton and Smythe made a gallant attempt from a camp at 27,400 feet, but were defeated by a storm. Both climbers were too exhausted to climb the final peak.

Climbing on Everest is a gruelling and dangerous occupation. Why then, do people do it? Why was the opportunity to return to the mountain immediately grasped when the climbers were offered it in 1951? The answer is: " Because they must ". Mallory said he tried to climb Everest " Because it's there," and this is as good an answer as any. It is man's nature to challenge the unknown, and to mountaineers Everest is the ultimate challenge.

PLANNING A NEW ROUTE

One exciting feature of the 1953 expedition was that it would attack the mountain from the south side—from

Nepal, where mountaineers had never been allowed before. Eric Shipton, an old " Everester ", was leader of a six-man party that went out in the winter to try and plan a route which could be attacked the following summer. They found a way into an enormous icefall, which was described as being like a " squashed meringue ", and they believed that the mountain could be climbed provided this obstacle could be overcome.

As it happened, the British party was not to have the first chance of proving the route, as Swiss climbers had been given permission to make the first attempt. They launched a full-scale attack in the summer of 1952, and they were still trying to climb the mountain in the depths of winter.

The route was certainly a tough one, since the " squashed meringue " kept collapsing, but the Swiss forced a way through. They reached the exposed South Col and established a camp at 27,560 feet; a wonderful effort. Unfortunately, they were so weakened by this time that they had to give up when success seemed within their grasp. In 1953, Everest was " over to the British " again.

You can imagine then how Hillary and Tenzing felt on top of the mountain that had beaten all who had tried to conquer her in years gone by. Their names would soon be known throughout the world as the first to climb Mount Everest; but Hillary and Tenzing knew that the honour must be shared with climbers of many nations who had striven to reach the peak.

No sooner had Everest been climbed from the south side, than men wanted to climb it from the north. The Chinese claim to have climbed it by Mallory's route, but have not supplied photographic evidence of their achievement. British climbers would be swift to take advantage of any opportunity offered to them to have another go at the North Face, but access to Tibet is difficult at the present time.

The story of man's attack on Everest is a reflection of the approach to mountaineering generally. The moment any mountain is scaled by its easiest route, the climber looks for a harder way. Every peak in the High Alps of Europe has been climbed, but men are ever trying to find more difficult routes. The North Face of the Eiger, for example, was climbed for the first time in 1938, but climbers are still tackling it every year. The 6,000-foot wall rises from Grindelwald, as an almost vertical precipice. Anyone who attempts to scale it must spend several nights on minute ledges, in constant danger of being frozen to death or swept away by avalanches of snow or rock.

CHALLENGE OF THE EIGER

More than a score of fine climbers have been killed on the North Face of the Eiger, and every year sees fresh tragedies. Yet the fascination exerted by the death-wall is increasing steadily. It attracts young climbers, as it is regarded as the most terrible climb in the Alps, the greatest test of skill and courage. Climbers knowing its background of death and disaster were astonished to read in the papers in 1961 that an Austrian-German group were strung out on the north wall, trying to make the first winter ascent.

Through a telescope, a party of four men could be seen clinging to the cold, dark wall which gets no winter sun, but is a place of ice-crystals and iron-hard snow plastered on steep rocks.

Leader of the party was 31-year-old Tony Hiebeler, who knew he was attempting something more difficult than man had ever tackled before on any mountain. It was the challenge of the unknown which attracted him. Hiebeler had climbed the North Face of the Eiger in summer and he knew what a test of mountaincraft and stamina it was.

He had chosen his companions for their physical hardness; Anton Kinshofer (27), Anton Mannhardt (22) and Walter Almberger were all men who worked with their hands, as carpenter, sawmill worker and iron miner respectively. They would need all the strength they possessed to hack a way up the Eiger wall. Hiebeler estimated that the climb would take a full week. If the weather broke, the climbers would have little chance of survival.

In summer, the Eiger is a dangerous place because of falling stones and snow avalanches which sweep down the North Face. Hiebeler had reasoned that the keen frosts of winter must seal the loose material in ice. The climb would be more difficult than in summer but less dangerous, provided the climbers were not frozen to death. Men had never before tried to live on such an exposed mountain wall in winter.

WINTER ASSAULT

Hiebeler was astounded by what he found as he began the assault on the North Wall. He could not recognise anything of the summer route for the mantle of foot-thick ice covering it.

One great problem of the climb is the Hinterstoisser Traverse, called after a man who died on it. Kinshofer took the lead on this, hammering a metal peg into the ice, he hooked his rope into it, so that if he slipped he would dangle from the peg. His companions knew that this metal was their only hope of survival if he slipped off. Tensely, they watched Kinshofer clinging to the handholds he had cut in the ice, while the points of his boots clawed for hold. Suddenly he shot into space, and for a moment death had them by the throat. If the peg came out, the climbers would fall down the North Face. But the peg took the strain. Kinshofer dangled, managed to regain his holds, and then continued calmly across the terrible traverse.

Four days later, the party was still climbing the middle section of the wall and approaching the " crux " of the problem, the recess known as " The White Spider ". The only exit from this is by cracks in the vertical rock. In summer, it is dangerous as well as difficult, because it is a natural trap for falling avalanches. The climbers were worried about the severities of the actual climbing, but they were even more worried about the weather, which was showing signs of breaking. A thaw would have been a disaster, bringing certain death to them.

Luckily, the weather cleared. The bold Kinshofer led the way up the crevices, fighting for every inch. On the sixth day, the climbers came out of the shadow on the mighty wall and reached the summit. It was like a reprieve from death to all of them.

People who had climbed to meet them by the easy route from Grindelwald were amazed by their fine physical condition. The climbers were thinner, but not at all weak. This was undoubtedly due to the food they had carried, and to their bivouac equipment. They had relied upon a liquid diet to avoid dehydration. They knew they must avoid losing body fluid, which causes sickness and headaches on mountains. So they heated a syrup, containing powdered chocolate, over a tiny stove and drank this mixture. Sometimes there was no room to operate the stove, and the chocolate syrup had to be taken cold.

For an expedition into previously unclimbed regions, or for assaults on formidable giants such as Everest, a party of local porters accompany the climbers. The porters carry equipment, food and fuel supplies.

The climbers slept on any ledge that was big enough to take their bodies; where no ledge was available, they would sit with their feet hanging into space. They slept in eider-down jackets and eider-down trousers, each with a sack covering the head like a tent, to keep out the wind. The men knew they must conserve the heat in their bodies if they were to survive the cold.

WINTER CLIMBING

So the North Wall of the Eiger was climbed in winter, and mountaineers looked for other "impossible" tasks to perform. In the following year, Hiebeler was back in Switzerland trying to make the first winter ascent of the North Face of the Matterhorn. He was beaten to the post by a rival party of Swiss climbers who were equally deter-mined to be first up this sheer face. On this treacherous climb the ledges are even scarcer than on the Eiger, though the angle is not quite so steep.

The familiar pattern was being followed. No sooner have mountaineers conquered the hardest climbs in summer, than they are trying to prove that it is possible to make the same climbs in the depths of winter.

Climbing in the coldest months of the year has spread

even to the Himalayas, the highest mountains on earth. The Swiss tried to climb Everest in winter, but failed. They climbed it successfully, however, in the summer of 1956. The finest example of winter climbing so far has been the ascent of Ama Dablam, which had defeated two previous summer expeditions. This mountain, over 23,000 feet high, is a terrifying wedge of rock and hanging ice. It was climbed at the same time as Hiebeler was fighting for his life on the North Face of the Eiger. So two great break-throughs in mountaineering were achieved at the same time in opposite corners of the earth.

The siege of Ama Dablam took three weeks, as compared with six days for the Eiger. On the first part of the climb, the party followed a narrow edge, a rock arête exposed to a sheer drop on each side. Then the climbers moved out on to a great face of ice which led them to the summit.

The party were members of Sir Edmund Hillary's International Expedition. It included four climbers representing America, Britain and New Zealand; Dr. Michael Ward, Barry Bishop, Mike Gill and Wally Romanes. These men spent the entire winter in the Himalayas, testing the effect of the rarefied air on their strength. They were so strong, despite the difficulties, that they still had stamina in hand after the climb to carry down a Sherpa who broke his leg. They found, however, that anyone staying too long at high altitudes experienced a gradual deterioration, and was apt to get pneumonia. Even Sir Edmund Hillary had a cerebral attack, a form of " stroke " which knocked him out.

THE HIMALAYAS

Gradually, climbers have continued the penetration and exploration of the Himalayas, and the great summits have fallen one after another. After Everest, came the ascent of the second highest mountain in the world, K2, height 28,250 feet, which was climbed by Italians. This was followed by Kanchenjunga, third highest at 28,146 feet, climbed by the British. French climbers reached the 27,790-foot summit of Makalu, and the Swiss climbed Lhotse, a neighbour of Everest, 27,890 feet high.

The Himalayas have presented to mountaineers the prospect of a new Golden Age of climbing, an age akin to the exploration of the European Alps in the time of our great-grandfathers. The sport of mountaineering is very young and man has gone a long way in a short time. For long, the mountains were seen as the haunts of ghosts and demons, and in many parts of the world people still hold their high mountains in great awe. The Himalayas are venerated as the " Abode of the Gods ".

FATHER OF MOUNTAINEERING

One of the first climbers to explore the great spine of rock and ice which makes the frontiers of Italy, Switzerland and France was a Scot, Professor J. D. Forbes. Forbes has been called the father of mountaineering; he opened up many new routes over the unmapped ice-fields. He came to the Alps in 1839 to study the Mer de Glace, the river of ice descending from Mont Blanc, highest peak in Europe (15,781 feet), taking with him August Balmat, a local hunter who was to become an important figure in the Alpine Golden Age.

Forbes was then thirty years old, but was already a Professor at Edinburgh University. He planned to study the movement of ice and debris left by retreating glaciers. He had theories of how the British landscape came to be formed, and wanted to test them among the ice-fields of the high mountains. To do this, Forbes penetrated into regions where men had never been before, including the vast glacier world which has come to be known amongst Alpinists as the High Level Route.

Forbes, the detached scientist, became increasingly the mountaineer, climbing for the love of adventure. When he was no longer able to climb, he wrote: " My heart remains where my body can never be ". Forbes felt homesick when he was not amongst his beloved mountains. His book, " A Tour of Mont Blanc and Monte Rosa " remains one of the classics on mountain adventure.

THE FIRST ALPINE CLUB

Meanwhile, other climbers were following his example in exploration, and in 1857 a very important event took place in London. The first Alpine Club was formed, a club where mountaineers could meet and exchange information.

The club published a journal describing the activities of its members, who were all men of means, with money and leisure enough to be able to climb for several weeks of each year. They could afford to engage local chamois hunters and shepherds to help them explore the peaks. As the first climbers and guides learned their new trade together in this way,

many lives were lost by falling stones, avalanche and storm.

Men died on mountains because they were ignorant of them. They had to learn by experience, and the Alpine Club became a sort of university of climbing. The members found they needed all the intelligence they possessed, as they sought to develop a technique of climbing. There was no question of climbing a peak by a difficult route if an easier way could be found. The art of mountaineering became identified with the climbing of peaks as safely and efficiently as possible.

VICTORIAN CLIMBERS

The sport of climbing was born when all the easiest routes had been worked out, and climbers sought steeper and more difficult ways. A. F. Mummery was the father of climbers, and his book " My Climbs in the Alps and the Caucasus " should be read by all young climbers. This superb writer and climber was killed trying to scale the Karakorum peak of Nanga Parbat.

Edward Whymper was another of the great Victorian mountaineers; he thought Mummery was a suicidal maniac. Whymper arrived on the mountaineering scene when one great Alpine problem still affected the minds of Alpinists to the exclusion of all else. This was the Matterhorn, 14,780 feet, the " Lion of the Alps ". It is the most awesome peak in Europe and even the boldest climbers were dismayed by it. " Do you think that you or anyone else will ever get up *that* mountain? " his guides asked Whymper as he gazed at the peak rearing high above him.

Whymper was then 25 years old and he had just completed 100,000 feet of climbing in eighteen days. This was an astonishing feat, especially as it included the passage of the Col Dolent, a severe route over Mont Blanc from France into Italy which still taxes good climbers to-day. After being caught in a terrible storm on Dent Blanche, which nearly cost him his life, Whymper made his way over a glacier to obtain a closer look at the Matterhorn.

From Zermatt, the mountain rears up in a sharp pyramid, black and pointed as a spear. Whymper had tried to climb the Matterhorn six times, but never from this side. He had attacked it from Italy, where the mountain appears easier. He had pressed his attack from the Italian side, going higher than any other man before him, and continuing to climb even when his guides refused to follow.

Looking up at the mountain from this new viewpoint, Whymper suddenly noticed something which made him think; snow was clinging to what was apparently a vertical rock face. He knew that snow could not possibly lie on a vertical wall, so he moved round the mountain until he could see the ridge in profile. And what he saw astonished him, for the place which had looked vertical when seen from the front was now seen to be a slope which could presumably be climbed. The mountain was an impostor.

WHYMPER DOUBLE-CROSSED

Whymper hurried off instantly to the Italian side to pick up his able guide, Jean-Antoine Carrel, who was as keen as Whymper to climb the Matterhorn. Carrel agreed, but double-crossed him. Taking advantage of Whymper's absence on a visit to a sick friend in the village, Carrel set off with some fellow Italians, planning to be the first to reach the summit. They were already climbing Whymper's old route from Italy when Whymper recrossed the pass to make his attempt from the Swiss side.

The foothills of mountains, such as Everest, are perfect training to ensure the fitness of the men for the harder job to come—the climb to the summit. Camp sites dot the entire route to the top.

Meanwhile, Whymper found that other British climbers were hoping to climb the mountain by the route which he had just discovered. Whymper offered to join forces, and a combined party was formed comprising four amateurs and three guides.

This big party was a strange mixture of strength and weakness. It had experienced Alpinists in the Rev. Charles Hudson, Lord Francis Douglas, and the guides Croz and Taugwalder. But it also included a nineteen-year-old youth by the name of Robert Hadow, who was to hold up progress by his lack of climbing experience. On the 4th of July, the assault on the peak began. Everyone was amazed by the easiness of the route, and the climbers scrambled swiftly up a face which had looked almost unclimbable from below. By 10 a.m., they had climbed to within 800 feet of the summit, and Whymper's main anxiety now was the fear that they might be too late to be first on top. Carrel might have beaten him to it.

As the party neared the summit, things began to become more difficult. The staircase of easy rocks had ended, and the face of the mountain now rose sheer before them. The only route was across the exposed north face of the mountain, which falls away almost vertically for 4,000 feet. The guide Croz took the lead, and climbed it magnificently. The others followed, including Hadow who had to be assisted as he made his way up the face. Once over this steep section, the climbers could see the summit, with no obstacle between them and the top only 200 feet away.

CONQUEST OF THE MATTERHORN

Whymper could wait no longer. He took off the rope and with Croz raced to the summit. Where were the Italians? Nowhere in sight. The summit was unmarked by any footstep. The Matterhorn was theirs, conquered at last. The time was 1.40 p.m. The climbers looked round them, peering down to the steep rocks of the Italian side; suddenly,

133

they saw their rivals as mere dots crawling on the vast black wall. " We must make these fellows hear us! " exclaimed Whymper, and next instant Croz and he were hurling stones to attract the attention of the Italians—an extraordinary thing to do, as dropping stones deliberately down mountains is regarded as a crime.

Whymper could shout his triumph over Carrel in the excitement of his achievement, but he felt for him just the same when he said afterwards: " I would that the leader of that party could have stood with us at that moment. He was the man, of all those who attempted the ascent of the Matterhorn, who most deserved to be first upon its summit ... He made a false move, and he lost it."

Alas, Whymper's party, too, were to make some false moves on their descent of the mountain, and four of them were to die within a short time of leaving the summit.

TRAGEDY STRIKES

The accident happened on the steep section of the face which Hadow had found so difficult on the way up. Croz led, followed by Hadow. Whymper heard a shout and saw the two men tumbling downwards. In an instant, the rope tightened on Hudson, dragging him off, followed by Lord Francis Douglas.

Whymper and old Peter Taugwalder braced their bodies to take the shock of the jerk. The strain came on the rope, and it snapped under the weight of the four men. Had it not done so, it seems certain that the whole party would have been killed. The horrified survivors saw their companions sliding out of sight. They fell 4,000 feet.

After the tragedy, old Peter Taugwalder was accused of deliberately choosing a weak rope to protect himself in event of an accident. This accusation was regarded by experienced mountaineers as a travesty of justice. In fact, the guide saved the lives of his other companions by his prompt rope handling; he could easily have been caught off balance. Basically, the accident was due to bad rope-handling by Whymper, who should have ensured that the rope was securely fixed to the rocks or " belayed " when any member of the party was moving in this steep place.

Whymper was much criticised after the Matterhorn accident, but this did not deter him from continuing with his explorations; the challenge of the mountains was in his blood, and he now went off to the Great Andes in Ecuador. Here, he became the first European to climb a mountain over 20,000 feet high, which he did to find out " whether human life can be sustained at high altitudes ". He climbed Chimborazo, 20,702 feet, and he camped on the summit of Cotopaxi, 19,612 feet, in a blizzard. His companion on this arduous journey was none other than his Matterhorn rival, the guide Jean-Antoine Carrel. Later, Whymper went to Greenland; then, at the age of 62, he walked from London to Edinburgh covering 55 miles a day.

NEW PEAKS IN THE HIMALAYAS

Curiously, the epic drama of the Matterhorn was repeated in the Himalayas in the New Golden Age, when British and French climbers were each trying to be first on the summit of the Mustagh Tower, 23,860 feet. This enormous fang of ice-covered rock has been described as " Nature's Last Stronghold ". It is a peak not unlike the Matterhorn.

Climbers in the Karakorums were familiar with the Mustagh Tower, but none had considered climbing it until 1956. Then, in the same season, four British climbers intent on reaching the top found they had French rivals, consisting of a formidable team comprising Magnone, Keller, Paragot and Contamine. The four Britishers, also experienced climbers, included Joe Brown, Tom Patey, Ian MacNaught-Davis and John Hartog. As the French were already trying to climb the south-east ridge, the British team had no alternative but to tackle the north-west ridge.

Neither of the ridges was of the type normally climbed in the Himalayas. Camped on knife-edges of rock and snow, the climbers faced difficulties that would be considered hard even in the Alps. McNaught-Davis and Brown made the first bid for the summit, setting out without any knowledge of how the French party were getting on. The climb was steep and dangerous, with deep snow lying at an angle where it was liable to avalanche.

MUSTAGH TOWER CONQUERED

It took the two men six hours to climb 800 feet in the top section, and they were so weak when they got to the top that they had not strength enough left to climb the full length of the summit ridge. They were forced to spend a night near the top of the mountain, and it says much for their training and fitness that they were not even frostbitten. Patey and Hartog moved up in their steps next day, and they traversed the two little tops which mark the summit of this barrel-shaped tower. They had enjoyed their climb immensely and were at peace with the world on the icy summit when Patey suddenly heard a shout. Looking down, he realised where it had come from; the tents of the French climbers were perched on the mountainside 3,000 feet below. Their rivals had actually been looking through their binoculars at the summit when they saw Patey and Hartog appear on it like tiny fleas. The French climbers reached the summit a few days later.

So, the most difficult mountain known to man was climbed by two different routes within a week. The French climbers gave their British rivals every assistance in helping John Hartog back to civilisation; he had been badly frostbitten after his victorious climb.

MODERN EQUIPMENT

In the modern age of mountaineering, climbers are placing more and more reliance on mechanical aids. Good equipment enables the climber to sleep out on the most exposed mountain walls in summer or winter. With vertical walls almost commonplace, he is now tackling overhanging ones, where he must depend on metal pegs, expansion bolts, wooden wedges, rope ladders and pulley equipment. Typical of this sort of climb is the Direct Way on the Tre Cime di Lavaredo. It requires hundreds of feet of rope, 200 metal pegs and many expansion bolts, yet it is still very much a true climb for a rock gymnast.

Climbing becomes more and more popular every year, and at the moment of writing it is estimated there are over 1,000,000 alpinists in Europe. The world still has plenty of unclimbed mountains for the man who wants to explore rather than cling to overhanging walls. The aeroplane makes travel to new lands easy, and great new climbing territories are now within reach. To the Himalayas and the Great Andes have been added such places as Patagonia, Fire Land, where whole ranges of mountains have yet to be trodden by human foot. For the men who seek high places the opportunities are boundless, ranging from the homeland hills to the distant corners of the earth.

TREES AND THEIR TIMBER

How soothing and peaceful are the murmuring sounds of a wood. The twittering of birds among the branches, the rustle of unseen creatures in the undergrowth; the occasional drone of an insect as it hurries about its business. In the heart of a wood, the world of towns and cities, of roads and railways, of factories and mills can seem a thousand miles away.

But there are few places nowadays where we can escape the noise and bustle of modern life. Even in the depths of the forest, we may suddenly hear the thud of steel as it bites into the trunk of a tree. And we know that the woodmen are at work.

As we listen, we realise that the birds and insects, and the animals of the forest floor appear to be listening too. It is almost as though they understand that their ancestral home is being destroyed; a tall tree, which may have sheltered generations of woodland creatures, is falling to the woodman's axe.

THE END OF AN OAK TREE

Suddenly, the rhythmic blows of the axe come to an end. There is a sharp crack, followed by a moment of silence. Then, with an ear-splitting crash a great tree plunges to the ground. A shower of twigs and leaves flies into the air and the tangled mass of broken branches is lost in a cloud of dust.

Already, the woodmen are attacking it with saws and axes, stripping away branches. Soon, the trunk of the tree is shorn of all its foliage; it lies ready for the tractor that will drag it to the sawmill.

THE BALANCE OF NATURE

There is something tragic in the felling of a tree, especially when the victim is a lordly giant of the forest: an oak, a beech or perhaps an elm. The life of such a tree can be ended in a minute or two, but it takes a man's lifetime to grow another to replace it. The timber that it yields is valuable to us; but the living tree can be of even greater service.

The leaf of the tree is a tiny chemical factory. It draws carbon dioxide from the air, converting it by the process of *photosynthesis* into sugary materials that are the raw materials of the tree's living matter. At the same time, the tree releases oxygen into the air. The quantities of gases involved in the activity of a single leaf are very small. But the count-

less millions of leaves in a large forest are manipulating large amounts of gas. They play an important role in maintaining the balance of gases in the atmosphere.

The tree's roots, too, perform a useful service. Reaching deep underground, like a network of tentacles, they hold the soil in place, preventing it from being washed away. During rainy periods, soil and roots form a spongy carpet on the forest floor. This absorbs water and feeds it to the trees in immense quantities, especially when the snow begins to thaw and the water seeps into the subsoil. In some places, where whole woods have been cut down, the water now runs freely over the surface of the land, swelling the rivers and causing floods. Often, the water will carry away soil that has taken thousands of years to form, leaving a base, infertile subsoil. By cutting down our trees, therefore, we can

Trees breathe through their leaves, absorbing carbon dioxide and releasing oxygen. Cross-section of trunk shows the annual rings, each ring representing one year's growth. Water and substances such as calcium, potassium and iron are absorbed from the soil by the roots.

135

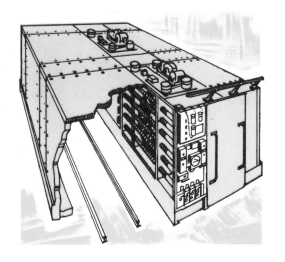

Left, *sectionised timber drying shed showing the electric coils, control panels, and the floor runners on which the timber is run into the shed.* Right, *exterior of drying shed showing panels of polished aluminium and rails set in concrete.*

interfere with nature's balance of vegetation, causing floods and soil erosion. Trees should be felled only when due consideration of the consequences has been taken, and when a tree *is* felled, the stump should be left in the ground to maintain its grip on the soil.

If our oak tree had fallen a few million years ago, it would probably have ended up as coal. But modern trees are much too valuable to us to be left to decay on the ground. The demand for timber rises from year to year, and the material of the tree is now the starting point of many industries.

As soon as the tree is felled, the trunk is cut into lengths suitable for transportation. By counting the rings in the cut surface of the stump, we can tell the age of the tree. Sometimes, we have more dramatic evidence of the tree's age as in the oak tree which was split by lightning, revealing one of Charles I's cavaliers in full armour. The tree must have been already old when he hid in its hollow trunk 300 years ago!

When all is ready, the trunk is dragged away to the sawmill. Soon, it has become little more than a stack of planks in a corner of the timber yard. The newly sawn wood is full of moisture, and it must be allowed to dry and "season" before being used. Otherwise, the timber would warp after it had been cut to shape—this often happens to cupboard doors, for example, which have been made from badly seasoned timber. Seasoning may take a long time, but it is an essential part of timber-production. When the wood is finally seasoned, it will contain between 15 and 18 per cent water if dried in the open air, and from 7 to 10 per cent if dried specially in a kiln.

HARDWOODS AND SOFTWOODS

Several species of tree, in addition to oak, are grown in Britain for furniture making; beech, elm, ash and chestnut are examples of important timbers for this purpose. Others such as mahogany, abura, afara, obeche, afrormosia, and iroko are imported from Africa. Teak is imported from Burma, Siam and Java. Finland also is a major importer of birch for the furniture trade. South America produces the strongest wood of all; it is called greenheart, and comes from a tree that grows abundantly in British Guiana. This valuable timber, which is so heavy that it sinks in water like a stone, is used for making lock gates, wharves and other port installations.

The timbers mentioned above are all *hardwoods*. Some of these timbers are used in building; for structural purposes, and for doors, panelling, etcetera. But hardwoods are costly, and for this reason the cheaper *softwoods* are usually employed in building. These timbers include spruce, pine and larch, which are broadly classified as conifers. Compared with hardwood, about four times as much softwood is used for industrial purposes. But hardwood is preferred as fuel, and when this is taken into account, the total production of the two classes of timber is roughly the same—about 16,000 million cubic feet per year. In North and Central America alone over 10,000 million cubic feet of softwood is felled annually. But even this tremendous production makes only modest inroads on the total amount of timber available; nearly 40 per cent of Canada is covered by timber forests!

Softwood timber is used not only for constructional purposes, but as an industrial raw material. It is a source of cellulose, the substance that is found in virtually every plant that grows on land. Crude cellulose, in the form of wood pulp, is made into paper; this is the way in which most Canadian trees end their days. Huge mills turn out vast quantities of wood pulp to make paper for books, magazines, newspapers, wrapping and cardboard cartons. In America, the consumption of paper is equivalent to 3 hundredweights for every man, woman and child per year. This means that every person needs a good-sized tree-trunk annually!

Without our softwood trees, we would indeed be faced with many problems. We would have no paper on which to print the millions of text books required by our schools and universities. Our newspapers would be smaller, as they were a hundred years ago, when paper was made from rags and worn-out clothes. As the demand for paper grew, it outstripped the supply of cast-off clothing; this was the spur that forced the papermakers to look for new raw materials in the forests of Canada. As wood-pulp made possible the mass production of paper, timber became the basis of one of the world's great industries.

So, when we look at a tree, we should remember the immense contribution it makes to modern life. Book publishing, the press, the building industry and the furniture trade all depend on trees. Their practical value to man is incalculable. But trees are also a source of great beauty. We realise this when we see an oak or a beech tree that we have known for years being felled and dragged off to the sawmill. It is almost as if we have lost an old friend.

It is not surprising that the love of trees is ingrained in most people. There are organisations whose members make a point of planting a tree in any available space. They know that they will not themselves live long enough to bask in its shade; but they are happy in the knowledge that the trees will be there for their children to enjoy.

THE STORY OF COAL

The story of coal began millions of years ago. At that time man did not exist, but the world was rich in vegetation. Trees grew thickly and ferns much larger than any we now know covered the earth. Year by year these trees and plants died and fell to the ground creating immense deposits of rotting trunks and foliage. Earthquakes and geological changes brought the sea flooding in over regions which had once been forest land. Deep down on the ocean bed the remains of thousands of generations of trees decayed under the pressure of the water. Upheaval followed upheaval, so that in one era Britain lay beneath water and in another beneath a tropical sun. And with every great change Nature applied the process of carbonisation to a new layer of organic substances.

This process, which is going on around us every day, is a simple one. Cut off from light and air, the residues of trees and plants gradually lose much of the oxygen and hydrogen which they once contained. Simultaneously, the proportion of carbon in the residues is increasing, creating eventually the solid carboniferous materials we know as peat, coal and anthracite. The concentration of carbon in every form of carboniferous rock is different, and by estimating the carbon content of a coal it is is possible to tell how old it is.

Carboniferous materials are divided into four main categories: anthracite, bituminous coal, lignite and peat.

FOUR TYPES OF FUEL

The oldest of these four types is anthracite. Its origin dates back to about 280 million years to that period of the Palaeozoic era which preceded even the age of the reptiles. It is placed in the Carboniferous Period which saw the creation of forest swamps that afforded perfect conditions for the evolution of early amphibians. Anthracite contains up to 98 per cent. pure carbon. It is gleaming black, with a hard metallic look and bears no traces of the wood from which it originated. An excellent fuel, it burns best in stoves with a controlled draught, leaving very little residue. The largest deposits are found in the United States, Russia, France, Germany and Britain.

Bituminous coal, of which there are many varieties, is the second oldest formation. It goes back 200 million years to the early Mesozoic era when the first dinosaurs were emerging. The product of this period is that black, streaky house coal which breaks easily and gives off a good deal of smoke. It contains from 70/85 per cent. carbon and is used, according to quality, for domestic purposes, steam transport, blast furnaces and the manufacture of coal gas. The United States, Russia, Germany, China and Britain are the main producers.

Lignite and brown coal are of more recent formation. Geologists place their origin in the Tertiary Period, which started about 70 million years ago with the appearance of the first mammals. The woody texture can actually be seen in this type of coal, and its carbon content is a good deal lower than that of the older kinds where decomposition is more complete. It gives off little smoke and is well-suited for making briquettes. Parts of Russia, Germany and Czechoslovakia are rich in lignite. It is found to a lesser extent in Italy, which is a country of later geological formation than, for instance, Britain.

Geologically, peat belongs to the Quaternary Period which extends back for a mere million years. It is quite unlike the older types of carboniferous material, as anyone who has seen it stacked alongside the red peat bogs of Ireland will

During the Carboniferous Period, primeval forests of palms, conifers, shrubs, vines and other plant materials flourished and died. The decayed vegetation changed gradually into the substance we know to-day as coal.

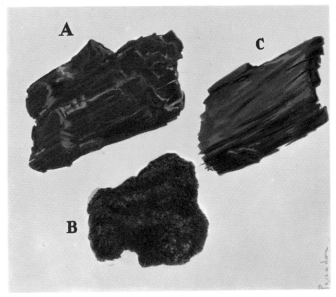

Carbonisation is most complete in anthracite and bituminous coal (A), which is hard and black. Coke (B) is the solid residue of coal heated until most volatile matter has been driven off. (C) Lignite is a low-grade brown coal.

An aerial view of one of the pitheads in Pennsylvania, U.S.A., where immense quantities of anthracite are mined; usually the thickness of the seams vary between 3 feet and 6 feet. In the U.S.A. anthracite is used mostly for home-heating.

appreciate. Peat does not derive from trees, but from an accumulation of moss and bog plants in which the process of carbonisation is at an early stage. Peat is of a yellowish-brown colour and when cut contains a good deal of moisture which has to be dried out before the peat is burned. Peat emits much smoke and leaves more ash than coal; it has a carbon content of 50/60 per cent. By-products obtained by distillation of peat in a coking plant include combustible gases, ammonia and acetic acid. Vast deposits of peat are found in Canada, the United States, Sweden and Finland. In Russia alone the peat bog deposits cover an area twice the size of Ireland.

WHY COAL TYPES DIFFER

The most important factor in the formation of coal is the time that has gone into the making of it. But the slowly-moving stream of time is not the only factor: pressure and temperature also play an important part. In fact, where conditions of pressure and temperature have been favourable, the process of carbonisation has often been retarded or irregular. This largely accounts for the differences in coal from different parts of the world.

A good example is to be found in the region around Moscow, where coal deposits laid down during the Carboniferous Period 250 million years ago are being mined. Had the pressure and temperature conditions been different, the deposits would by now have turned into hard coal or anthracite. But, in fact, they have not developed beyond the stage of lignite.

Pennsylvania, which is the only anthracite-producing area in the United States, provides another curious example. In one sector of these coalfields the earth has undergone great changes due to the folding of the overlying rock strata. Here we find anthracite, while other sectors in the vicinity which have not experienced these geological upheavals yield ordinary bituminous house coal.

Another factor influencing the nature of coal is the type of vegetation which supplied the material for decomposition. This has differed from one geological age to another. Anthracite and bituminous coal derive mainly from ferns

and to a lesser extent from pine and fir trees, whereas lignite comes from trees of the oak and palm species as well as conifers. Peat depends for its formation on an abundance of turf and bog plants.

Both anthracite and bituminous coal seams often occur in great numbers between rock layers going down to depths of several thousand feet. Smaller numbers of lignite seams are generally found together, and peat is usually a single layer. The reason for this is that the swampy terrains supporting primeval forests around sea coasts and lake shores subsided from time to time and were submerged beneath the waters. Through the ages myriads of particles of sand and other sediments drifted into these depressions and hardened into rock. Later, the sea receded and vegetation spread over the reclaimed land, only to be inundated again as the sea invaded it in the wake of a new upheaval. In some regions this cycle was repeated scores of times during the 60 million years of the Carboniferous Period: the age of the coal swamps and the amphibians.

THE RAW MATERIAL OF INDUSTRY

Coal has now become an industrial raw material with many important uses. For several hundred years, it has served as an economical form of fuel for industrial furnaces and domestic fires. In the early 1800s, man learnt to convert coal into gas and chemical by-products such as coal-tar and ammonia. The residue, coke, became of great value to industry. Meanwhile, with the discovery of the steam-engine, coal came into its own as a fuel. Industrial plant, railway locomotives and ocean-going ships were all capable of being driven by steam. The smoky atmosphere of manufacturing towns and the pit-scarred surface of mining districts were part of the price we paid for the nineteenth-century revolution that followed the development of coal as a fuel.

The main coal-producing countries are America, Russia, Britain, Germany, France and Poland. Between them they extract about four-fifths of the world's output of 1,800 million tons per year. Britain's contribution of approximately 180 million tons is almost double what it was in 1860. Geologists estimate that there are still over four million million tons of coal waiting to be brought to the surface.

IN THE BOWELS OF THE EARTH

There are three types of underground mine, as distinct from the surface mines which can be opened up by bulldozers and power shovels. They are called shaft mines, slope mines and drift mines. The first of these has two or more shafts, usually equipped with lifts to raise the coal and carry the miners up and down. Ventilators force fresh air into the mine and draw the fumes and bad air out. In Britain, the average depth of the shafts is about 1,200 feet, though in really deep mines the shafts go down to 4,000 feet.

Slope mines are not nearly so deep and are approached by a bore that slopes gradually down to the level of the coal seam. The advantage of this type of mine is that the coal can be hauled to the surface in trucks. Drift mines are made when the seams can be reached by horizontal tunnels, as is often the case in hilly districts in the United States. Both slope and drift mines usually make use of small cars, drawn by special locomotives, to take miners to the coal face.

THICKNESS OF SEAMS

Coal seams vary greatly in thickness. In Fife and in Staffordshire there are seams twenty-five feet thick, while in

A simplified diagram explaining the principles of getting coal from the face into railway trucks, ready for lorry transport to your home.

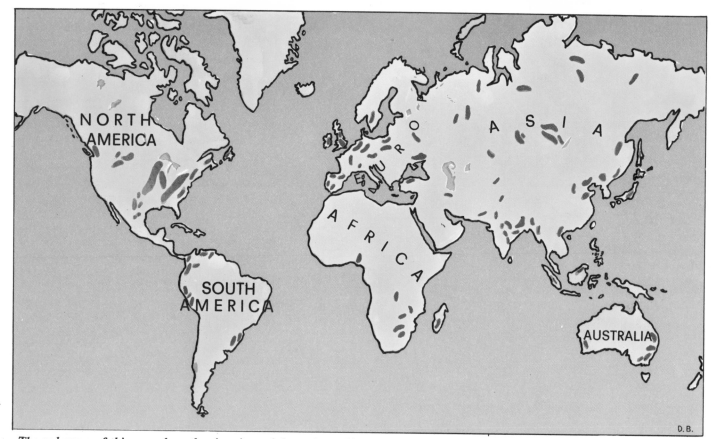

The red areas of this map show the situations of the main coalfields now in production throughout the world. The greatest coal-producing countries are the United States, Germany, Russia and Great Britain.

the Durham coalfields there are places with fourteen-inch seams. American coal is mined from seams averaging about six feet thick, though in the State of Wyoming there are two of nearly one hundred feet. The thickest seams in the world are believed to be in China where there is one coal bed which is actually 400 feet thick. Anthracite seams are usually thinner than those of bituminous coal.

WORK AT THE COAL FACE

In Britain, where workings almost always necessitate the use of shaft-mines, the main underground tunnels branch off into secondary tunnels which follow the course of old coal seams that have been worked out. At the coal face, miners bore into the seam with the aid of an electric drill suspended from a beam, rather like a mammoth dentist's drill. Small shots of high explosive are inserted into these holes and fired to bring down the coal. In many modern mines, compressed air, injected at a pressure of 10,000 lb. per square inch, is used for this purpose. Throughout the coal-mining operation, the air of the mine is tested to detect any gas which may have seeped in from the surrounding rocks.

When a suitable length of coal face has been prepared, mechanical coal cutters come into action and start slicing away at the seam. As the coal falls to the ground it is loaded on to a conveyor belt, which, in turn, delivers it to wagons that carry it to the lift shaft. A miner may handle about fifteen tons of coal per shift in this way.

MECHANISATION

Mechanical techniques, which are even more advanced in the United States than in Britain, have eliminated many of

the hardships once suffered by miners. In ancient times only slaves or prisoners of war were employed in the mines, and in most cases those who went down the mine never again came up into the light of day. They were treated as animals—like the ponies of more recent times, which were kept permanently underground hauling loaded trucks through the darkness.

PIT ACCIDENTS

With all the improvements that there have been in the working conditions of modern pits, the miner's job remains a hard and at times a dangerous one. Accidents, though much reduced by the introduction of safety devices and strict regulations, still happen. Firedamp is a constant threat to the miner; this is the gas, methane, which forms in pockets in the coal. Seeping into the workings, firedamp may cause explosions which result in great loss of life. Another danger, less easy to control, is what is known as " top fall "; this is the collapse of the tunnel roof just above the place where the miners are cutting the seam at the coal face. About one half of all accidents in mines happen in this way.

Coal mining is one of the principal activities of the leading industrial countries in the world. The economic importance of coal increases year by year; it is now no longer used only as a fuel, but as a chemical raw material as well. It provides us with drugs and disinfectants, plastics and synthetic fibres, vitamins and hormones. As time goes on, the importance of coal as a fuel will diminish, and we shall derive much of our power from oil, electricity, atomic energy and solar energy. But the diminishing importance of coal as a fuel will be more than counterbalanced by its increasing importance as a raw material for industry.

THE DISTILLATION OF TAR

For more than a century, we have been burning coal-gas as a source of light and heat. We make this gas by heating coal in closed retorts; when the coal decomposes, gas is given off, together with a thick black liquid that we call coal-tar. (The name *tar* comes from the Arabic *qatram*, meaning pitch.)

When the demand for coal-gas grew during the 19th century, tar became an embarrassment to the gas manufacturers. Great quantities of it were produced as a by-product, and for a long time nobody had any use for it.

At the end of the 17th century Becker, a German chemist, first showed that coal-tar could become a useful source of chemicals. But Becker's suggestions aroused little interest at that time; the organic chemical industry was still in its infancy. About a century later, at the end of the 1700s, the manufacture of coal-gas began, and the quantity of tar accumulated. Many people realised that there were fortunes to be made if uses could be found for the tar, and small amounts of tar were used in the manufacture of tarred paperboard and moisture-resisting papers. These relatively minor uses led to more important ones.

In about 1815, a better method of drying the moisture-laden tar was discovered. It was placed in closed cauldrons, from which the water vapour and other volatile products were distilled and collected in containers. So from the tar came liquid chemicals which in turn were investigated by scientists. It was found that coal-tar distillate could be used in paints and varnishes in place of the more expensive turpentine. And as the techniques of distillation improved, it became possible to separate the liquids into a number of products. Creosote, for example, was being used in 1840.

In 1845, the first industrial tar distilleries were founded in England and Germany. It was at this time that the German chemist Hofmann isolated benzol from the light oils of tar, and the investigation of the many substances found in coal-tar distillate really developed. Some years later aniline was isolated, and this in turn was followed by naphthalene. From these chemicals were made the first synthetic coal-tar dyes, which brought a vast new range of colours into use.

As the chemical industry became increasingly important during the late 19th century and 20th century, the demand for coal-tar chemicals outran the supplies available from the gas works. The distillation of coal and related materials—such as lignite, peat and even wood—became important. And when you consider that 220 pounds of tar yields only 650 grams of benzene, you realise what enormous quantities of tar are needed to satisfy industrial demands.

Tar is now known to be a highly complex mixture of an incredible number of substances which are present in widely varying proportions. Hundreds of these substances have been isolated and investigated, but there are many more of which we still know comparatively little.

INDUSTRIAL USES

The hydrocarbon chemicals obtained from coal-tar are now of immense industrial importance. The so-called aromatic hydrocarbons, including benzene, toluene, xylene, cimene, naphthalene, anthracene and phenanthrene, are raw materials from which modern industry makes all manner of synthetic products. Coal-tar chemicals give us fuels and medicinal drugs, explosives and pharmaceutical products, synthetic resins and paints, varnishes, dyes, perfumes and hundreds of other materials which are so important to us to-day.

The direct use of unrefined tar as it comes from the furnaces of gas works is now of almost insignificant importance. In a partly-processed state it is sometimes used for water-

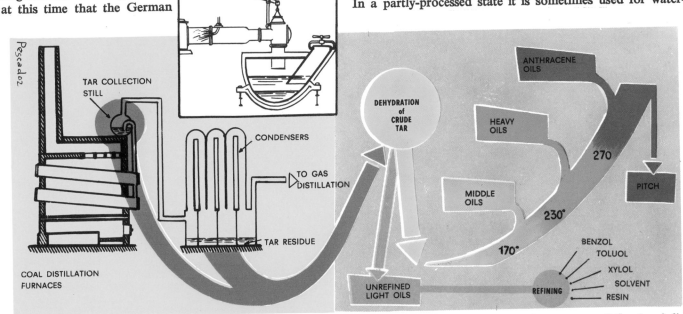

The coal-tar obtained from coal distillation furnaces is dehydrated and ammonia is removed. By the process of fractional distillation, it is separated into light, middle and heavy oils which distil in that order as the temperature is increased.

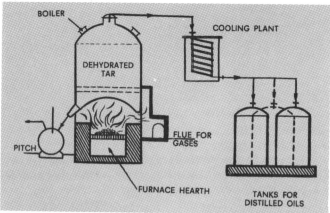

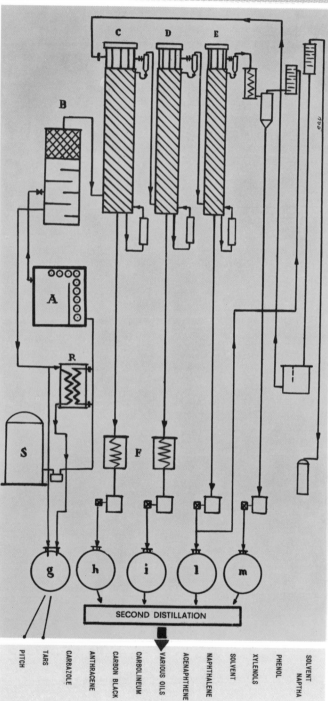

proofing purposes, for the preservation of wood and for making tarred paperboard. But the bulk of the coal-tar now produced is sent for fractional distillation which separates the various chemical products one from another. The distillation of coal-tar has itself become an important industry in most industrial countries. The products obtained from coal-tar distillation may be classified broadly into four main groups or " fractions ".

1. *light oils* (benzol, toluol and xylol) which distil at below 170°C.
2. *middle oils* (mainly phenol and naphthalene) which distil at between 170° and 230°C.
3. *heavy oils* (naphthalene and lubricating oils) which distil at between 230° and 270°C.
4. *anthracene oils* which distil at over 270°C.

   Pitch is the residue of the distillation process.

Distillation, which may be continuous or intermittent, is carried out in many types of plant. In industry, distillation is usually a continuous operation, superheated steam often being used to heat the tar. The fractions obtained are redistilled, and the process may be repeated time and time again in order to isolate and purify the materials that are obtained.

Light oils, which are the most important industrial raw material, represent from 2 to 4 per cent. of the distillate. Redistillation of light oils yields a number of products, including benzene, produced at 30°C., toluene at 110°C., and xylene at 138°C. Various other hydrocarbons, forming solvent naphtha, are obtained at over 142°C.

The *middle oils*, which form 4 to 5 per cent. of the distillate, provide naphthalene in the form of a crystalline deposit. This is purified by sublimation. The liquid remaining after separation of the naphthalene contains about 40 per cent. of phenol, in addition to cresols.

The *heavy oils* also contain naphthalene and cresols, in addition to other hydrocarbons of importance to industry.

The *anthracene oils*, forming 6 to 10 per cent. of the distillate, are thick and fluorescent. They contain anthracene which separates as greenish crystals. This is a raw material for the manufacture of dyes.

Pitch is the residue from coal-tar distillation; it forms about one half of the total quantity of tar used. Pitch contains a number of hydrocarbons mixed with fine particles of carbon. If the distillation has been carried out at high temperature, a hard pitch is obtained; if lower temperatures have been used, the pitch is softer.

Pitch has a number of industrial applications. It is sometimes used as a substitute for bitumen.

To-day, the thick black coal-tar that was such an embarrassment to our coal-gas manufacturers a century ago has become a vitally important raw material of modern industry. In it, we find a store of chemicals which have come from the remains of plants which flourished millions of years ago. We are now turning these chemicals into all manner of synthetic materials—from plastics and fibres to dyestuffs and drugs—that have become such a feature of our modern age.

Top blue panel: *Design of a plant for the distillation of dehydrated tar.* Yellow panel: *Diagram of the tar distillation. The tar (S) passes through a heat exchanger (R) and a boiler (A) to (B), where the pitch is extracted and collected (g). The distillation towers (C, D, and E) separate the remaining constituents of tar which are cooled (F) and collected (h, i, l, m) for further refining into the products listed.*

PAX ANTARCTICA

CONSIDER THIS WORST STAGE OF JOURNEY AND EXPECT RAPID TRAVEL FROM HERE ON. WE LEAVE HERE WITH FOUR SNO-CATS, THREE WEASELS, ONE MUSKEG. WILL PROBABLY REACH YOU WITH FOUR CATS AND ONE WEASEL. TWO DOG TEAMS WILL TRAVEL AHEAD. HAPPY CHRISTMAS TO YOU ALL.

On 21st December, 1957, this radio message was sent out by the British explorer Sir Vivian Fuchs as he fought his way, with eleven companions, across the Antarctic continent. The message was to Sir Edmund Hillary, who was more than a thousand miles away on the other side of the South Pole. Fuchs and his party, in a weird assortment of tracked vehicles, were attempting to do what no expedition had done before—make a complete crossing of Antarctica from north to south, a continuous journey across more than two thousand of the stormiest miles in the world.

SNOW VEHICLES

The great Antarctic explorers of the past—men like Amundsen, Scott, Shackleton and Mawson—could hardly in their wildest dreams have foreseen travellers of the future clanking up glaciers and crawling over crevasses in such huge pieces of machinery.

Dangerous? Yes; there is always danger lurking in the Antarctic. But modern tracked vehicles can travel more surely than men on foot, or even sledges hauled by dogs. The tracks have the effect of skis, spreading the weight of the vehicle over a large area of snow or ice.

Fuchs had found the climb from the Filchner Ice Shelf difficult and slow. The surface was seamed with networks of crevasses, where the solid ice had split apart; the only way across was by slender snowbridges. Sometimes the entire crevasse was hidden; without warning, the ice would crumple and the vehicle would be poised on the edge of a crevasse so deep that the bottom could not be seen.

DANGEROUS EXPERIENCES

On their first experience of this sort, Fuchs and Stratton

in the cabin must have thought their last moment had come, like motorists swerving off the road into a canyon. By a miracle, they were left hanging in space as the front track jammed against the far wall of the crevasse. Hardly daring to breathe, they climbed out of the cabin and crawled along the rear pontoon to safety.

Then came the problem of getting the vehicle out. This was done by supporting the front by steel cables fastened to two Weasels, after which a Sno-cat was used to heave the four-ton vehicle backwards from the crevasse.

After this experience, the explorers linked the vehicles together, like climbers on a rope, so that if one fell into a crevasse the others could support its weight. Some of the party walked ahead of the vehicles armed with long metal probes with which to test the firmness of the snow. Often, men would have to jump for their lives as the ground gave way beneath them. Metal bridging equipment might then be laid over the crevasse to enable the vehicles to cross.

ACCIDENTS DELAY PROGRESS

After 300 miles of very slow progress, held up by accidents which cracked steering platforms and damaged caterpillar tracks, the expedition made its way over the ice-field. At last they found themselves among the black peaks of the Whichaway Nunataks, almost 5000 feet above sea level. Four thousand feet more, and another 500 miles, and they would be at the South Pole, completing the first lap of their tremendous journey. Two dog teams were sent ahead to mark the best route for the vehicles; the Sno-cats and Weasels were filled with 320 gallons of petrol, and on sledges behind them they carried another 5200 gallons of petrol, plus two tons of lubricants and spare parts.

Flanked by weasels and sailing along like a mighty battleship, a Sno-cat pulls sledges of supplies and equipment over the ice.

143

You might think this was a lot of petrol and an unnecessary number of vehicles for only twelve men. But the party was carrying a large quantity of scientific equipment in addition to skis, paraffin and everything else needed by a party of explorers making a polar journey lasting four months.

NEW OBSTACLES

Beyond the Nunataks were new obstacles in the form of uneven furrows of ice and snow like a crazily ploughed field. This is known as " sastrugi ", a surface created by wind and blowing snow, which makes progress a series of jolts and judders. Nevertheless, the party made 25 miles that first day on sastrugi; this was good progress considering that it was to take two months to cover the 900 miles from their starting point on the Weddell Sea to the South Pole.

Not all hold ups were due to bad conditions. Much scientific work had to be done, especially the time-consuming job of drilling holes in the ice to put in explosive charges, so that the men could measure the time for shock waves to travel through the ice. This is known as seismic sounding. It enables the scientist to measure the depth of ice and so build up a picture of the mysterious land hidden below.

Seismic soundings were taken every 30 miles. There was also a gravity survey, with tests every fifteen miles, and tests with an instrument called a ramsonde to measure the structure of the snow layers, providing a record of the weather of previous years. Contrary to popular belief, very little snow falls in the Antarctic. Scientists believe that the actual precipitation is roughly equivalent to the amount of rain which falls on some desert areas such as the Sahara. The snow-fall for the Ross Shelf is thought to be only 7-8 inches a year, though this is hard to prove because of the effect of wind blowing on snow which has already fallen.

ANTARCTIC BLIZZARDS

Blizzards in the Antarctic are sudden and terrible. As the wind rises, the surface begins to move like angry waves on the sea. Whipped into sudden hurricanes with a force of a hundred miles an hour and more, the air becomes a mad fury of whirling powder as fine as dust. In this " whiteout ", all movement by man becomes dangerous. The heat is blown out of his clothing, and snow penetrates through even the smallest chink.

These were the storms that early explorers battled against to try and reach the South Pole. Captain Scott and his brave companions dragged their heavy sledge back from the Pole in the worst weather that has been recorded since Antarctic records began. The blizzards and the intense cold wore them down and they died within a day's march of safety. After a journey of 2000 miles, they found the remaining twelve miles too much for their exhausted bodies.

From the time when Captain Robert Falcon Scott and his four comrades left the South Pole on 17th January, 1912, no man was to stand there again until 1956. The men who revisited the South Pole in that year did not stay; they were American explorers who landed by plane and took off again shortly afterwards.

AMERICAN BASE

When Fuchs was making his journey across Antarctica, the Americans already had a base at the South Pole. A team of scientists was established in a cluster of huts forming the Amundsen-Scott South Pole Station, an outpost of the American base 1200 miles away on McMurdo Sound.

The Polar station was named after the two great explorers who had reached the South Pole in 1911-12. While Captain Scott was marching in from one side of the great Ross Shelf, the Norwegian, Amundsen, had sledged in from the other side using Husky dogs. He had beaten the British party by a month, and when Captain Scott reached the pole he found a tent, with the Norwegian flag already flying there.

FUCHS ARRIVES AT THE POLE

Now, in 1958, Fuchs was traversing roughly the same routes as these two great explorers, approaching the pole from the same general direction as Amundsen. His party had passed the crevasses and sastrugi and were now on the plateau at ten thousand feet. This is how Fuchs describes his arrival: " Suddenly it was there—a small cluster of huts and radio masts; the United States Amundsen-Scott International Geophysical Year Station at the South Pole.

" Glancing back at our little convoy, I could not help thinking it a brave sight. The Weasel heaved and plunged like a small ship in a brisk sea, churning out great sprays of snow, while the Sno-cats sailed majestically, like battleships over the snowy waves."

SIR EDMUND HILLARY

Over the ice men came out to greet them, but one tall man strode before the others. It was Sir Edmund Hillary.

" Hallo, Bunny! " he called.

" Glad to see you, Ed," replied Fuchs.

The two halves of the British Commonwealth Trans-Antarctic Expedition had linked up. Hillary had worked his way over the plateau, following a line east of that taken by Captain Scott in 1912. His job was to mark a route and lay supply depots so that Fuchs and his men could complete their great crossing of Antarctica before the winter cold set in.

Hillary had found a good route over the mountains and had managed to establish his supply depots by 20th December. On his side of the Pole the spring had come earlier, and he was ahead of schedule. So, with three tractors and four companions, he had forged ahead, reaching the American South Pole Station on 4th January after covering a total distance of 1250 miles.

One member of the Fuchs party, George Lowe, had a special welcome for Hillary, for they are both New Zealanders and had been on Mount Everest together. Lowe stepped out of his vehicle wearing the first Panama hat ever seen at the South Pole. He then established a new record by running round the world in two minutes, circumnavigating a circle of petrol drums which the Americans had put out to mark the lines of longitude at the South Pole!

The international date line runs through Antarctica, which meant that the 19th of January, the day on which Fuchs arrived, was the 20th to the Americans. Fuchs was anxious to continue his journey without delay, in order to beat the winter and get to Scott Base before the ship sailed for home. If they missed it, they would have to wait until the following summer before leaving the Antarctic. Their hopes were high because the route was already marked, and food and fuel had been dumped by Hillary along the way.

TROUBLE EN ROUTE

The known route is always easy compared with the unknown. Fuchs was now able to make up for lost time, and in fifteen days had covered over 500 miles. But the

Photographers with the Antarctic expedition record the historic meeting of Dr. Fuchs and Sir Edmund Hillary at the Amundsen-Scott station at the South Pole.

party now ran into trouble when the magnetic compass became unreliable in the vicinity of the shifting South Magnetic Pole. One day, Fuchs found three Sno-Cats coming towards him. They were from his own party; he had gone round in a complete circle. After this it was necessary to flag the route on carefully taken bearings.

Suddenly, the explorers saw the first rocks they had seen in 1400 miles; great peaks hemming in the long glaciers which lead down to the sea. But new difficulties had to be faced, including sixty-mile-an-hour winds and temperatures below —38°C.

Despite the difficulties, the party made good progress. Soon, they were approaching the Ross Shelf, and on their second last day they made their longest run of the whole trip, 75 miles, leaving only another 22 to complete their crossing. All was over bar the shouting, and at exactly three minutes to two on 2nd March they arrived at Scott Base to be welcomed by every vehicle and man on the British and American station.

A ROYAL WELCOME

A band improvised by the Americans clashed out a brassy version of " God Save the Queen ". There was also a message from Her Majesty which read:

ON COMPLETION OF YOUR HARD AND ADVEN-TUROUS JOURNEY ACROSS ANTARCTICA MY HUSBAND AND I SEND OUR WARMEST CON-GRATULATIONS TO YOU AND TO ALL MEMBERS OF THE COMMONWEALTH TRANS-ANTARCTIC EXPEDITION. YOU HAVE MADE A NOTABLE CONTRIBUTION TO SCIENTIFIC KNOWLEDGE IN A GREAT ENTERPRISE WELL DONE

As welcome as that telegram was the sight of the ship HMNZS *Endeavour* standing ready to take the explorers back to civilisation.

Before setting out, Fuchs had estimated that the 2158-mile journey across the frozen continent would take him

100 days. It had taken exactly 98 days of travelling, plus one for the calendar correction: an average daily journey of 22 miles. Shackleton's dream of crossing Antarctica had come true, on land as well as in the air. For while Fuchs had been making his way over the ice, the R.A.F. members of the party under John Lewis had flown an Otter aircraft non-stop from South Ice to Scott Base; this was the first complete Trans-Antarctic crossing in a single-engined plane.

While Fuchs was in Antarctica, the American nuclear submarine *Nautilus* made its historic voyage beneath the ice of the North Pole, travelling from west to east. One week later, another American submarine *Skate* repeated the feat, surfacing in open leads within 40 miles of the Pole. *Nautilus* took over 11,000 soundings, and proved that the waters of the Arctic Basin are very deep indeed. Using the route under the Pole, the distance from Tokyo to London is only 6,500 miles compared to 11,200 miles by normal surface sailing.

The region of the North Pole is covered by a mass of ice which is very far from land. Projecting towards the Pole are the land masses of Norway, Siberia, Alaska, Northern Canada and Greenland.

The region of the South Pole, on the other hand, is covered by land, forming the huge continent of Antarctica. The Pole itself lies over 900 miles from the nearest water. There is no land near to Antarctica, which is surrounded by a great ocean dotted with a few islands. Antarctica is the most elevated land mass in the world, reaching an average altitude of over 6,000 feet above sea level in its 6,000,000 square miles. Its high latitude, high altitude and enormous area make it the coldest place on earth. By comparison with Antarctica, the Arctic is warm. Temperatures of —38°C. were recorded by the Americans at the South Pole and by the Russians at their station during I.G.Y. (International Geophysical Year).

Eskimos live in the Arctic, and have done so for centuries. Until recent times, man has never tried to live in the Antarctic except for short periods. The reason for the almost total absence of life in the Antarctic lies in the winter of terrible blizzards which makes movement impossible for weeks at a time.

To-day, the Antarctic Continent is busier than it has ever been before. Scientific work is being carried out by well-equipped teams from France, Britain, the Argentine, Australia, Japan, Norway, the U.S.A. and the U.S.S.R. Only in the Antarctic is there complete co-operation between nations, thanks to an international agreement which has " frozen " all claims to land. The pact allows explorers of any nationality to do scientific work anywhere, sharing their discoveries with each other.

In an age of suspicion, this is a marvellous achievement. Scientific work which has been done shows there is wealth beneath the ice in the form of oil, coal, metal ores and other valuable minerals.

Scientists are trying to find out everything they can about the shape of the land that lies under the ice. During his Trans-Antarctic journey, Fuchs showed by his seismic soundings that although the ice was 2,000 feet thick twenty-five miles from the Pole, the ice at the Pole itself was four times as thick. Apparently, there are mountains under the ice; the land below the Pole itself is a valley.

INTERNATIONAL EXPERIMENTS

The Americans found an even greater thickness of ice on the 80th parallel at their station " Byrd ", when they sounded over 10,000 feet over a wide area. By 1959, they had also shown that the Ross and Bellingshausen Seas were linked by a broad ice-trough more than 350 miles wide. The Norwegian-British-Swedish Expedition to Queen Maud Land revealed the astonishing fact that the mountain ranges are so deep as to be far below sea level.

The Russians working from their base at Mirny took soundings over 250 miles, but failed to find any land above sea level, while the French in Adelie Land discovered depressions 2,000 feet below the level of the sea. The Australians, working 800 miles along the 62nd Meridian, found the ice depth to be 8,600 feet.

In this desert of thick ice there are fossils which prove that the white wilderness was once covered by tropical vegetation; among those discovered are fossilised plants of a type found in Australia, a winged spore from a Rhaetic tree and coal seams seven feet thick. How did it happen that a tropical country changed to a polar land?

One theory is that the change was due to a shift in the earth's orbit, which altered the position of Antarctica with respect to the sun. As the climate cooled, the vegetation died; the land became covered by ice, which remained frozen throughout the year.

SEASONAL CONDITIONS

In this frozen waste of Antarctica, there is no blade of grass, no flower, no tree; only ice, ice and more ice, depressing even to the most self-sufficient explorer. Yet there is magic—in the moments of incredible calm after storm, when sounds carry for miles in the still air—and in the short days of approaching winter, when one side of the sky is lit by the fire of sunset while the other is green and yellow with the curtains of light known as the aurora. Then suddenly it is a world of storm, and frozen seas heave up immense blocks of ice stretching for miles—huge icequakes caused by the terrible winds against which no man can stand.

The worst weather in Antarctica is found at the coast, especially west of Adelie, where the Russians have endured many hurricanes of over 100 m.p.h. In these conditions, huts must be strong and well anchored if they are not to be blown away. These mighty weather disturbances in the Antarctic, affect the climate over most of the earth's surface.

The exceptional winds of Antarctica are caused by a mixture of warm and cold air at different heights. North winds, deflected from the cold plateau by the spin of the earth, conflict with warm air moving south from the tropics.

The work of a modern Antarctic expedition consists of gathering information. Members of Sir Edmund Hillary's party found hitherto unknown mountains west of McMurdo Sound, and they climbed Mount Newall to map them. At the same time, they did what every other exploration party was doing; measuring daily temperatures, air pressures, relative humidity, wind speed, amounts of frost, sunshine, cloud formations. These routine measurements were made even if it meant risking life in blizzard conditions.

By this kind of careful measurement, it has been established that the South Magnetic Pole has moved 400 miles in fifty years. It is known also that many of the terrible Antarctic storms are due to electrical disturbances originating from the sun. These electrical disturbances often coincide with wild displays of the aurora at both North and South Poles, and with the radio blackouts that affect communications from time to time. The auroral displays—which we also know as the Northern and Southern lights—are caused by streams of particles originating from the sun. Every eleven years or so there is a period of maximum activity in the flares and eruptions on the sun, coinciding with the maximum area of the dark patches we know as sunspots. In the polar regions, the aurora is most vivid when the sunspot activity is at its height. Scientists in the Antarctic are studying the relationship between the sun, the aurora and the magnetic storms, so that they can increase our understanding of these great forces which affect the atmosphere of the earth.

Summer in the Antarctic begins in the last week of September, and continues until the last week of March. During this time the sun never sets, never drops below the horizon. Winter is a time of continual darkness. With the disappearance of the sun, the sea freezes into a solid mat which is shattered periodically by violent storms.

When summer gives way to the dreaded winter, the most extraordinary event in the Antarctic year occurs: the emperor penguin arrives at its rookery. This is the only creature other than man which deliberately chooses to stay on the Antarctic continent in winter; the emperor penguin actually lays its egg in the coldest period of the Antarctic year. It was not until 1952 that we learned something of the life cycle of this largest and hardiest of the penguins. It was the French expedition to Adelie Land that made the first real study of these extraordinary birds.

EMPEROR PENGUINS

The French scientists found that the rookery held no birds until the 10th March when the first three emperors appeared, walking with the deliberation of solemn old men, bills held high to give them a height of 3 feet 6 inches, from large feet to superior nose. By 25th March, there were more than 1,500 birds and the number grew eventually to about 15,000 birds. But it was not until May that they began to lay eggs. The birds arrive early and so take advantage of the fact that in March the sea is open, allowing the birds close to land. The sea would be frozen for many miles if they waited until nearer laying time. Less than twenty of these breeding

In modern Antarctic expeditions, careful surveys and measurements are taken every day. Sir Edmund Hillary's party discovered a new range of mountains.

stations have been discovered, all of them on floating ice or on land.

Streamlined as a torpedo in the water, the 60/90 pound emperor penguin is a slow-coach on land; he moves fastest in an emergency by lying down on his belly and rowing himself along the ice with his flippers.

Prévost, the French ornithologist, discovered that the male penguin depends on his hearing and not his eyes for recognising a female. Catapulting from the sea on to the ice, a newly arrived bird would waddle towards a group of penguins and stand listening, beak raised. Then it would rub its head from side to side on its flippers, as if tuning up in preparation for singing.

Next, the bird would join the group and search until it had found a partner. Standing face to face, the two birds would then sing solemnly to each other, long notes from the male, cooing sounds from the female. The voice was the significant sexual factor of recognition.

Birds kept arriving from the sea until there were more than 13,000 of them, and they had their own way of dealing with the terrible winter blizzards. They simply pressed together until they were one tight mat of birds, with everyone struggling to be on the inside. By constantly pushing and jostling, the inside birds were forced to take a turn outside, so that every one survived. At night, even when there were no blizzards, the large rookery of birds tended to break up into little tight packs, each shaped like a giant turtle, each a centre of warmth against the bitter cold.

The first eggs were laid on 5th May, and by the end of the next fortnight practically every female had laid a large egg weighing about one pound. All these birds were living on their fat. They had not eaten for eight weeks, nor had they built any nests.

The new-laid egg drops on to mother penguin's feet and there it stays, pressed against her warm belly. The arrival of the egg excites the parent penguins, who sing loudly to each other. Then a moment comes when the male feels about with his bill and tries to touch the egg. He may try several times, until at last he is shown the egg. The mother bird then begins shifting from one foot to another as if she were on hot bricks. This is the moment when she lets go the egg which rolls on to the ice, to be grabbed by the male and hoisted on to his legs for incubation. At this point, he sings loudly; in reality, he has little to sing about, for he has been left to hold the baby, as the hungry mother sets off across the ice, vanishing over the horizon in search of food.

Not until the chick is hatched one month later will the mother return, by which time the father is only a shadow of the portly bird he was. The mother, returned from the sea, recognises her mate by the sound of his voice, even though she may have to search for hours among thousands of crying penguins. Now, she proceeds to feed her young one on the fruits of her wanderings: a rich fish paste of plankton and shrimps. Bill to bill, she hoses food into the little grey chick while the father departs to take his turn of feeding and bringing back food to the chick.

Prévost tried to keep count of the birds, and by marking certain ones and keeping others in cages he was able to learn more about emperor penguins than anyone had done before him. He was, in fact, carrying on the work begun by Dr. Edward Wilson of Captain Scott's 1902 expedition, when the very first emperor penguin chick was found. Wilson realised that it must have hatched out in winter to be so well-grown in early summer.

THE WORST JOURNEY IN THE WORLD

Ten years later, with Bowers and Cherry-Garrard, Wilson undertook a winter sledge journey to visit the rookery, and the story of that journey is wonderfully told by Garrard in a book called " The Worst Journey in the World ". It took the party five weeks to reach the penguins; five weeks of the greatest hardship ever undertaken by polar explorers. They hauled their sledges by a harness attached to their bodies, and because of the terrible conditions of blizzard and low temperatures they covered only short distances every day. Wearing all their clothes, they shivered in their sleeping bags; when they tried to cook, their hands froze to the pressure stove. One day they hauled for eight hours to gain only one and a half miles. The temperature dropped to the lowest ever recorded in the Antarctic at that time,

To determine the varying depth of the ice, seismic soundings were taken every 30 miles by members of the 1958 Antarctic Expedition.

80°C. of frost. Worse was to come on the return journey when the tent blew away. By a miracle, they managed to recover it. Without the tent they could not have survived. This incredible journey was made simply to study penguins, and bring back the first three emperor eggs ever seen by man.

Dr. Wilson died with Captain Scott and Bowers in their tent only 12 miles from safety; terrible blizzards prevented the exhausted men from reaching their depot of food. How Dr. Wilson would have loved the task that Prévost set himself fifty years later, camped in a little hut in the midst of thousands of penguins marching from the sea with food for their grey chicks.

Prévost found that although the chicks are fed by both parents, many die of starvation waiting for food. Many more are killed by accidents, such as walls of ice collapsing to bury hundreds of well-grown chicks. Others are blown away in storms; in one case, over 300 in a single blizzard. The young have a wonderful instinct, keeping together in tight masses to keep warm and as defence against the wind. The chick recognises its parents by voice when one of them comes with food, and can single out the special sound however loud the noise in the rookery.

The return of spring brought another enemy in the giant petrel, a large seabird with the ability to kill and eat young emperor penguins. The seals were back too, lying in wait out on the ice. Life was returning to the Antarctic as other seabirds arrived, the small and dainty snow petrels, cape pigeons and fulmars. But for the adult penguins their stay on land was over.

By now, they had little interest in their chicks, which were nearly as large as themselves. It was time for the adults to go back to the sea and build up their own strength before breeding again the following winter. Soon, the rookery held only gawky and abandoned chicks, who must take the plunge into the sea themselves and learn to fish, or die of starvation.

STUDYING WHALES

Man is now studying whales as intensively as the French studied the emperor penguins, but for a different reason. Whales are commercially valuable. They provide food in the form of oil and meat, and by-products such as artificial wool can be made from their blubber. Man has hunted the whale too enthusiastically in the past, killing them without thought. Some species of whale might have faced extinction but for an International Agreement which sets a limit on the numbers that may be caught in any season. Even so, too many whales of certain species are being killed. The blue whales, which form the chief quarry of the modern whaler, are becoming scarcer. Scientists are now studying their migrations, breeding habits and distribution.

Research work of this type is carried out by specially-equipped oceanographic expeditions, paid for by whalers who want to ensure that the future stock of blue whales can be harvested scientifically rather than destroyed by the stupid greed of uncontrolled killing.

The greatest achievement of Antarctic exploration is the friendly spirit of co-operation which exists between men of all nationalities. They share the common task of discovering the secrets of the great white south.

Captain Scott and his men were cut off from the world when they made their great polar journey. To-day the explorer has radio and aircraft to keep him in touch with his fellow-men, and there are few dangers which cannot be met with skill and know-how.

The case of Geoffrey Pratt is an example of a modern polar rescue operation. Pratt was found unconscious in the cabin of his Sno-cat, 142 miles from the South Pole. He had been poisoned by carbon monoxide fumes and needed oxygen if his heart was not to be damaged.

Fuchs was able to take immediate action by sending a radio message to the Americans, who summoned an aircraft from a thousand miles away. The Neptune plane was there by midnight, found the party despite poor visibility, and dropped the needed oxygen bottles. The stricken man quickly recovered.

The new tools of the explorer include rockets, balloons, artificial satellites, Geiger counters, cameras and magnetic instruments. But there is no substitute for man. Only the best men are good enough to face the rigours of the great Antarctic Continent. The scientists who volunteer to man our outposts in Antarctica must still be ready to withstand the bitter cold and blizzards, the loneliness and monotony of life in the least attractive country in the world.

THE POTATO

Shortly after the Spanish invasion of Peru, a small party of officers set off to explore the countryside. One of the first discoveries they made was a plant that was quite new to them: a low, bushy plant with silvery-green leaves and bluish-white flowers, from which hung little clusters of berries.

Attracted by the fruit-like appearance of the berries, the Spaniards decided to try some. But they had a bitter, unpleasant taste, and the soldiers soon spat them out. They decided that the only possible reason that the natives cultivated such a disagreeable plant was to provide poison for their arrows. The invaders were alarmed at the discovery of this " secret weapon ", as the Peruvians had seemed to be a fairly harmless people; the Spanish soldiers began to wonder if they ought to destroy this crop wherever they discovered it.

A few days later the Spaniards found, to their astonishment, that Peruvian children were pulling up the plants, collecting them in bundles and burning them. And behind the children came their mothers, gathering brown tubers from the ground in which the plants had grown. With primitive implements the women dug the tubers from the ground and collected them in baskets. Not far away, one of the women was boiling some of these tubers in a cooking pot on an open fire.

The appetising smell was too much for the Spanish soldiers. They tasted the cooked tubers, and found them very good indeed. They were filling, and tasty too. " What are they called? " asked the Spaniards, pointing towards the pot. " Pappa, " replied the Peruvians, delighted that their guests had enjoyed their food.

NEW ROOTS IN SPAIN AND ENGLAND

This " pappa " was the first helping of potatoes ever to be eaten by white men. The potato, now one of the commonest vegetables in the world, was completely unknown to Europeans until these Spanish officers found it in 1541. Intrigued by their discovery, the Spaniards took specimens home to Spain where the plant soon became acclimatised. The potato arrived at a fortunate time, for Spain had been impoverished by the wars that Philip II was waging in his efforts to build an empire. The Spaniards cultivated the potato diligently, and within twenty years it was growing in every part of the Iberian peninsula. It did much to appease the hunger of the Spaniards, who were facing famine.

At that time, Spain was England's great rival as a colonial power. Communications between the two countries were almost non-existent, and it was not until after 1586, when Sir Francis Drake found the plant during one of his voyages, that cultivation of the potato started in southern England. Its fame spread rapidly as its value as a food was recognised. And, by the middle of the eighteenth century, the potato was second only to wheat in its importance as a food crop. Served at the tables of kings and peasants its cultivation became established in every country of Europe. It came as a god-send to millions who were often short of food.

GROWTH AND VARIETY

The potato belongs to the botanical family of *Solanaceae*. Strangely enough, this family includes the poisonous hedgerow plant we were all warned against as children: deadly nightshade. Possibly it was the resemblance between the flowers and berries of these two plants that first aroused the suspicions of the Spanish officers.

Solanum tuberosum is the name that botanists give to the potato; it is an annual plant whose tubers are commonly sown in Britain in the spring to crop in summer or autumn according to the warmth of the climate. The tubers throw out shoots in two directions—up and down. Those that grow upwards emerge from the soil, produce silvery-green leaves and, as the plant matures, form clusters of flowers that may be white, yellowish or violet. At the same time, small nut-coloured berries, containing the tiny seeds of the plant, begin to ripen. Meanwhile, the downward-growing shoots, called *stolons* or suckers, form tubers at their extremities.

The Spanish learned of the value of the potato as a food from the Indians of South America.

Towards the end of the sixteenth century, potatoes brought from the New World were grown in the Iberian peninsula.

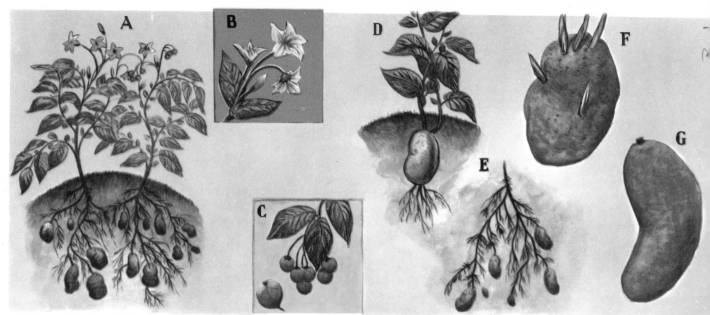

The potato plant, Solanum tuberosum, *showing potatoes, roots, leaves, flowers and fruit. B. flower; C. fruit; D. tuber or potato; E. fibrous roots; F. tuber with sprouts; G. French variety of potato.*

These are the potatoes, which are rich in starch and nitrogenous substances of high food value. They should not be mistaken for the roots of the plant, which are long, thin, and fibrous, and do not produce tubers.

To most of us, potatoes are just potatoes. But there are, in fact, many different kinds in cultivation, varying greatly in the shape and colour of the tubers. Some are round, oblong or egg-shaped; others may have yellow, pink or violet skins with white or yellow flesh; some ripen early and some late. These characteristics determine the many varieties of potatoes which are recognised by the seedsman. And it is because of these differences that we are able to enjoy potatoes all the year round. When local supplies run short in one part of the world, different varieties may be brought in from countries where they are still being harvested. Shiploads of imported potatoes fill the gap until our own new potatoes are ready.

Usually some of the potatoes from the crop are held back for use as seed. These are carefully selected and put aside during the winter. They are called seed potatoes, even

One method of storing seed potatoes is to seal them in glass vessels and keep them at a steady temperature in a well-lit store.

though they have nothing to do with the natural seeds of the plant; these, as we have seen, are contained in the berries that grow above the ground. Potatoes are grown from true seed by breeders seeking new varieties. Potatoes may be bred with characteristics that make them suited to some particular soil, climate or season.

The potato grows from a tuber just as a tree or shrub grows from a cutting. The tuber acts as a food store for the plant. It may be cut into several pieces, and each piece will grow into a new plant if placed in a rich and fertile soil. Normally, potatoes are sown in parallel rows, with tubers set about nine inches apart. Protected from the cold by the soil above, the tubers form buds and begin to sprout. The shoots draw on the rich reserves of food inside the tuber, which withers and shrinks. Soon, the shoots break through the surface of the soil and emerge into the light of day.

Once it is growing above ground, the potato plant faces many hazards, some of which threaten its very existence: sharp frosts, biting winds, cold, dry air and, worst of all, pests like weevils and Colorado beetles which attack the young plants. At a later stage, the potato may be attacked by mildew, which is caused by a minute fungoid growth known as *peronospora*. Plants may be protected from mildew by spraying with a solution of copper sulphate; if the mildew is allowed to gain the upper hand, the entire crop may be lost. Potato blight, is another infection that causes great loss.

Potatoes which survive these perils are eventually ready for digging. In England, this usually takes place between June and September, according to the variety of the crop. Dry weather is preferred, so that the soil can easily be shaken off, the potatoes being left to dry for a while in the sun. If the crop is a large one, the farmer uses machinery for lifting and carrying the potatoes to storage. But potatoes are a favourite crop of the amateur gardener too, who needs only a spade or fork for digging and a shed in which to store his crop. The vagaries of the weather and the uncertainties of agricultural economics make it difficult for anyone to know if potatoes are going to be plentiful or in short supply. And a reserve of home-grown " spuds " can be a useful standby when the potato crop is poor.

We live in an exciting world these days, with new inventions and discoveries changing our lives at bewildering speed. But it is fair to say that no small engineering development has had such a dramatic effect as the coming of the motor-car. Starting in a humble way towards the end of Queen Victoria's long reign, the motor-car has influenced the lives and habits of all of us.

For thousands of years, our ancestors depended on the horse as the basis of their transport system. They rode on horseback, or used the horse (and other animals too) for pulling carriages. It was only by employing the power of animal muscles that they could keep the wheels of their vehicles turning. And it was only when inventors provided an engine capable of using other sources of energy that the motor-car was born.

GROPING IN THE DARK

The problem of finding a machine which used energy other than muscle power, had occupied men's minds ever since the time of ancient Greece. Archimedes recognised the power of steam, but neither he nor his followers were able to make practical use of it.

One hundred years later, about 150 B.C., Hero of Alexandria devised a primitive engine operated by steam: but this was no more than a toy. For more than 1800 years, little further progress was made in the development of steam power until, eventually, Savery and Newcomen turned their attention to the problem in about the year 1700. Their early steam-engines, which made use of Papin's invention of the first cylinder and piston, were heavy and cumbersome. But they paved the way for James Watt, whose inventions made the steam-engine a practical device for providing mechanical power. Watt used steam-engines for driving all kinds of machinery and so brought self-propelled vehicles within the bounds of possibility.

RAIL AGAINST ROAD

In 1769, a Frenchman named Nicolas Cugnot built an enormous wooden tricycle driven by two pistons operated by steam produced in a primitive boiler. Cugnot's steam wagon crept along at about three miles an hour, stopping every minute to cook up more power. This first self-propelled road vehicle now stands in a museum in Paris. Others whose names are associated with the development of the steam-engine are William Murdoch, Richard Trevithick, a Cornishman, and Oliver Evans in America. At this time, however, the future of the steam-powered vehicle was seen to lie in the heavy locomotive running on rails, rather than in the road vehicle. When George Stephenson drove his " Rocket " on the Liverpool and Manchester Railway in 1829, he showed how the steam locomotive could provide man with his first mechanised transport system.

The railways brought immense benefits, but their development held up progress on the mechanised road vehicle. Railways were favoured by regulations such as that which made it an offence to drive a horseless carriage on the roads without having someone walking in front with a red flag.

This law was passed in 1831, when railways were just beginning. Even worse, excessive tolls drove the few steam carriages in existence right off the roads. In Mr. Pickwick's day coachmen openly scorned these " monsters ". The efforts of Victorian business men were diverted towards the railways; the roads were allowed to fall into disrepair with the passing of the stage-coach.

THE BIRTH OF MOTOR-CAR ENGINES

It was during this period that inventors began to experiment with the internal-combustion engine, driven by a mixture of fuel and air which burned inside the cylinder itself. The first important step was taken by Samuel Brown, who built a gas-burning engine in 1823. It was a primitive affair, but it assured Brown of a place in the history of internal-combustion engines, comparable with that which Newcomen had already won in steam. Brown's engine operated by creating a vacuum inside the cylinder. It was followed by the invention of an engine using pressure, which was built in 1833 by W. L. Wright. As time went on, this new type of internal-combustion engine was improved and modified. Many people played their part; Lenoir, Hugon, Barsanti and Matteucci all contributed to its development prior to 1862. In that year, Alphonse de Rochas, a Frenchman, published a theoretical study of the subject and established the principles of internal-combustion engines which are applied to this day.

Up to this time, these engines had been employed only in industry and not for mechanical traction. Otto and Langen, who started building a free-piston internal-combustion engine in Germany in 1867, sold 50,000 of them in the next fifteen years. But these engines were much too big and

Oliver Evans, an American engineer who specialised in building boilers, constructed a steam wagon in 1804. The people of Philadelphia were astonished when the vehicle appeared in the streets.

awkward to be adapted for use on the roads. The first vehicle to be powered by an internal-combustion engine was built by an Austrian named Siegfried Marcus in 1875. A few years later Murnigotti, an Italian engineer, constructed a similar machine and patented it. Then, in the middle "eighties", Gottlieb Daimler and Karl Benz, whose names were to become world famous in the motor-car industry, brought out their much-improved models.

PANHARDS LEAD THE WAY

We should hardly recognise the ancestor of the modern motor-car if we were to meet one on the roads to-day. The early car often had only three wheels, and they looked like giant tricycles. The builders might also install an engine in the front of a horse carriage, so that the vehicle looked like a stage-coach from which the animals had bolted. This was the position in 1894 when the French engineer, Krebs, designed the Panhard, the grandfather of all modern cars. It was fitted with a vertical, petrol-driven internal-combustion engine. The right-hand gear change, clutch, foot brake and accelerator were all there. The body was antiquated, but the chassis had features similar to those of a modern car. A Panhard of this type won the first road race in the history of motoring, run from Paris to Bordeaux in June 1895.

Credit goes to Panhards—the veritable Jaguars of the 1890s—for putting a practical vehicle on the road. We should not, however, think of any one man as the inventor of the motor-car. Twenty or thirty pioneers are remembered for the contribution they made to the development of the internal-combustion engine, and the transmission of its power to the wheels. Daimler, Benz, Panhard, Krebs, Levassor, Albert de Dion, Sir Henry Royce, Gibbon, J. D. Rootes and Lord Nuffield all played an important part in the development of the motor-car in Europe. In America, Henry Ford and many others were active too. We have only to think of the many complex parts that make up the engine, chassis, and body of a motor-car to understand why the modern car represents the work of many gifted men.

HOW THE ENGINE WORKS

The internal-combustion engine used most commonly in modern motor-cars is a *four-stroke engine*; it draws its power from energy released by burning a mixture of air and petrol. The mixture burns inside the *cylinder* in which there is a *piston* that moves up and down. Fuel and air enter the *cylinder* via an *inlet valve*, after being mixed in the *carburettor*. A *sparking plug* ignites the gaseous mixture of petrol and air inside the cylinder. A *connecting-rod* linked to the *crank-shaft* transforms the up and down motion of the piston into the power that makes the wheels go round. This is, in principle, the way in which a four-stroke internal-combustion engine works.

What, though, causes the actual combustion? How is the motion of the piston sustained, and how is that motion conveyed to the wheels? In a sense the engine breathes. On the first downward movement, the piston sucks in the explosive mixture of fuel and air from the carburettor. This is the *intake stroke*. The return movement, or *compression stroke*, compresses the gas at the very moment that the sparking plug ignites it. An explosion follows, and the piston is thrust down again in what is called the *power stroke*. The fourth movement of the four-stroke cycle is another upward one, its purpose being to expel the burnt-out gases from the cylinder. This *exhaust stroke* completes the

cycle, which is repeated again and again with lightning rapidity.

Of these four strokes, the really vital one is the power stroke. It exerts force on the connecting-rod and the crankshaft, which turns the propeller shaft. The latter takes up the power from the piston, except of course when the clutch is being used to change gear or to keep the engine running when the car stops. The power, now transformed into a rotary movement, is conveyed by the differential gears to the rear axle, and the rear axle keeps the wheels turning. These are the main functions of a car engine and its transmission system. These are its vital organs. Chassis and bodywork, which have developed side by side with the internal-combustion engine and the transmission system, add strength, purpose and beauty to one of the greatest achievements in the field of mechanical engineering.

THE VALUE OF MOTOR RACING

From the earliest days of the motor-car, owners have been competing with each other in races and road trials aimed at proving the speed and reliability of their cars. Competition was especially fierce in the 1890s, when the internal-combustion engine had yet to establish itself as the most efficient engine for the motor-car. Experiments were still being made with vehicles powered by steam, as well as by gas engines and electric motors. Public road tests were the only way of proving which form of propulsion was the best.

One of the first road races run was from Paris to Bordeaux and back, in June, 1895. This was not so much a speed test as a struggle to survive a succession of snags and breakdowns. The cars bumped along on their hard tyres over rough, unmetalled roads, and much depended on the skill of the mechanics who accompanied the drivers. It was considered no small achievement when M. Levassor, a Frenchman, returned to Paris in his Panhard forty-eight hours after leaving the city; he had maintained an average speed of 15 m.p.h. The car had a petrol-driven internal-combustion engine. In 1900, the electric road vehicle made a come-back, when Jenatzy broke all records in his flying torpedo. This electrically propelled vehicle maintained the then incredible speed of 65 m.p.h., and Jenatzy and his wife,

In 1900 the Frenchman, Jenatzy, set up a record speed of 65.8 m.p.h. in his electrically-propelled car, Jamais Contente.

Father and son, Sir Malcolm and Donald Campbell, set world speed records on land and water with their famous Bluebirds.

who sat behind him, became known as " the fastest couple of the century ".

But the century was very young, and it was not long before Jenatzy's record was broken by a car driven by an internal-combustion engine. In 1904, M. Rigolly won another triumph for France by reaching a speed of 103·56 m.p.h. Stimulated by the Gordon Bennett Trophy, which was offered by an American newspaper proprietor, car manufacturers now took more and more interest in motor racing. The Grand Prix had been established in 1903, and it was soon apparent that it had come to stay. The first race from Paris to Madrid had to be stopped at Bordeaux as many people were killed, and the French were afraid of what might happen over the Spanish border. The race was subsequently transferred to Le Mans, which was to become known throughout the world as the mecca of car-racing enthusiasts.

Tests and road trials, ranging from the old meetings held at Brooklands and Donington Park to the Monte Carlo Rally and the Italian " Mille Miglia ", proved the high quality of many makes of British, American, French, German and Italian cars. Meanwhile, great individual feats were achieved by Britons like Major Seagrave, who averaged 200·79 m.p.h. in 1927, Sir Malcolm Campbell who raised this record to 310·13 m.p.h. in 1935, and by John Cobb who, on one of his runs at Bonneville, Utah, in September, 1947, became the first man to travel on land at 400 miles per hour. These achievements were not just victories for Britain, but were triumphs for the engineers and manufacturers of the cars and all the components that went into them.

These racing drivers remind us that motoring started as a sport and that they are determined to keep it so. These sporting traditions can be judged from the fact that few of the really old vintage cars had closed bodies. Until about 1910, most of them had open tops, and few had windscreens. In those days people enjoyed their motoring as an open-air adventure—a more modest one, perhaps, than the Paris-Peking rally of 1907, which took competitors over a 10,000-mile course across the breadth of Europe and Asia—but still an adventure. And so it remained, well into the 1920s, long after the motor-car industry had become established.

COMFORT AND UTILITY

Up to this time, the aim of car manufacturers had been primarily speed and reliability. Now, comfort and utility were to become steadily more important. With these principles in mind, manufacturers produced better and better models. People wanted cars not just for sport or for recreation. They needed them too for the everyday business of life. Mass-production and the assembly line came into their own in the motor-car industry as manufacturers set out to meet the growing demand. " Motor-cars for the million " poured from the factories. In Britain, the number of all registered vehicles—motor-cycles included—rose from 1½ million in 1925, to about 2¼ million in 1930. By 1939, there were more than 3 million, and by 1967, over 14 million motor-vehicles on the roads.

Meanwhile, the popularity of the car seemed to have no limits in the United States. There, registered vehicles numbered 26½ million in 1929, and by 1954, this huge figure had more than doubled. If there are 130 million motor-vehicles in the world to-day—and the total cannot be far short of that figure—more than half of them are registered in North America. Allowing the average life of a car or lorry to be about six years, this would mean 20 million new vehicles every year simply to replace those that are scrapped.

A WORLD-WIDE INDUSTRY

Achievement brings great opportunities for others who follow afterwards, and the motor-car industry is no exception. Not only is this so in the assembly factories and workshops, but in a score of industries that contribute essential materials to the motor-car manufacturers. They range from special steels to copper, nickel, zinc, aluminium and other metals. They include the electrical and rubber industries and all those firms that make special instruments and fittings. Petrol production, tankers to transport it, oil refining, garage pumps . . . . men have enriched themselves in scores of activities connected with the motor-car. And, of course, governments would be a lot poorer if it were not for the taxes that car owners pay on petrol to keep the internal-combustion engine ticking over.

THE GREAT ALPINE TUNNELS

The mountains we call the Alps rise like a jagged wall that separates Italy from her neighbours to the north. These towering peaks have always been a formidable obstacle to travellers in central Europe. But in the last century or so, man has overcome the Alpine barrier in the simplest and most effective way, piercing the mountains by tunnels that are among the engineering marvels of our age.

The greatest tunnel of modern times passes under the massive peak of Mont Blanc. This road tunnel, inaugurated in September, 1962, is one of the most wonderful achievements of French and Italian civil engineering; it shortens the route from Paris to Rome by nearly 150 miles.

A CENTURY AGO

First of the Alpine tunnels was that which runs beneath the Mount Cenis Pass; this was the pass used by Hannibal when he crossed the Alps with his elephants. Work on a tunnel beneath the Mount Cenis Pass began in 1857, and the traveller following this route into Italy at that time, would hear of the tunnellers burrowing deep beneath the Fréjus range, building the tunnel that was to carry a railway line from Modane in France to Bardonecchia above Turin.

The tunnellers had no pneumatic drills. They hacked with pickaxes at the granite, making their way through the mountain at a rate of less than one foot per day. To many it must have seemed an impossible task. But not to Sommeiller, the engineer in charge. Within three years he had perfected his compressed air drill, and the tunnel was soon creeping forward at the rate of seven or eight feet every twenty-four hours.

Underground, the heat was intense; rock falls held up progress and endangered men's lives; sudden spouts of water burst from pent-up streams and flooded the workings. Even to-day, the tunnelling costs of £75 a foot sounds a lot of money, especially when it is multiplied by the number of feet in eight miles. It is easy to understand why some of the people of Savoy, now part of Italy, thought it a mad and wasteful project. Their government had to find over £3 million to pay for the first great Alpine tunnel.

MEETING UNDER THE MOUNTAIN

Throughout the 1860s the work went on, Italians tunnelling from the south, Frenchmen from the north. Behind them came masons and builders who lined the walls with brick and stone. This in itself was no light task in a horseshoe-shaped tunnel twenty-six feet wide and twenty-four feet high. There was always the nagging doubt that the calculations might be wrong, and the two parties would miss each other!

By 1870, people were beginning to wonder whether the work would ever be completed. Then one morning, Sommeiller, who was in Turin, received a telegram from his engineer on the site. The drills had just penetrated the last rock face. French and Italians were cheering each other amid the dust and stone. They were shaking hands through the gap. It was 4.25 a.m. on Christmas morning, 1870. As the news of this great feat reached the outside world, people were amazed to learn that the two boreholes were only two feet out at their meeting point.

THE ST. GOTTHARD TUNNEL

The double-track Mont Cenis tunnel, which was opened in 1872, still carries a large volume of railway traffic between France and Italy. In that same year, work was started on the St. Gotthard tunnel which pierces the Lepontine Alps in the Ticino province of Switzerland and is an important link in the communication system between northern European countries and the Mediterranean ports. The problem here was a different one. The Mont Cenis tunnel is straight and the track almost level. But at St. Gotthard, it was necessary

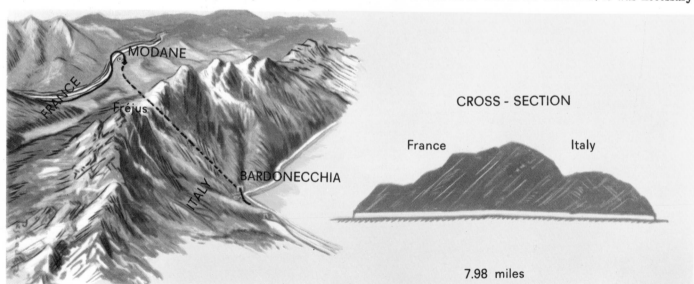

CROSS - SECTION

France   Italy

7.98 miles

The first Alpine tunnel, Mont Cenis, was opened in 1871. It passes under the Fréjus Alps between Modane in France and Bardonecchia in Italy. The tunnel is eight miles long and slopes gently to a central point to ensure that water drains away.

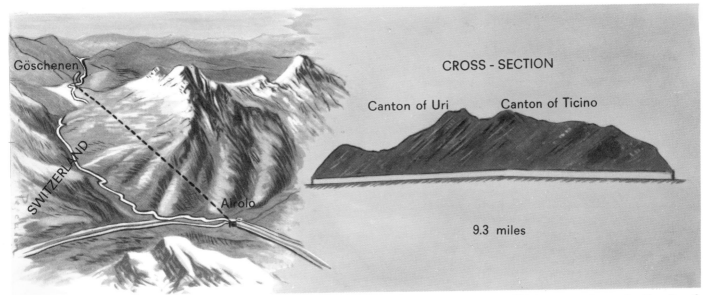

In spite of difficult conditions, the central zone of the St. Gotthard massif, which rises to 10,600 feet, was chosen for the site of a nine-mile long tunnel.

to build the line between two points at different heights; Göschenen to the north and Airolo to the south.

The only way to gain the necessary height was to cut a series of seven loops through the heart of the mountain. These spiral curves were to rise nearly two hundred feet in the course of each loop. Planned so that the line would emerge at intervals into the open, the track was to run along the side of the mountain at the turn of each loop. In all, there were to be 9¼ miles of tunnel proper.

A WALL OF GRANITE

The ambitious St. Gotthard scheme was financed by a company whose shareholders were mainly Swiss, German and Italian. The work was carried out by Italians, who have a proud tradition in constructional engineering that goes back to Roman times. They threw themselves into the task with energy and enthusiasm. Dynamite had recently been invented, and, with the aid of explosive charges and rock drills driven by 2,000-horse-power water turbines, powered by the Rivers Reuss and Ticino, the tunnellers gnawed their way slowly into the rock face. In one section, they ran into a wall of granite over fifty feet thick. It took them two years to get through it. The engineers had planned the tunnel in seven separate sections, and work could go ahead on all of them at the same time. The separate loops, each emerging every mile or so, kept seven gangs of tunnellers in action. They worked in underground temperatures of over 100°F.; they suffered injuries from flying chips and falling stones; in the evening they staggered exhausted and half-choked with dust into the clear air of the Swiss Alps. Many accidents took their toll of life before the first train went through the St. Gotthard in 1881.

TRAPPED IN A SEWER

Tunnelling has always had its hidden dangers. The weight of the mountain builds up immense pressures in the rocks and underground streams. In the Tanna tunnel in Japan, for example, water gushed into the workings at a pressure of 275 pounds per square inch, and seventy men were killed in the sixteen years it took to complete the project.

One of the worst disasters of this kind occurred in the Lötschberg tunnel which links Goppenstein with Kandersteg

in the Bernese Oberland. After burrowing for two miles, the advance party broke into an underground river which engulfed them and turned the workings into a vast sewer. Twenty-five men were drowned and large quantities of gear were lost. Before the breach could be closed, 8,000 cubic yards of debris had to be cleared away. Work was later resumed at a lower level, so that the tunnel would pass beneath the river whose bed had been scooped out in past ages by a glacier. Opened in 1911, the Lötschberg now carries traffic between Berne in Switzerland and Brig on the Italian frontier. Like the St. Gotthard, it is looped and rises nearly 1,400 feet in nine miles.

EXCAVATION TECHNIQUES

Building a tunnel of this sort proceeds in four stages, as shown in the first illustration. First, a wedge-shaped hole with sloping sides is cut and shored up with stout wooden beams. The *cuniculus*, as it is called, is then enlarged to open the tunnel to its full width and height. In the third

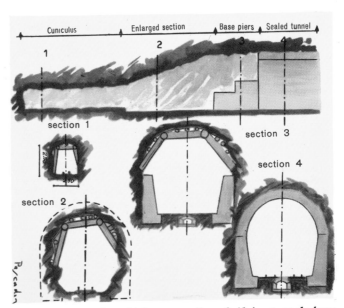

The four stages by which many miles of Alpine tunnels have been built.

CROSS - SECTION

12.3 miles

The Simplon Tunnel measures 12.3 miles and is the longest in the Alps. The two tracks are carried by separate tunnels, connected every 220 yards by cross galleries. It is an important link between France, Switzerland and Italy.

stage, the solid stone or concrete piers on which the central arch will rest are built to half the height of the tunnel. Finally, the overhead structure is removed and the semicircular roof and floor are sealed with concrete.

By the time the Lötschberg tunnel was excavated, hydraulic drills and percussion air drills were in use. Ventilation had been improved and pumps installed to clear the shaft of water. An efficient system of tip wagons had been developed to remove the debris and to carry up the building materials. Working conditions were much better, and the miners felt safe from all but the unpredictable hazards of working underground. As always, the danger of sudden flooding remained; during the construction of the Hudson River tunnels in New York, the river poured into the tunnel through a hole in the roof, drowning twenty men in a few minutes.

A TUNNEL WITH A DIFFERENCE

The danger of flooding was the only serious obstacle to the boring of the longest and most famous of all the Alpine tunnels. This was the 12¼-mile-long Simplon tunnel which was started in May, 1898, and opened to traffic on 1st June, 1906. The original scheme for a Simplon tunnel dated back to 1893, when a company supported by the Swiss and Italian governments began working on this project. Their plan was to build a double tunnel, leaving a rock wall about 55 feet thick between the two tracks. This would remove any risk of collapse which might occur if the pressure of the mountain above was spread over a wider surface.

Another new feature of the Simplon project was the construction of broad passages linking the tunnels at intervals of two hundred and twenty yards. This had many technical advantages, including better ventilation. Also, the miners had more room to move about and working conditions were less cramped. Altogether, there were more than one thousand miners, who lived with their families in special villages erected near the workings. They had their own shops, hospital, baths and other facilities, for the excavation of the Simplon was to take about seven years.

HOT SPRINGS AND COLD

Some parts of this tunnel lie beneath 7,000 feet of solid mountain. The temperature rises rapidly with increasing depth, and as the men progressed the thermometer climbed

to 38°C. After tunnelling for about two-and-a-half miles, they struck a spring which gushed out at a rate of 10,000 gallons per minute. In another sector, water flowed in at a temperature of 45°C. Fortunately, equipment was available to deal with these obstacles. And when they were overcome, a series of pressure sprinklers was installed to lay the dust and to keep the air temperature constant.

It was soon obvious that the engineers had chosen a good site for the construction of the Simplon Tunnel. This time, there was no hard granite, only layers of gneiss, limestone and mica-schist which were relatively easy to penetrate. The drilling machinery developed by the famous engineer, Alfred Brandt, was already in use. Brandt's rotary hydraulic drills had proved their worth in the Arlberg tunnel twenty years before. Since then these drills had been greatly improved, enabling the tunnellers to progress at a rate of 30 to 35 feet per day and a cost of £50 per foot, as they bored their way through the Alps for a distance of over twelve miles.

THE SIMPLON OPENS

Nowadays, we are inclined to take these great achievements lightly. But in their day, they aroused as much interest as space flights do to-day. During the winter of 1905, all Europe was waiting to hear whether the two shafts, one starting in Switzerland and the other in Italy, were going to meet. They did so on the 24th of February of that year, a date which marks a great victory in the annals of tunnelling. The Simplon was ready to take traffic in the following year. But for the time being, only one of the two adjacent tunnels was used. The second was not completed until shortly after the end of the First World War, since when the Simplon has been open to two-way traffic.

The ceremonial opening of the Simplon tunnel, in the presence of the king of Italy and the president of Switzerland, was a notable event. The Alpine ranges had now been breached at many points by some of the world's longest tunnels. Others, in Austria, had linked that country to the west, via the Arlberg tunnel, and to the south-east by a series of tunnels that carried the railways of central Europe down to the sea at Trieste.

EUROPE'S GREATEST SUBWAY

The nineteenth century saw immense progress in the

In 1898 work began on the Simplon Tunnel. It was opened in May, 1906, in the presence of the King of Italy and the President of Switzerland. In June the first regular passenger train began to use the tunnel.

building of tunnels, which were designed to carry the railways that linked up so many countries of the world. To-day great tunnels are still being built, often to carry the roads that have now become so important in the world's communications system. One of the most striking projects of modern times is the road tunnel under Mont Blanc. This tunnel was discussed and considered practicable in 1933. In 1945, a company was set up, and within a year the men of Entreves on the Italian side were tunnelling into the mountain. But money ran out after they had penetrated about a quarter of a mile, and the Mont Blanc project was dropped, at least for the time being.

Eventually, the French and Italians agreed that a motor highway through the mountain would be a great asset to the European road system, and must be built. It was to cost about £11,500,000, and the two governments, with some help from Switzerland, decided to make a fresh start. From the Italian side, work began in earnest in January, 1959, and from the French side in the following May. Eventually the two parties met in August, 1962, and a month later Europe's greatest subway was officially inaugurated.

UNDER THE WEIGHT OF MONT BLANC

The approaches to Mont Blanc are by the Val d'Aosta in Italy and the Val d'Arve in France. From Courmayeur to the south and Chamonix to the north one may see the top of Europe's highest mountain: 15,781 feet. Just above these two lovely resorts the great rock walls slope steeply down to a level of about 4,000 feet. Between them lie 7½ miles of solid mountain. And that is the length of the new Mont Blanc tunnel.

Its dual track rises very gently from either end allowing water to drain off through a six-foot duct beneath the road. On each side is a footpath so that people may, if they wish, walk through. The overall width of the tunnel is twenty-eight feet, and the height about twenty feet. The tunnel is so well ventilated that the petrol fumes of 400,000 vehicles a year can be removed quickly and effectively. Driving through the Mont Blanc tunnel, the traveller can breathe as freely as in a London underground train.

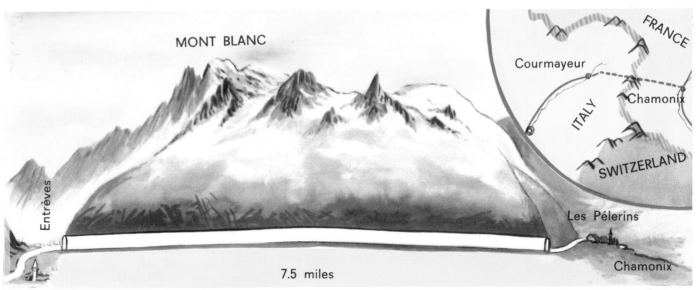

The 7½-mile long, two-lane road tunnel under Mont Blanc is perhaps the greatest achievement in Alpine tunnelling. It links the Val d'Aosta in Northern Italy with Chamonix in France.

COPPER

Copper is not a very hard metal and is quite easy to work. The colour of copper is familiar to everyone; in the days before aluminium found its way into the kitchen, copper pots and pans were in widespread use.

The metal is found only rarely in its native state. It occurs as an oxide in the minerals cuprite and melaconite, as a carbonate in minerals such as malachite and azurite, and as a sulphide in chalcopyrite, bornite and erubescite. Chalcopyrite is the most important commercial ore.

Copper is important to us in our modern world largely because of its ability to conduct electricity. It is vital to the electrical industry. But copper has many other uses too, which are of great importance; many of these since the dawn of civilisation. From the earliest times, man has been making all kinds of vessels and utensils from copper. This and other applications of copper stand out as milestones along the path of technical progress.

THE COPPER AGE

Gold has been known for as long as copper, but being a rare metal it was reserved exclusively for ornaments and fine work. The more abundant metal, copper, became the preferred material for making useful articles. Man's constant search for the most suitable medium of this kind is reflected in the names we give to great eras of history: The Stone, Copper, Bronze and Iron Ages.

The Copper Age is, in fact, a transitional one between the Stone and Bronze Ages. It flourished in ancient Babylon and Egypt where copper was one of the first metals to be put to practical use. Most probably, copper was worked at a very early date in Mesopotamia, whence its use spread through Asia Minor to the Mediterranean countries. Archaeological evidence shows that copper was used in the Aegean Islands three thousand five hundred years before Christ, but the period of its greatest development was between 2500 and 2000 B.C. in Spain and Western Europe.

In early times, small amounts of copper found in a pure state were beaten, either hot or cold, with a hammer and thus worked into the necessary shape. Later, the metal was extracted from chalcopyrite. Meanwhile it had been found possible to melt copper, enabling great progress to be made in its application. The melting point of copper is 1,083°C., and as it was not possible to reach such temperatures by means of an open fire, it was necessary to use special forced-draught furnaces for melting copper. By making use of these furnaces, copper could be liquefied, and at some stage, either by chance or by design, copper was mixed with other metals, and in this way came the discovery of bronze, an alloy of copper and tin.

Copper articles unearthed in recent times have shown how skilful were the primitive peoples who made use of the metal. Weapons, knives and household utensils of many kinds, all made of copper have been found in Egyptian tombs and among the ruins of Nineveh. The Egyptians searched far and wide for deposits of copper and its ores. Between 3000 and 2000 B.C., when they were mining copper in the wild deserts of Sinai, soldiers accompanied the miners and engineers to protect them from attack. Copper was almost as important to those early civilisations as oil is to us to-day.

KING SOLOMON'S MINES

In King Solomon's day, around 1000 B.C., an industrial town was built in a region rich in malachite not far from Aqaba on the Arabian gulf of that name. It is believed that this was the mysterious town of Asiongaber which is mentioned in the Bible. Here, archaeologists have discovered traces of old mines, of copper slag, moulds and dies. But the most interesting remains are those of a large smelting-furnace so placed as to take advantage of the north winds that blow from the interior of Arabia. The general concept of this "blast" furnace was not unlike that of a modern one, except that we use compressed air in place of natural draughts. King Solomon is believed to have employed Phoenician smelters to build this industrial centre for him at Asiongaber, the metal for the copper altar and other sacred fittings in the Temple of Jerusalem being produced there.

It is natural to suppose that some of the metal smelted in Asiongaber was exported to other parts of the Mediterranean and the Middle East. It is possible that the palaces of Alcinous, which Homer tells us had copper walls, were supplied by Phoenician traders from this source. At all events, this seafaring people may well have carried the secrets of copper-smelting to the Greeks, who valued this metal highly. So, too, did their contemporaries, the Etruscans, an ancient race living in central Italy. Tombs are still being discovered, containing weapons, mirrors and ornamental objects made with beaten copper extracted from the ancient mines of Tuscany.

The use of copper by King Solomon for his temple was followed up later by western civilisations, who made use of

Early examples of copper work: A. Sixteenth-century flagon; B. Venetian brazier of same period; C. Embossed mast-head from a sixteenth-century galley. Right: Seventeenth-century statue of an Italian cardinal.

copper for almost every form of embossed metal-work and sacred decoration.

ESSENTIAL TO MODERN INDUSTRY

Throughout the ages, copper has always been in demand by civilised peoples, but it was not until well into the nineteenth century that it became a really essential industrial metal. The discovery that stimulated this new demand was Alessandro Volta's invention of the electric battery in 1799. This marked the beginning of the electrical age, bringing revolutionary changes in industrial development. The demand for copper increased steadily as copper conductors carried electricity into every corner of the world.

Power cables, telegraph lines and telephone installations make great use of copper. So, too, do dynamos, transformers, radio and TV sets and many different kinds of machinery. Copper and its alloys are used in the construction of motor cars and railway engines. The building trade makes use of it, and chemical factories consume a very large amount for the manufacture of copper compounds, including oxide and sulphate. The greatest demand of all comes from the electrical industries, in which the need for copper grows year by year. This increasing demand for copper has depleted the world's resources; many deposits of copper ore have been worked out, and mining engineers are searching for new sources of copper to meet the growing needs.

EXTRACTION AND PRODUCTION

Copper pyrites often contain less than three per cent. of copper, and extraction of the metal is a long and complicated process. (Iron pyrites, by contrast, contains as much as 30/40 per cent. of iron.) After being mined, the copper ore is graded and passed through crushers. It is then heated to about 800°C. during which its sulphur content is greatly decreased. Next, it is treated in special smelting furnaces, forming " black copper ", which is impure and must be refined by further chemical treatment. If pure copper is required—for use in the electrical industry, for example—the metal must be further refined.

A century ago, the world production of copper amounted to about 100,000/150,000 tons per annum; to-day, it is

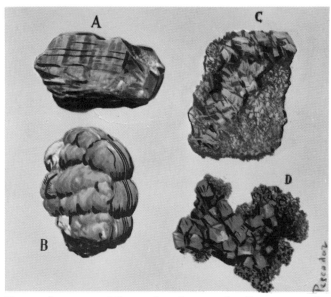

Copper is extracted from mineral ores. A. Copper-containing iron ore; B. mammiform malachite; C. copper pyrites; D. metallic copper.

about 2½ million tons. This twenty-five-fold increase gives an idea of the way in which the demand for copper has grown. One third of the present output comes from the United States, the richest mines being in Arizona, Utah, New Mexico, Montana and Michigan. The next largest producers are Rhodesia, Chile, Russia, Canada and the Congo. In Europe, where demand exceeds output, the most productive mines are in Yugoslavia, Finland, Sweden, Norway, Spain and Germany. Mines at Mansfeld in the German Harz Mountains and others in Sweden have been worked for over 700 years. Sweden's mining industry is very highly developed; in the seventeenth century she was the largest copper-producing country in the world.

The word copper comes from the Latin *cyprium*, later modified to *cuprum*. *Cyprium* was derived from Cyprus, where copper was being mined three or four thousand years B.C. It is remarkable to note that these mines, which were abandoned in the distant past, are working again for the benefit of the people of that island.

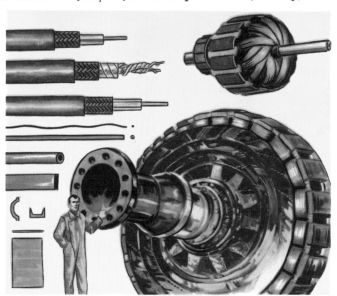

Because it is a good conductor, copper is used for (left) cables; (top right) dynamos; (bottom right) alternators.

Miners, using a compressed air drill, extract the ore from a copper mine deep beneath the Hertz mountains in Germany.

TOBACCO

In the growing plant, Nature has given us a wonderful chemical factory that can manufacture all manner of products. Some plants, like wheat or rice, provide us with our foods; others, like cotton or flax, give us fibres from which we make textiles; still others produce strange chemicals that can affect our bodies in many ways—and such a one is the tobacco plant.

SMOKING IN ENGLAND

When people smoke cigars, cigarettes or pipes they are burning the leaves of the tobacco plant, in order to distil the nicotine and other natural drugs from the leaves. These drugs are inhaled into the body, which they affect in various ways, some pleasant, others unpleasant or even dangerous.

Sir Walter Raleigh is generally believed to have introduced the habit of smoking into England. But people in other parts of the world began to smoke long before the days of Sir Walter Raleigh. Greek and Latin writers, including Plutarch and Pliny, tell us that in parts of Asia it was the practice to smoke hemp and opium for their pleasant aroma.

At that time the Scythians, who were a Mongol people, would sit round fires inhaling the smoke of burning herbs until they became light-headed. " They grow drunk with the fumes as the Greeks do with wine," wrote Herodotus in the fifth century B.C. But at least they were not addicted to the *Nicotiana tabacum*. The tobacco plant was unknown to the ancients.

A MEDICINAL HERB?

The story of tobacco begins in much more recent times; it is less than 500 years since Christopher Columbus set foot in America and found the Indians smoking tobacco. Many were the occasions when early explorers were met by groups of natives offering gifts, among them the green leaves of the tobacco plant. It was a medicinal herb with health-giving properties, said some. Others smoked it in the pipe of peace.

There were so many things to be discovered in the new world that no one at first took the tobacco plant very seriously. A Carmelite friar, returning in 1519 from a voyage to America, is said to have offered some tobacco seeds to King Francis I of France. But they were left to rot in a corner of one of the royal hothouses.

In Portugal, a member of the Court tried sowing some of these seeds in a garden reserved for botanical experiments. In due course, the tobacco plants grew to a good size, burst into flower and caught the eye of Jean Nicot, the French Ambassador to Lisbon.

" MONSIEUR NICOTINE "

Nicot, who was a keen botanist, managed to obtain some of the seeds which he planted in his Embassy garden. The shape of the leaves, their strong pungent smell, and their characteristic oiliness aroused his curiosity. He felt sure that the plant had healing properties, and began to try it out in the treatment of all kinds of illnesses. Nicot found that the tobacco had an effect which was soothing in cases of headache, gout, sores on the skin and bites from a mad dog. When the dried leaves were powdered and used as snuff they relieved the common cold.

There was apparently something in what the Indians had said about the healing properties of this plant. So it acquired its first fame in Europe not as a herb to smoke but as a remedy for many ailments. Names like " the ambassador's herb ", " the Queen's herb " and *clysterium nasi*—" nose clearer "—were given to it. People began to believe that tobacco could cure almost anything: asthma, bronchitis, constipation, pimples, stiff neck and malaria. Its reputation as a cure remained even after smoking for pleasure had come into fashion. During the Great Plague that swept England in 1665, students were ordered to disinfect themselves with tobacco smoke before entering class.

As Jean Nicot was the first to study these curative effects of tobacco, it was only natural that the plant should have been called after him. His friend, the Duc de Guise, proposed the name *Nicotiana*, and so it has remained in the vocabulary of botanists. Tobacco, the more common word, is probably of American-Indian origin. This is the name that has persisted ever since smoking came into fashion during the reign of Queen Elizabeth.

DID SHAKESPEARE SMOKE?

Some say that the idea of smoking tobacco was first brought to London by Sir Francis Drake when he returned from his great voyage round the world in 1580. But it was Sir Walter Raleigh who introduced smoking to the Court of Queen Elizabeth. We have all heard about the servant who thought Sir Walter was on fire, and rushed up and tried " to put him out " with a jug of water or beer. It is more than likely that Raleigh had indeed set himself on fire with fragments of burning tobacco, for the Indian custom at that time was to roll the dried leaves into loose tubes and light

Spanish sailors were the first Europeans to see the Indians of South America smoking the tobacco leaves.

them. In Holland there are records of people smoking tobacco in tubes of palm leaves in 1570, and cigars are still a very popular " smoke " in that country to this day.

The first regular smokers used long clay pipes which were later known as " churchwardens' pipes ". By 1590, they had become quite a fashion, and we know that smoke from these pipes hung heavily over the audiences that went to London theatres at the time that Shakespeare was writing his plays. Shakespeare himself may have weakened his lungs by smoking, for it is said that he died of bronchitis. From the very first, there were many people who regarded smoking as an objectionable habit, among them King James I, who in 1604 published a book called *Counterblast to Tobacco*.

GRAVE PENALTIES FOR SMOKING

Responsible people in those days knew what they were talking about when they condemned smoking. It is always easier to judge problems fairly when they first arise, before prejudice, self-interest and public opinion have hardened around them. So it is understandable that the government of Louis XIV of France prohibited the sale of tobacco except on doctor's orders, just as we do with certain dangerous drugs to-day. In seventeenth-century France, severe penalties were imposed on those who were caught smoking. And in distant Abyssinia the Coptic Church issued a decree announcing that anyone who smoked would have both their hands chopped off!

In spite of these warnings the habit grew. Doctors realised at an early stage that smoking might be harmful to the health. Nicotine, one of the drugs in the tobacco plant, was found to be an extremely poisonous substance. It is now used as an insecticide: it is apparently for this purpose that the tobacco plant manufactures it. But it is not easy to stop people from poisoning themselves if they want to. King James I had made the attempt, only to become known as " the wisest fool in Christendom ". So the authorities gave up trying to prevent people smoking and clamped on a tobacco tax which has grown steadily ever since.

SNUFF WAS HARMLESS ENOUGH

Meanwhile, the custom of taking snuff had become widespread in many European countries. Snuff, now sold in powdered form, was considered harmless enough. The custom was to buy the dried tobacco leaves and carry them round with a tiny grater in a small box. Antique silver, gold and jewelled boxes of great beauty show how fastidious were the eighteenth-century snuff-takers. Theirs was the century of snuff. The nineteenth was the century of the cigar and the twentieth century that of the cigarette. Only the pipe has belonged to all of them.

A WORLD OF SMOKERS

As the smoking habit spread, the demand for tobacco grew at a fantastic rate. Vast tracts of land were brought under tobacco cultivation, especially in North and Central America. The produce of the tobacco plantations soon became a vital commodity with which to pay for manufactured goods imported from Europe.

From the first plantations in Santo Domingo, Cuba and Brazil, tobacco-growing spread rapidly to Maryland, Virginia and other States in North America. In due course the United States became the world's largest producer, with an output of 2,000 million pounds annually. This represents about one-fourth of the total world production of 8,000 million pounds. At least one quarter of the American crop is exported, and it is a valuable source of income to that country.

China, India, Russia and Japan between them produce more tobacco than North America. Fine-quality oriental tobaccos are grown in Turkey, Greece and Bulgaria. Italy and Spain grow almost enough to meet the needs of their people. In fact, tobacco seems to grow in most countries except those such as Britain, Holland and Scandinavia where smoking is heaviest. Thus Britain has to meet a very heavy import bill for her tobacco, most of it coming from the United States and Canada.

ONE OF A POISONOUS FAMILY

The two important species of tobacco plant, *Nicotiana tabacum* and *Nicotiana rustica* both belong to the same family as the poisonous deadly nightshade. Of these two species, *Nicotiana tabacum*, or common tobacco, is the most

The United States grows a quarter of the total world tobacco production of 8,000 million pounds a year.   China, India and Russia, respectively, are the next biggest tobacco producers.

widely cultivated. It has larger leaves with less nicotine in them than the *rustica* species which is grown in some oriental countries.

Common tobacco is an annual. It dies after yielding about half-an-ounce of very fine seed—300,000 seeds to the ounce—which is enough to raise 20,000 seedlings for transplanting into the field. The plant grows quickly in a sandy or light clay soil, according to the strain, reaching a height of about four feet in three months. When the white flowers begin to bud, the top of the plant is nipped off, leaving up to twenty leaves attached to the stem.

GROWING AND CURING TOBACCO

With most varieties of common tobacco, the mature leaves are at least two feet long and roughly half that width. The wild species, *Nicotiana rustica*, which is grown in the East, has a much smaller, though more highly fragrant leaf.

A few weeks after topping, when the plant has been in the field for about four months, it is ready for harvesting. The plant may be cut down whole or stripped at intervals from the bottom upwards as the leaves mature. The leaves are commonly left in the field to wilt, and next day they are strung together in rows and hung up until they turn yellow. This begins the curing process which consists in wilting, yellowing, colouring and drying the tobacco.

THE TRADE HAS ITS SECRETS

The simplest curing method is to leave the cut tobacco out in the sun. Climatic conditions are seldom entirely suitable for this, so the leaves may be air-cured in sheds, a slow process, or in the smoke of wood fires. Another technique is flue-curing, which is widely practised in the United States. The leaves are packed into sheds heated by flues which throw out hot air at ground level. All these methods are used in different parts of the world, and each of them produces tobacco leaf of characteristic flavour, aroma, colour and quality.

Curing takes about three weeks, after which the tobacco is made up into bales for sale by auction or for direct delivery to the manufacturers.

Each manufacturer has his own trade secrets, and big

Tobacco leaves are usually cured in three ways—by air, fire and flue.

firms are jealous of the methods they use for flavouring and blending their brands of cigarette and pipe tobacco. The conditioned leaf is shredded and passed on to machines that roll and pack up to 1,200 cigarettes per minute. Cigarettes represent about 45 per cent. of all " smokes ", cigars 20 per cent., and pipe tobacco and snuff the remaining 35 per cent.

CIGARS ARE COMING BACK

In some countries, cigars have always remained in great demand, and may be smoked—as in Denmark—by women as well as men. Their popularity is increasing generally throughout the world, as people consider them less harmful than cigarettes. At one time, the smell of cigar smoke lingered in the air of every club and office where men met to talk business. This gave a tremendous stimulus to cigar-making in the last century, and by 1870 over 1,000 million were being made every year in the United States. American cigar consumption is now six times that figure.

A good cigar should have a pleasant aroma and leave a white ash. Among the best are the Havanas which come from Cuba—one of the first countries to grow tobacco commercially. According to the Cubans, it was they who made the first cigarettes. To avoid wasting cigar remnants, manufacturers started cutting up leaves that had previously been thrown away; the finely-shredded tobacco was then rolled in selected uncut leaves. The Spaniards took up this idea and began to put handmade, paper-wrapped cigarettes on to the market in Europe.

AN ORIENTAL " WHIFF "

There is another story of how cigarettes first came to be made. During the Turco-Egyptian War in 1832 the town of Acre (now in Israel) was the scene of a bitter siege. At that time, it was the custom to charge cannons with powder wrapped in tissue paper. One day, a corporal whose hubble-bubble pipe had been broken twisted up some of his tobacco in a piece of this paper. The Egyptian commander, Ibrahim Pasha, happened to hear of this and promised his soldiers as much tobacco and tissue paper as they wanted if they succeeded in breaching the city walls. Two days later the Egyptians entered Acre and the general kept his promise.

Since then, the habit of cigarette smoking has spread to every country in the world. In the 1950s Americans were smoking 400,000 million cigarettes a year—enough to make a string of them twenty million miles long. If we add to these Britain's consumption of close on 200 million pounds of tobacco annually, and the contribution of a few other countries whose people are heavy smokers, we find ourselves with an enormous cigarette stretching so far into space that we could light its tip from the sun.

WHY PEOPLE GET THE CRAVING

In recent times, the smoking habit has come under heavy criticism, and there is no doubt that it can have extremely harmful effects. Nicotine itself is an insidious drug, which is responsible in large part for the habit-forming effects. When the human body is forced to fight against such drugs it sets up its own mechanism to combat them. Having done this, it wants to keep that mechanism in action. And its urge to do so creates the craving that the smoker feels for another cigarette—and then another. This is the secret of the tobacco plant's success in establishing such a hold on the human race.

PHOSPHORUS AND MATCHES

Every living cell of every living thing contains the element phosphorus. It is one of the fundamental elements of all living matter, playing a vital role in the chemical processes that go to make up life itself.

For this reason, every plant and animal needs a supply of phosphorus to provide raw material for the construction of its living matter. This phosphorus comes from the phosphorus-containing chemicals in the soil, which are absorbed as solutions through the roots of plants. We human beings, and other animals, obtain our supplies of phosphorus second-hand when we eat plants or animals as food.

Phosphorus is a non-metallic element which reacts readily with oxygen. It does not occur in a free state in nature, but is a constituent of many minerals in the form of phosphates. Apatite is a common phosphate rock.

A "LIGHT-BRINGING" SUBSTANCE

Phosphorus was discovered by the German chemist Hennig Brand in 1669, in the residue left from the evaporation of urine. A century later, the Swedish chemist, Scheele, obtained the same substance from bones, thus confirming its presence in the human body. For a time, this remained the chief source of phosphorus, but it was later shown that phosphorus could be obtained from minerals such as apatite. This is the source of commercial phosphorus to-day.

Although of light yellow colour, the phosphorus obtained from mineral sources is called "white phosphorus". It is waxlike, semi-transparent, and soluble in carbon disulphide. In sunshine it becomes a deeper yellow, and a pinkish-white film forms on the exposed surface. In air or oxygen, white phosphorus emits the light we know as phosphorescence; the name of the element comes from two Greek words meaning "light-bringing". An extremely poisonous substance, white phosphorus is the cause of a grave illness called

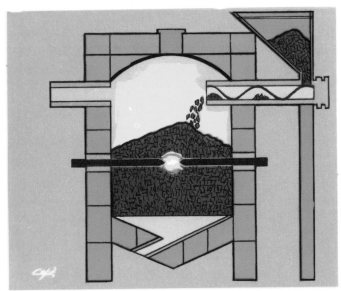

Pure phosphorus is obtained by heating rock phosphate, coke and silica in an electric furnace. The resultant vapour is freed of dust and the phosphorus condenses to solid.

phossy jaw, and people handling it must take rigid precautions. Phosphorus is usually stored in water to keep it out of contact with the air.

Phosphorus exists in two forms, the white phosphorus described above, and a second variety called red phosphorus, which is a reddish-brown powder. The properties of red phosphorus are very different from those of the white form of the element. Red phosphorus is not phosphorescent or poisonous, nor is it soluble in carbon disulphide. Red phosphorus, made by placing white phosphorus in a closed container and heating it to about 300°C., is widely used in the match industry.

Top: Rock phosphate is mined in the United States, North Africa, Germany and Russia. Bottom: Tricalcium phosphate, a form of apatite mined in Spain.

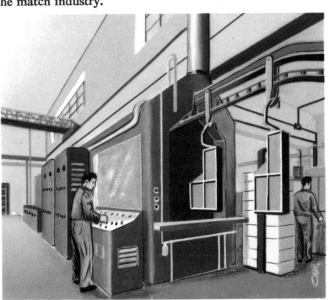

In this process, metal parts of cars, motor cycles, etc., are sprayed with iron or manganese phosphate to give a protective finish.

In the form of phosphate, phosphorus provides us with a vitally important fertiliser, giving plants the supply of phosphorus needed for both the animal and plant world. Phosphorus goes into many metal alloys, and into dyes and other synthetic chemical products. Nerve tonics commonly contain phosphorus in the form of phosphates, hypophosphates and glycerophosphates. It also goes into some explosives, and—most important of all—it is a constituent of the pastes from which we make our matchstick heads.

FIRE SPITTING " LUCIFERS "

Fire has always played a vital part in the life of man. Long before the Stone Age, our primitive ancestors knew the value of fire, and went to great lengths to keep a fire going once they had got it alight. To-day we do not give the matter a thought; we carry with us a source of fire in the form of a box of matches or a cigarette-lighter. Although we accept these fire-makers so casually, we have had them only for a very brief period of our long history.

About ten years after Brand made his discovery of phosphorus, a chemist called Haukwitz discovered that he could use it to light a piece of wood that had been soaked in sulphur. This fire-lighting process did not always work, and it was, in any case, too complicated to be of practical value. Further attempts to produce fire were made with phosphorus, sulphur, wax and other inflammable materials—but always with unsatisfactory results. Then, in about 1805, a chemist named Chancel invented a primitive match, consisting of a splinter of wood that had been soaked in sulphur and tipped with a blob of potassium chlorate mixed with sugar. When dipped into sulphuric acid the blob immediately caught fire and ignited the wood.

This was followed by the invention of a phosphorus match, consisting of a stick impregnated with sulphur and a head made of phosphorus mixed with antimony sulphide, potassium chlorate and gum arabic. This was a great advance on all previous matches, as it was ignited simply by rubbing the head of the match against a rough surface; the heat produced by friction caused a chemical reaction in the phosphorus mixture of the match-head, releasing sufficient heat to set fire to the matchstick. Credit for this discovery goes

Wax matches are made in a different way to wooden matches. After being soaked in tallow the wax sticks are chopped in cutting frames (above) before the heads are dipped in paste.

to a German, G. F. Kammerer. A factory was set up in Austria, but it was a risky venture. Explosions and fires were always breaking out, and the employees began to suffer from *phossy jaw* and other illnesses caused by handling white phosphorus. Moreover, Kammerer's matches were apt to burst into flames as a result of spontaneous combustion, lighting fires that were not wanted. Appropriately enough, these matches became known as " lucifers ", from the Latin *lux* and *fer* meaning " light-bringing ".

INVENTION OF THE SAFETY MATCH

Experiments continued and, in 1844, the discovery of red phosphorus—which does not ignite spontaneously—brought a real prospect of producing much safer matches. The difficulty now was to find a substance which could be mixed with red phosphorus to produce a self-ignited composition. It was found that potassium chlorate could be used, but the

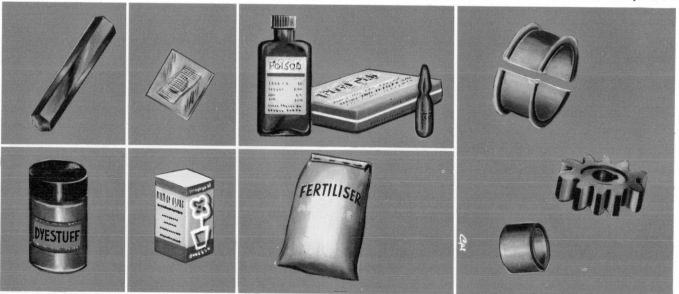

Other uses of phosphorus: Top (*left to right*): *filling for incendiary bomb; a fire raiser (when the wet gauze dries, the phosphorus ignites); pharmaceutical products.* Bottom (*left to right*): *dye; ammonium phosphate; fertiliser.* Right: *phosphor bronze gear and bearings.*

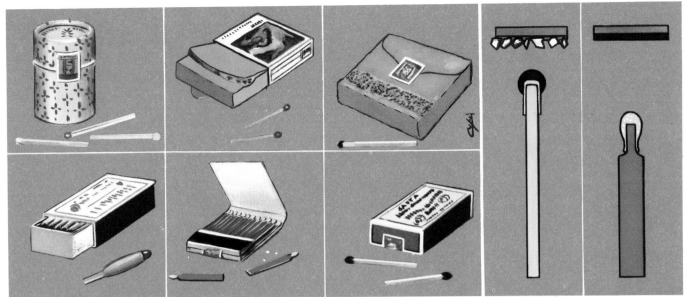

Top: *Decorative matches; Italian* cerini *for handbag; kitchen matches.* Bottom: *wind matches; book matches; safety matches.*
Right: *vertical section of kitchen match with sandpaper striking strip; red book match with phosphorus in the black striking section.*

effect of ignition was startling—showers of sparks flew in all directions. A simple solution to this difficulty was found by spreading phosphorus over the rough surface against which the match was to be struck, and putting the other constituents of the self-igniting mixture in the match-head. J. E. Lundstrom, a Swede, discovered this technique in the 1840s, and opened a factory which began Sweden's long association with the production of safety matches. In many parts of the world they are known as " Swedish matches " to this day.

White and red phosphorus remained in use as constituents of match-heads until dropped by international agreement in 1898. In that year two French chemists, E. D. Cahen and H. Savene, discovered that sesquisulphide of phosphorus made a satisfactory substitute. Also, it was non-poisonous, a characteristic which at once commended it to an industry in which thousands had lost their lives or suffered disablement from diseases caused by phosphorus. The sesquisulphide formula was adopted, and it is used in many types of match now on the market.

Best known of all are the wooden matches made from pine or poplar wood. The timber is sliced into long strips of the same width as a matchstick. These strips are fed into a machine which slits them, producing as many as two million matchsticks an hour. The sticks are then dried, cleaned and transferred to an endless chain of perforated plates which is the main feature of the match-making machine. Here the sticks are treated with hot paraffin wax, and then dried and dipped into the hot paste which will harden into the striking head. Machines of this kind pour out matches at the rate of 750,000 an hour.

Sesquisulphide of phosphorus is the most vital ingredient in the manufacture of match heads. But it is far from being the only one. On igniting, a good match must produce intense heat and then burn out quickly without leaving an afterglow or an unpleasant smell. All match factories have their own laboratories so that careful control of the entire match-making process can be maintained. The chemicals used may be classed in four groups. First, the inflammable materials: sesquisulphide of phosphorus, sulphur and antimony sulphide. Second, the substances that support combustion: potassium chlorate, manganese dioxide and bichromate of potash. Third, various gums and rosins used to bind and harden the paste. Fourth, calcium carbonate, powdered glass and pulverised earth, which are added to increase the temperature produced when the match ignites.

MATCHES BY THE MILLION

Different countries all have their favourite types of match and, as collectors know, of match-boxes too. Generally speaking, wooden matchsticks are most popular in America and Britain. In continental European countries, vast quantities of matches are made from paper, board or cotton thread " sticks " impregnated with wax or tallow. The famous Italian *cerini* is an example. Book-matches are made of impregnated cardboard, and it is an astonishing fact that about 200,000 million book-matches are given away every year by American firms. This represents about two-fifths of the total annual match output of the United States. Complete books, each containing twenty matches, are turned out by machines producing 350 books per minute. There are wind and water resistant matches, the former having large heads which will stay alight in a strong breeze. Waterproof matches were developed for use in damp and rainy climates by the American army during the last war. They will strike after eight hours' immersion in water.

It is impossible to estimate the number of matches made in the world every year. If everyone were to use only one match per day the number would run to over one million million. This gives an indication of the size and importance of the modern match industry. In Britain, match production is in the hands of firms whose names are household words. In America, the industry is controlled by a few trusts of great wealth and size. In some other countries, match-production is the exclusive right of state monopolies.

By trying to acquire match monopolies in certain European countries after World War I, Ivar Kreuger caused one of the biggest financial scandals of the century. In a last effort to save himself, he forged over £28 million worth of Italian state bonds. This brought his many frauds to light and the Swedish " match king " shot himself rather than face the consequences of his crimes.

RECORDS AND RECORDING

The gramophone record has become an important factor in the spread of modern culture. It is simple to use, and there is no limit to the variety of its contents; it appeals to the music-lover as much as to the teenager who has caught the latest dance craze. But music is only one aspect of the modern record industry; speech and language training by disc are now becoming increasingly popular. The disc is comparatively inexpensive, and the instrument on which we play it—the gramophone or record-player —is within the reach of almost every pocket.

EARLY EXPERIMENTS

Sound was first recorded by Leon Scott as early as 1857, but it was the famous inventor Edison who produced the first phonograph; this was a primitive instrument equipped with a rotating cylinder wrapped in a thin sheet of tinfoil. Then, in 1887, Emile Berliner patented a gramophone which used a flat disc instead of a cylinder, and it is this type of record which is used today. In the meantime, manufacturing technique has improved beyond recognition, and modern methods of sound reproduction have now been brought to a high pitch of perfection.

STUDIO PRODUCTION

There are two main stages in the production of modern records. The first of these takes place in a studio where the artists perform to an audience composed only of sound technicians, whose apparatus is installed in adjoining rooms. The second stage takes place in workshops and factories where the finished product is manufactured.

The studio is usually a fairly large hall fitted with acoustical apparatus that can be adapted to meet any need. The players and their instruments are arranged around the pianist and conductor as if taking part in a concert: violins, 'cellos, trombones, flutes and so on. Several microphones, each designed to respond to a particular type of sound, are suspended over the instruments. The soloist sings into another microphone which stands in the middle of the floor. The microphones transform the sound-waves into electrical impulses which are conveyed along cables to amplifiers in the control room. Here the recording engineer and his technicians preside over a battery of apparatus which enables them to adjust the strength and pitch of the sounds, and to obtain an artistically perfect recording.

THE TAPE-RECORDING

Sound analysis requires a highly-trained ear and a precise knowledge of the operation of the control equipment. In the hands of an expert, the controls can be made to increase the harmony of a piece, or to raise the volume of certain notes and give them dominance over others. It is seldom necessary to ask the artists to repeat their performance with more emphasis, let us say, on the violins and less on the kettledrums.

Anyone who uses a tape-recorder knows how sounds are registered and reproduced on the tape as it unwinds from a revolving reel. In the same way, the electrical impulses of our studio concert are recorded on long tapes at a speed of rather less than three feet per second. So a musical note lasting one-tenth of a second takes up about three inches, and a long note lasting ten seconds uses about twenty-seven feet of tape. This leaves plenty of space for a careful analysis of the sound and, in fact, makes it possible to check the quality of every single note or group of notes recorded. If, for instance, a false note is played, or a singer falters for an instant, that section of the tape is snipped off and a new piece is inserted in its place, so that the final tape is as near perfect as possible.

THE "MASTER" RECORD

The magnetic tape on which a performance has been recorded is known as the master tape. This is sent on to a workshop equipped with electro-mechanical apparatus—a kind of sound-printing machine—which transfers the recording of the tape on to a metal disc covered with a thin layer of lacquer. An electrically-heated sapphire needle moves over the revolving disc, vibrating in response to the electrical impulses imprinted on the tape. This needle cuts the spiral music grooves which are eventually transferred on to the soft surface of the records that we buy.

Before this stage is reached, the newly-made disc must be submitted to treatment by several complicated processes. First the lacquer disc is coated with a film of silver, which makes it a good conductor of electricity. It is then placed in an electro-plating solution, and a layer of nickel is grown on to the silver face. When it is thick enough (1/40″) the nickel layer is stripped from the lacquer. In this way an exact copy in metal is made of the recording on the lacquer disc, but in place of the spiral grooves, we now have a disc with spiral ridges. This is called the " master " and is not used to produce records. The master in its turn, is put into the electro-plating bath and a layer of nickel is grown on to the ridged surface. This is stripped off, giving the positive or mother. This is an exact copy of the lacquer disc, with spiral grooves, and can, in fact, be played.

A PLASTIC IMPRINT

Finally the mother is placed in the elecro-plating bath and a thin layer of nickel (1/100″) is grown on the face. This is stripped off giving the matrix or stamper. This metal stamper, which again has the music in the form of spiral ridges, is the one that is used to press the records. Needless to say, two stampers are necessary, one for each side of the record. These are placed, facing one another in the two halves of a hydraulic press. The stampers are heated by steam and the two labels and a piece of softened vinyl plastic are inserted between them. The press is then closed and a hydraulic pressure of about 30 tons, for a seven inch record, is applied. This has the effect of forcing the soft plastic to take the exact shape of the music grooves. The press is then cooled by water, opened and the hard record taken out. In this way, many hundreds of records may be pressed from these two stampers to supply the very rapidly growing demand for records of both classical and popular music.

After being taken from the press the record is smoothed at the edge, inspected, and inserted into an attractive envelope which may carry information about the artist and the music on the record.

Finally, they are carefully packed in boxes and sent to the record shops. As there are at least six stages between the master tape and the finished record it will be appreciated that great care must be taken at every stage to ensure that there is no loss of quality between the actual recording and the record sold in the shops.

END OF THE "78"

The long-playing records so popular to-day are now standardised at 45 and 33 revolutions per minute, the most popular being the 33 r.p.m. type which plays for about twenty minutes on each side. These records have largely re-placed the older, heavier 78 r.p.m. types. And the 33 r.p.m. in their turn, may now be challenged by the even longer-playing 16 r.p.m. record for which many modern gramophones are now equipped.

Long-playing records were introduced by the American firm of Columbia in 1948; production in Britain followed in 1952. Issued in albums containing a series of discs, they are ideal for enthusiasts collecting works by famous composers. Indeed, the long-playing record, which is produced by techniques similar to those described above, has brought the study of music within the reach of more people than ever before. This has also been stimulated by improvements in the record-player. The self-change mechanism, for example, enables us to listen for a couple of hours at a stretch without having to change the record every few minutes as our parents had to do.

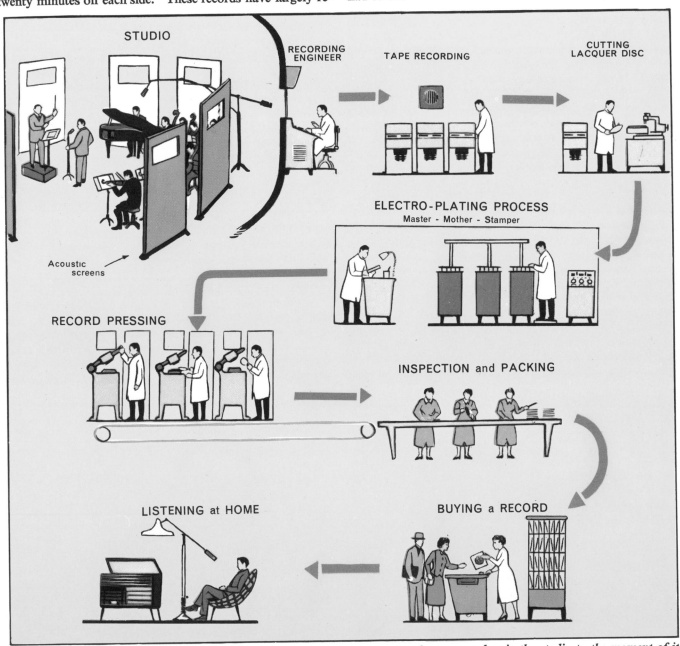

Here we see the whole process of record production, from the performance of a new number in the studio to the moment of its sale in a shop. From the studio, the sound passes in the form of electrical impulses to the recording engineer, who sits at his control panel. It is first recorded on magnetic tape and from this it is cut on to a metal disc coated with cellulose lacquer. This disc is then copied by various electro-plating processes to give finally a matrix or stamper which is used to press the records with which we are all familiar. After inspection and packing, they are sent to the shops for sale.

THE MECHANISED FARM

Not so very long ago, most of the world's inhabitants lived in village communities linked to each other by the most primitive of tracks. Each village was as self-sufficient as possible, providing for itself all the things that its inhabitants needed in their everyday lives. And most important of all, of course, was food.

The responsibility for producing food was shared by everyone in these village communities. But as the world became industrialised, many people moved away from their villages and congregated in towns and cities. They could no longer grow food for themselves, and depended on others to grow it for them. Gradually, the farmer himself was caught up in the Industrial Revolution, and his farm became an industry as mechanised as any other.

The population of the world is now growing so rapidly that there are twenty million more people to be fed every year. This means that more and more land must be brought under cultivation to supply the basic foodstuffs that are needed. Land which has never before been tilled must be turned over to the production of human food and animal feeding stuffs.

OPENING UP VIRGIN LAND

New land of this type may have to be cleared of trees and scrub, and broken up by deep ploughing. Or it may need draining, or even reclaiming if it is marsh and swamp. If a large area of land is to be brought into production, roads, railways, waterways, bridges, aqueducts, electricity supply lines and houses may be needed. Without the help of modern earth-moving and cultivation machinery, a project of this sort would require years or even generations before it could be completed. In fact, vast areas of the earth might never be developed at all but for the heavy-duty equipment that we now use on the land: the bulldozers, power-shovels and trenching machines; the graders, scrapers and stone extractors. These wonderful machines, powered by huge engines, or by a crawler tractor, enable us to change the face of the earth at incredible speed.

THE TRIUMPHANT TRACTOR

When new land has been cleared, all manner of strange machines are brought in to help at every stage of its cultivation. It is their job to prepare the soil before the grain is sown. Among them we find ploughs, weeders, manure- and fertiliser-spreaders, harrows and hoeing machines. Insecticide-sprayers and water-sprinklers may be used, depending on the crop that is being raised. Later, come the mowing and threshing machines, and the big combine harvesters. All these machines, and many others as well, may be harnessed to the tractor, that versatile machine which has taken over from the horse as the symbol of modern agriculture.

The tractor is a vehicle built of steel and driven either by a petrol or a diesel engine. It moves slowly but it gets there in the end; its power is enormous, and it can travel over the roughest ground. Some tractors run on wheels, others—called caterpillars—on tracks. In the United States, one in twenty of the country's five million tractors is of the caterpillar type. There would be even more if it were not for the fact that caterpillars cannot be driven on roads, nor used in fields with row crops without causing damage.

DIESEL OR PETROL ENGINES

While the caterpillar tractor is most useful in breaking up rough ground, the lighter four-wheeled tractor is favoured by the farmer. The huge rear wheels of these farm tractors are equipped with heavy-duty tyres with deep treads to give them a grip on mud and broken soil. The small front wheels act more like bogies, guiding the vehicle. Tractors may be

A caterpillar tractor, equipped as a bulldozer, can uproot small trees and clear virgin ground of scrub.

Before ploughing new ground, stones and tree stumps are removed by a tractor fitted with a giant ripper.

powered with diesel- or petrol-engines. In America all but one in thirty of farm tractors burn petrol, whereas in Europe diesel oil is favoured. The reason is purely economic: diesel fuel is cheaper than petrol in Europe, whereas the reverse is true in the United States.

American tractors are commonly equipped with 4-stroke engines, whereas many European countries prefer the two-stroke engine, which gives more power in relation to weight. America has the greatest number of tractors at work, but Britain, Western Germany and Switzerland have more tractors per cultivatable acre than other countries. Their terrain is well suited to tractors; this is not always the case, as for instance in Italy, where many crops are grown on hillsides so steep that they can be tilled only by hand or with the aid of oxen.

The modern tractor is more than a mechanical vehicle. In the farmyard it becomes a source of power for all manner of stationary equipment.

THE BULLDOZER FAMILY

The bulldozer is a familiar sight to most of us these days. Who has not been fascinated by the irresistible power of the huge blade? Pushed along by a throbbing caterpillar the bulldozer tears down shrubs and pushes over trees with the greatest of ease.

The bulldozer digs ditches and clears tracks for roads. Its heavy blade is set at an angle, so that it pushes the debris to one side. The biggest bulldozers weigh up to forty tons and develop 400 horse-power. But these monsters, built as a single unit, are used primarily on heavy civil engineering work. The caterpillar fitted with a removable blade is generally adequate for most agricultural purposes. Carrying eight or ten stout prongs, the bulldozer can also be adapted for clearing the ground of large stones and tree stumps. The prongs dig deep into the soil and as the tractor moves forward, they tear up the unwanted material and throw it on one side. In the reclamation of really rough land a ripper is of great help.

LEVELLERS AND POWER SHOVELS

Once the worst of the rubbish has been removed from the

Harrowing is done with adjustable discs angled to give maximum effect, to break up the clods left after ploughing.

top soil, a leveller or scraper may be the next machine to move in. It works like a huge carpenter's plane, levelling off the ridges and mounds as it moves along. Like an immense wheelbarrow, it creeps along behind a caterpillar, scooping up surplus soil which it collects in a huge container. When full, it is dragged away and unloaded by a mechanical tipper. In addition to the scraper that is pulled behind a tractor, there is a self-powered scraper mounted on four large rubber-tyred wheels.

The power shovel is another useful member of the earth-moving family, which performs a great variety of jobs. The loading of sand and gravel for construction purposes, the clearing of building sites and the excavation of channels are a few of its main tasks. Down goes the dipper stick, the teeth of the bucket bite into the ground, the boom arm swings and several tons of material are shifted by one man operating his power controls from inside a cabin. Equipment of this kind, which may be built to handle 100 cubic yards or more an hour, is put to great use in modern quarries.

This leveller scoops up earth to a depth of several inches, leaving behind an even surface. Machines of this type can remove about ten tons of soil at a time and they are often used in the preparation of road surfaces.

*Used on land that has been long neglected, the single blade of
this plough share bites three feet into the earth.*

THE PLOUGHMAN SITS IN FRONT

When the ground has been cleared and levelled, the farmer
can begin the real work of cultivation. Here again, machinery
has taken over all the heavy work of tilling and cultivating
the soil. The drudgery of hoeing, mowing, raking, harrowing
and ploughing are all things of the past. Gone are the
primitive tools that were used when these jobs were done by
hand. Only the tractor-drawn plough bears any resemblance
to its horse-drawn predecessor. The others have changed
so much that they would hardly be recognised by the farm
worker of old.

In one form or another the plough has been used ever
since man learned to break up the ground in which he planted
seeds. A simple plough consists of a blade called a coulter
for vertical cutting, a share for loosening the furrow and a
mould-board for turning the soil over in a ridge. Ploughs
with a single share are used to cut deep furrows; in some
soils it may be necessary to go down three feet. Ploughs with
as many as six shares and a spread of eight feet are used for

*Fertiliser distributors are replacing the old manure-spreaders.
The fertiliser is in the long box, where a series of revolving
paddles distributes it evenly through the exit tubes.*

the shallower furrows needed in the normal cultivation of
large fields. Disc ploughs, consisting of a series of concave
discs, weighted to increase penetration, are used under certain soil conditions.

HARROWING AND GRUBBING

Ploughing leaves the surface rough, and the clods must be
broken down by another machine, the harrow, before
sowing can begin. The harrow was once a spiked framework
which was drawn over the soil by a horse. The modern
harrow may have spiked teeth like a large rake, or it may
consist of blades and discs which chop the lumps into smaller
pieces as they are drawn over the soil. The harrow is often
used before ploughing, for loosening corn stubble and the
stalks of vegetable crops.

A machine similar to the harrow, called a grubber, is
equipped with broad, curved fangs which tear up dead roots
and weeds that remain in the harrowed soil from the previous
season. Finally, if the soil is to have a trim, flat surface, a
heavy iron or cement roller is drawn backwards and forwards
over the field.

ENRICHING THE SOIL

We could not grow the crops we need as food to-day if
we did not enrich the soil by adding fertilisers. These
materials replenish the stores of chemicals in the soil which
are the food of growing plants. Every crop extracts the
chemicals it needs, and may leave the soil exhausted by
removing from it supplies of nitrogen, phosphorus, potassium,
iron, silicon, magnesium, calcium and other essential
materials. Most of these plant food-chemicals can be put back
into the soil by adding manure and compost. But changes in
agricultural techniques, and the disappearance of the horse,
have made it impossible for the farmer to rely upon these
natural materials to provide the soil with all the plant food
that it needs. He must therefore apply synthetic fertilisers.

The three major constituents of fertilisers are nitrogen,
phosphorus and potassium. In the form of solid chemicals,
they are distributed from a wide hopper which ejects a
steady flow of powder from a row of tubes at the bottom.
As the distributor moves over the field, it dusts the ground
uniformly with a supply of fertiliser. Liquid fertilisers may
be applied as a spray, and in certain cases—such as anhy-
drous ammonia—the fertiliser is released into the soil as
gas.

SOWING AND HOEING

When the soil has been thoroughly prepared, the field
looks as neat as a newly-made bed. It is now ready for
sowing. Here again, the human sower has been replaced by a
machine—the grain drill. In its simplest form, the drill
consists of a large seed box mounted on four wheels. Seed
falls from the box down a narrow tube, and into a shallow
furrow cut by a disc wheel. A short length of chain dragged
behind each of the twelve discs covers the seed with loose
top soil. For potato planting, a more complicated machine
is used. Many farmers still prefer to plant their seed potatoes
by hand, however, as mechanical planters may damage the
tender shoots.

Young plants need plenty of air and sunlight, and every
good farmer makes sure that his crops have all they require.
By hoeing his field he loosens the soil and cuts down weeds
that would starve and choke his crops. Hoeing is done
mechanically, using a machine on which metal blades move

to and fro as they are pulled between the rows of plants. The blades loosen the sun-baked soil, letting the air penetrate to the roots of the plants.

MAKING HAY

In springtime, the grass grows lush and green in the meadows. Like wheat or potatoes, grass is an important crop, and the farmer looks after it with great care. Before it has time to ripen and produce seed, it is cut by means of a large mowing machine. As the scissor-like blades cut their way through the crop, the grass falls to the ground and is left to dry. It is turned by a tractor-drawn rake, and in due course is collected by a baler which picks it up, compresses it and throws it to the ground in bales bound with twine or wire.

THE COMBINE HARVESTER

Slowly but surely the sun ripens the wheat, barley and oats. When these crops have turned to a rich golden brown, and the grain in the ear is hard, the combine harvester rolls out into the field. By evening, a huge expanse of corn will have vanished as though by magic. In Britain, combine harvesters have been in general use since about 1950. Before that time, many farmers would cut their corn with a reaper and take it to a threshing machine which extracted the grain. The advantage of the combine harvester is that it cuts, cleans and threshes the grain as it moves along. Some harvesters carry a grain bin in which to store the threshed corn; others pack it into sacks. Some throw out the loose straw and leave it on the ground; others compress it into bales, which are thrown out and collected later.

The combine harvester is the most ingenious of all agricultural machines. Its use is not confined to the harvesting of wheat, barley and oats; maize cobs, beans and other crop plants may be reaped in a similar way. The combine represents the new generation of farm machinery and it is an example of the way in which agriculture is involved in the technical revolution of modern times. Automation is making its way into the farmyard.

SPRINKLERS AND SPRAYERS

An ample supply of water is essential to all plant growth,

The man with the old-fashioned pitchfork is vividly contrasted with the modern combine harvester speedily completing at least four operations to his one.

and much of the farmer's time is occupied in keeping his plants provided with water: in many countries, irrigation channels are used to bring water to the fields; elsewhere, water is sprayed on to the crops from sprinklers. Fed by pressure pumps, these sprinklers revolve slowly, sending out a steady shower of artificial rain over a wide area. They are widely used for fruit and vegetable crops, for example in the vineyards of France and Italy, in the orange groves of Mediterranean countries and in the market gardens of Britain. In the United States, even pasture land may be watered in this way.

Power sprayers are also used for pest control, distributing insecticides either in the form of a fine powder or a liquid. Liquid is more commonly used, as powder may be lost too easily from the leaves. Where large areas are to be dusted or sprayed, helicopters are now in common use. Early morning is a favourite time for spraying, as the dew lies on the plants and helps to ensure that the insecticide does its work.

Parts of a combine harvester: A. header or cutter; B. corn elevator; C. threshing cylinder; D. straw cutter; E. chaff separator; F. cleaning fan; G. straw spreader; H. grain cleaning sieves; I. L. M. elevator to N. grain tank with vents for loading to lorries or sacks.

SUGAR

Your body is a machine that needs a supply of fuel to keep it going. You get this fuel from the food you eat, which releases energy as it " burns " inside your body.

We measure this energy in calories, and scientists can estimate the calorie value of every form of food, so that we know how useful it is as an energy-provider. Also, we can estimate the number of calories needed by people of different ages doing different sorts of jobs, so that we know how much food they need to keep the body-machine working smoothly.

Young people, who are usually pretty lively " machines ", need a good supply of calories—between 2,500 and 3,500 a day. And much of this comes from sugar.

FOOD FOR ATHLETES

Some time ago a certain football team, which no one thought very much of, made a tour of Europe during which it played against the best teams of that year. To everyone's surprise, the under-rated team did so well that a rumour spread that its members were doping themselves.

Newspaper men began to watch this team more closely, and one day several boxes of white tablets were found among the players' luggage. Several tablets were given to an analyst to test. " Dextrose," he reported. " Pure dextrose! The sugar of the grape. Also called glucose."

How those football players must have laughed! Glucose tablets are as innocent and harmless as jelly babies. They contain sugar in its most easily assimilable form. And, as all athletes now know, glucose is the best and safest source of energy at moments when an extra burst of energy is needed quickly. Glucose is like anthracite in the fire of a stove or boiler. The body burns it up quickly, without any of the ill effects that are commonly associated with drugs.

Using Indian labour, the Spaniards obtained excellent cane crops from the fertile soil of the New World.

Like a good anthracite, glucose leaves hardly any " ashes " after its energy has been used up.

Normally we do not eat sugar in the form of glucose. The white crystalline or castor sugar that we put in tea, or sprinkle on our cereals, is another form of sugar known as sucrose. Its molecule is built from the combined molecules of glucose and fructose, manufactured by growing plants. Sucrose occurs in all vegetable life. It is an essential part of the fruit, the roots, and of the leaves and the sap.

Sucrose can be extracted from all types of vegetation. But some species are richer in this nourishing food than others, and two plants have now become the world's most important suppliers of sugar: sugar-beet and sugar-cane. Their contribution to our health and well-being is so great that we may wonder how past generations managed without them. Yet until man started to grow sugar-producing crops, he depended largely on honey for sweetening his food.

AN EXTRACT OF CANE

Sugar-cane grows best in a hot, sunny climate with plenty of rain to moisten the rich soil in which it flourishes. Sugar-cane grows wild in those parts of Asia where the monsoon controls the climate. It is found too in the Pacific islands, whose inhabitants have long enjoyed the sweet, delicious pith as a sweetmeat. People living in these places will cut pieces of the stalk and chew them just as we chew toffees and other sugary sweets. We can imagine how the travellers of bygone times would seek out sugar-cane as they made their way along the caravan routes of the East. It seems most probable that the Indians, the Persians and the Chinese were the first to cultivate sugar-cane deliberately as an agricultural crop.

Sugar-cane would be well known in many countries, from

The cultivation of sugar cane in the Mediterranean area seems to have coincided with the Arab conquests of the 7th century.

Persia to China, long before anyone in Europe had heard of it. The Greeks and the Romans sweetened their food with honey. And until the Arabs started moving westwards, sugar remained unknown to the peoples of Mediterranean lands. Then, little by little, the planting of sugar-cane began around the Mediterranean shores. First in Sicily, then in Spain, where it is still being grown in the hot country near Malaga.

The climate favoured by the sugar-cane is the same as that in which bananas flourish. And bananas, of course, grow best in the West Indies. The early explorers were quick to realise that the climate of Central America was better suited to sugar-cane than the Mediterranean. An early experiment was made in Mexico in 1506. Then it was discovered that the warm damp islands of the Caribbean were ideal; and Cuba was best of all. No further attempts were made to cultivate sugar-cane in southern Europe. Like tobacco, it became one of the staple crops of the tropics, being exported and sold to the Europeans who had introduced it to the New World.

During the eighteenth century, people began to drink more tea, coffee and chocolate. New sources of sugar were sought with which to sweeten these drinks. Fruit pulp and other vegetable materials were tried, and sugar-beet was found to be most promising. As long ago as 1747, a German named A. S. Marggraf discovered that beetroot was full of sucrose.

This plant has obvious advantages over sugar-cane. It grows in all the milder regions of Europe, where it was at one time used only as cattle fodder. Moreover, the juice of the white beet contains as much sugar as cane juice, and it is just as good. In short, it is an extremely useful and profitable crop. But it was not until the end of the eighteenth century that a Swiss chemist, Franz Karl Achard, found a satisfactory process for extracting sugar from beetroot. It came as welcome news to the French, who were then trying to close the markets of Europe to English merchant ships trading in colonial products. In 1806, Napoleon ordered 70,000 acres to be planted with sugar-beet, and from that time on its cultivation spread until in 1880 more sugar was being made from beet than from cane.

With the fashionable increase in tea drinking in the eighteenth century, sugar as a sweetener became more popular.

Sugar is also obtained from the sugar beet root, grown all over the world where there is a moderate summer temperature and a good rainfall.

First, the beets are brought in from the stockpile outside the factory and are washed and cleaned. They are not crushed, as sugar cane is, but go next to a machine which consists of a revolving drum fitted inside with knives. Here, the beets are sliced into chips and passed on to a diffusion battery of large cylindrical tanks.

In a battery there may be ten or twelve tanks, each of which can take between three and four tons of sliced beet. Inside each tank a mesh of loose chains prevents the beet from packing too tightly. One tank is loaded with beet, and hot water is fed in. The water dissolves the sugar from the beet, and it is then reheated and passed on to another tank. Thus the liquid circulates through the whole battery, becoming sweeter and sweeter as it absorbs the sugar from the beet.

At the end of this process the thick, yellowish solution is filtered to remove solid matter. It is then heated, and lime and carbon dioxide are added to clean the solution of remaining impurities. Sulphur dioxide gas is passed into the solution, bleaching it to a pale yellow. This purified solution is now ready to enter the evaporators, where it is boiled down to a concentrated syrup of sucrose. The sugar is now crystallised and separated from this mother liquor in centrifugal machines, like spin driers, which whirl round at about 2,000 revolutions per minute. Treacle and molasses are left behind as by-products after the sugar has crystallised.

WORLD SUGAR PRODUCTION

The method described is called the centrifugal process. It is used all over the world, and most of the world's supply of beet and cane sugar is made by this process. One quarter of the total is manufactured from beet grown in Europe. In addition, between six and seven million tons of sugar are produced by the older non-centrifugal method still used in Asia and South and Central America. On average, every person in the world is now consuming about 35 pounds of sugar per year; in America and Britain, the consumption per head may be as high as 100 pounds.

If we reckon that every pound of sugar releases 1,800 calories, then 100 pounds represents 180,000 calories. This is a handsome contribution to the fuel supplies of the human body.

THE TYPEWRITER

Walk into any office in almost any country in the world, and what is the sound that greets you? As like as not, it is the tapping of a typewriter—a sound as familiar to our twentieth-century ears as the ticking of a clock.

In the modern business world, everyone takes it for granted that letters and documents should be written in neatly typed characters. Yet, until about fifty years ago, thousands of office clerks spent the whole day writing out fair copies of correspondence and official documents. They would average 15 to 20 words a minute, compared with an efficient modern typist's 80 to 100.

MACHINES FOR THE BLIND

As with many other inventions, it is not easy to say who was the true inventor of the typewriter. We know that in 1714 Henry Mill, an English engineer, obtained a patent under the seal of Queen Anne for a mechanical device which, by means of levers, was able " to impress or transcribe letters singly or progressively one after another ". The idea was born, but not the machine. It never went into production.

Later in the same century we hear of a contraption fitted with levers and embossed letters; each letter was recognisable to the touch, and the intention was that it should be used by the blind. The early history of the typewriter is, in fact, the story of an attempt to find some practical method of helping blind people to put their thoughts on paper. A machine of this type was demonstrated at a meeting of the British Association in York in 1844. Another, built by a French teacher at the Paris Institute for the Blind, was shown at the Great Exhibition of 1851.

AMERICAN AND ITALIAN PIONEERS

Inventors now began to see that there was a much wider future for typewriters, if only a machine could be devised that would speed up the process of writing. In 1829, in America, William Austin Burt was granted a patent for a machine of this sort, called a " typograph ". Unfortunately, the one and only model was destroyed by a fire which broke out in the patent office itself. Meanwhile, a rather similar machine in which the type bars struck downwards against a central cylinder was constructed by Xavier Progin in France.

None of these machines bore any resemblance to the present-day typewriter. The letters were formed by shifting the keys round to the striking point. This principle was also applied by Charles Thurber, who was the first to build a typewriter with a carriage that moved lengthwise while holding the paper in a vertical position. An American patent was issued to Thurber in 1843. In Europe, too, real progress was being made, particularly by Giuseppe Ravizza, an Italian lawyer living in Novara.

Ravizza had combined the idea of a moving carriage with a fixed keyboard. But there was much room for improvement, especially in one important respect; on this typewriter it was impossible to see what was being written. The keys struck the underside of the carriage, which had to be raised to check mistakes. Ravizza was determined to remedy this defect and produced many models in his search for a solution.

MARK TWAIN'S TYPEWRITER

Numerous patents were now being taken out in America. One machine, which was built by Glidden and Sholes in 1868, holds a place of honour in the history of the typewriter as the first efficient machine to write faster than a pen. The inventors, who needed financial help to market their typewriter, approached the firm of Remington which had

The "writing ball" in the centre was invented in 1867 by Malling-Hansen, a Norwegian. The two more familiar machines on either side of it are American. The one on the left was built by Sholes in 1868 and was the first machine efficient enough to write faster than by pen.

made guns and pistols during the American Civil War and were now looking for new products.

Remington's took up this machine and by 1874 were marketing it under their own name. Among those who bought one was a Mr. Clemens, better known as Mark Twain. Somehow the rumour spread, and the author wrote to the firm asking them not to mention the fact as he was getting inquiries about it from all sides. " Since I do not like writing letters," he told them, " I wish no one to know that I am using this strange device." Presumably he wrote letters in longhand and kept the typewriter for his books. Meanwhile, curiosity was growing and, at the Philadelphia Exhibition of 1876, thousands of people were given the opportunity to type out and send a greetings message at twenty-five cents apiece.

" VISIBILITY " THE OBJECT

Unfortunately, it was still impossible to see what one wrote while using the machine. Moreover, the letters were all in block capitals. So when Ravizza, who was still busily experimenting in Italy, brought out his twelfth model with both a capital and a small letter combined on each key, Remington's decided to buy the manufacturing rights from him. The transaction enabled Ravizza to carry on with his inventions. He kept on building better machines until, with model 16, he scored a real success in the story of the typewriter. On this model, publicly exhibited in 1883, the *writing was visible.*

There was now no doubt that it was only a matter of time before these machines would be adopted in business offices all over the world. By the turn of the century, manufacturers were competing with each other in America, Britain, France, Germany, Italy and Switzerland to produce better and better models. Ease in handling, absolute precision, strength and cheapness were their aims. But there were other things to consider . . .

STANDARDISATION

People get used to the typewriters they have learnt on, and the manufacturer who wants to sell another model must see to it that his is not so different from the one that his customer has been using. For this reason, a tendency towards standardisation grew up in typewriter production. Then, as the habit of using the typewriter spread to social groups outside commerce, the need arose for lighter, simpler and less bulky machines. The portable made its appearance; at first this was a plain, dignified object, but to-day it is an elegant and decorative item of home furniture.

REVOLUTION IN THE OFFICE

No sooner was the typewriter firmly established as an article of daily use than a minor revolution began in commercial offices. Those patient clerks who spent their days writing letters and keeping account books were quietly replaced by typists: women typists, who were able to get through much more work than had been possible by the old method. The touch-typing system was then evolved and women, with their slender fingers, were much better able to master this technique than men. So business firms took on more and more women and girls for their correspondence departments. There is no doubt that the typewriter did more than anything else to start women along the path of economic independence.

The arrival of the typewriter also set off a whole series of

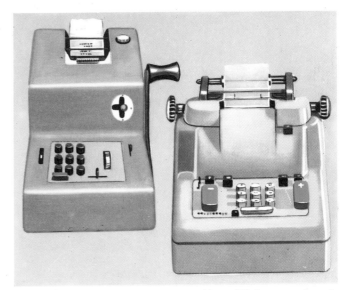

Left: *a hand-operated adding machine.* Right: *an electric calculating machine which adds, multiplies and subtracts.*

inventions in the range of office appliances and business machinery. Stenotype machines were introduced to take down reports in typed shorthand. Cryptograph machines provided for the quick decoding of cipher messages. Tape machines were developed to transmit and receive long-distance messages, especially news items and international stock market prices. Tabulating machines and comptometers were invented, combining calculating and writing mechanisms. These led, in turn, to the creation of computers which, when electronically controlled, are able to give written answers almost instantaneously to the most complicated questions.

THE ELECTRIC TYPEWRITER

All the machines described contain one or more features which were first inspired by the typewriter. Many of them are operated by electricity, and it was not long before the typewriter, too, was given an electric motor drive. The electric typewriter, now used in most large offices, is the most efficient instrument for writing that man has yet created. Speedy and smooth-running, its keys answer to a feather-light touch and strike the carriage hard enough to produce eight or ten carbon copies of perfectly uniform lettering. One of the most modern typewriters has a stationary carriage, the type being embossed on a small steel globe which travels backwards and forwards.

MACHINES OF THE FUTURE

Is it possible that the human mind will conjure up some new device to simplify writing further? Most certainly. Experiments are now going on in which the aim is to transform vocal impulses into electric impulses which, in their turn, will operate a writing machine. If this is achieved the experts will no longer have to worry about a feature of the modern typewriter which concerns them to-day. Many experts believe that the arrangement of the letters—the " universal keyboard ", as it is called—might be improved. But this is something which is as difficult to change as English spelling. Having learned to type with the keys in a certain position, most typists would find it very annoying if some clever designer reshuffled the letters and numbers into a more logical sequence.

COCOA AND CHOCOLATE

In the year 1520, the great Spanish soldier-explorer Hernando Cortés conquered Mexico by defeating the Aztecs under King Montezuma. And one of the rewards of victory the Spaniards enjoyed most was a delicious drink that the Aztecs called *chocolatl*. To-day, we know this drink—and the food that comes from the same source—as chocolate.

One of the first words every modern child learns to say is " chocolate "; even the single syllable " choc " is enough to start the young mouth watering.

Chocolate is indeed the " food of the gods ". It comes from the bean of the cocoa tree, known botanically as *Theobroma cacao*, which comes from two Greek words meaning " food " and " god ". The cocoa tree originally grew only in South America, where the Aztecs discovered that a nourishing drink *chocolatl* could be made from its beans. So highly did they regard these beans that they used them in place of coins as units of money.

MONTEZUMA'S NECTAR

Nowadays, the cocoa bean provides us with the drinks we call cocoa and chocolate, and with the solid food we know as chocolate too. The cocoa tree grows only in tropical countries, and few people living in temperate regions of the world will have seen one. The chief sources of cocoa are West Africa, Ceylon, Martinique, the Philippines and the Sonda Islands, Jamaica, Venezuela and Mexico. The tree flourishes in these and other countries within the tropical belt of 20° North and South of the Equator. It was from Mexico that Hernando Cortés wrote to the Emperor Charles V of Spain telling him about the favourite drink of King Montezuma.

On landing in Mexico, Cortés and his soldiers were as fascinated by the exotic vegetation of the country as they were by the customs and ways of its people. While exploring the gardens of the Aztec capital, they found some trees covered with reddish-yellow pods which grew on the trunks as well as on the branches. These pods were about the size of small melons: they were the fruit from which a royal drink was made for King Montezuma.

THE OLDEST COCOA RECIPE

The natives explained to the conquistadors how *chocolatl* was made. The fruit had to be picked ripe and its seeds taken out and spread on large trays in the sun. When the seeds were dry they were stripped of their husks and the kernels were toasted over a slow fire. They were then ground to powder in a cup-shaped vessel called a mortar.

A bitter form of the drink was made by adding peppers and other spices. But Montezuma preferred his *chocolatl* to be mixed with vanilla, honey and the sweet sap of the agave plant. Boiling water was poured over the mixture, which frothed up into a sweet and syrupy liquid, golden-brown in colour. A truly royal drink, Cortés agreed, and he sent the recipe with a packet of cocoa beans to King Charles V of Spain.

THE POPE GIVES HIS APPROVAL

In Madrid, the Emperor and his Court were pleasantly surprised by the taste of the new drink. But they soon found that it was much more to their liking when made with sugar. It became the custom to drink a little *chocolatl* in the morning, and the habit has remained to this day; many Spaniards still enjoy a cup of thick, sweet chocolate for breakfast.

Little by little, the popularity of chocolate grew. But cocoa beans were scarce, and the Spanish Court reserved them for friendly monarchs and high Catholic prelates.

The Aztecs of South America whipped the ground, roasted beans of the cocoa fruit in hot water, flavoured the mixture with vanilla and drank the liquid. They showed the Spaniards how to prepare the beans.

The seeds of the cocoa tree were used as food, drink and a form of "money" by the Indians, long before Columbus set foot on the shores of America.

Charles V sent a sample of the beans to his Habsburg cousins in Germany and Austria. Whenever they could, the papal legates took some back to Rome, and the Pope, who liked chocolate, declared that he would not consider it an offence if Catholics drank it before Mass. Tea and coffee were then practically unknown.

15/- PER POUND IN LONDON

The French acquired a taste for the new drink. Paris, which was even then the centre of the European social world, declared it very *chic* to drink *chocolatl*. The Archbishop of Lyons, a brother of Cardinal Richelieu, added to its popularity when he announced that it had helped to cure him of his stomach troubles. In due course, chocolate became so fashionable a drink in Paris that the smart set turned against it. Louis XIV would not allow it to be drunk at the French Court.

By that time, chocolate drinking was becoming popular in London. In 1657, solid chocolate could be bought at 10-15/- per pound from a French shopkeeper in the City of London. The price remained high mainly because of a big duty on imported cocoa beans, and it was not until 1853 that Gladstone reduced this duty to 1d. per pound. Since then, the demand for chocolate and cocoa has increased steadily in Britain.

WHERE THE COCOA TREE GROWS BEST

The habit of drinking cocoa and eating chocolate grew most rapidly in Western Europe which, including Britain, now uses nearly half the world's cocoa crop. Another third is consumed in the United States. These regions were in the best position to obtain cocoa beans; Europe had her colonial possessions, and the U.S. was near to the Central and South American sources.

Cocoa trees require a temperature of between 21° and 38°C. all the year round, and a fairly constant rainfall. These conditions are found in countries like Venezuela, Ecuador, the West Indies and Southern Mexico, where the tree grew naturally. But they were also to be found in Indonesia, Ceylon and parts of Africa, and the European colonial powers introduced the cocoa tree into these regions. Planting

zones had to be carefully chosen as the tree needs deep, rich soil, not too high above sea level, and plenty of shade.

West Africa proved to be an excellent cocoa-growing area; Ghana—once the Gold Coast colony—was especially suitable. One hundred years ago there was no cocoa in Ghana. But by 1891, cocoa was being exported, and by the end of the 1930s 287,000 tons were coming from Ghana every year. Although the figure is now rather less, cocoa still accounts for about three-quarters of that country's exports. It is grown mainly by small farmers who own between three and four acres of land. The crop yield is higher than in South America, but the finer flavours come from that continent.

"GODFATHER TREES"

Cocoa trees grow quickly, coming into production in eight years or so. They need plenty of shade, especially in the early stages, and the seedlings are planted near bananas and other leafy vegetation to give protection from the sun and wind. Sometimes, they are grown beside mature cocoa trees; "godfather trees", as they are called. These are cut down as soon as the young ones are established.

To simplify the harvesting of the crop, the cocoa tree is pruned back to about half its normal height of thirty or forty feet.

The cocoa tree has leathery leaves and small pink blossoms which are followed by the pod-like fruit. Inside the fruit, protected by pulp, are 25-50 almond-shaped seeds—the cocoa beans.

When the trees are two or three years old, they are topped to give greater strength to the main branches. This checks their upward growth and produces a more abundant crop which can be picked without difficulty. Twenty feet is the best height, though if left unpruned the cocoa tree would grow to forty feet. The fruit pods begin to form after five years and at the age of ten the tree is in full production.

UNDER TROPICAL SKIES

Hot, sticky weather is fairly constant in the tropics, and vegetation does not have to adapt itself to marked seasonal changes. The cocoa tree, like many other species of tree and shrub, bears fruit and flowers uninterruptedly. Pink and white blossoms appear, some of the flowers developing into pods about a foot long and four inches wide across the base. There are two main crop periods, one just before the rainy season, the other at the beginning of the dry season. These two periods fall between September and March.

The yellow and orange-red pods are cut from the tree with a stout knife. Upper branches are reached with a long stick to which the knife is attached. And providing the tree is not attacked by fungi, or by " swollen shoot "—a disease which is now doing untold damage to millions of trees in Ghana—harvesting goes on steadily for thirty or forty years. During that time a tree yields perhaps 10 pounds of pods, or 2/3 pounds of beans annually.

FERMENTING AND DRYING THE BEANS

After picking, the pods are opened immediately with the help of a broad knife called a machete. The beans are extracted and then put into a suitable vessel, where they are left to ferment for ten days or so. In Mexico, big earthenware jars are still used for this purpose. Fermentation frees the beans of a residue of pulp which rots away in the process. It also improves the flavour, gives the beans a uniform colour and loosens the husk.

The husks come off easily after the beans have been dried for a few days in the sun or in special drying rooms. Mexican boys are sometimes given the job of removing the husks and they get a lot of fun out of prancing around on the hot dry beans until the brittle husks have all flaked away. The

The tough pod is first opened with a machete and the seeds and pulp are scooped out and fermented for several days, when temperatures as high as 51° C. may develop.

After fermentation, the beans are full of moisture and they are then dried, either in the sun or artificially.

farmer then puts his beans into sacks which are weighed and sent off to the marketing depots.

MAKING CHOCOLATE AND COCOA

Modern chocolate- and cocoa-making processes are more complicated than the traditional cultivation methods. On reaching the manufacturer the beans are washed, sieved, graded and roasted at temperatures of around 150°C. While still hot they are put through rollers which break them into small pieces called " nibs ". Blowers remove the last fragments of shell and husk. The different grades of " nibs " are then mixed to produce those qualities and flavours that the manufacturer requires. Part of the secret of commercial chocolate-making lies in knowing what beans to buy and how to blend them.

EXTRACTING THE CHOCOLATE ESSENCE

The next stage is to release the chocolate essence, which is called cocoa butter. This is done by putting the " nibs " through a mill where they are heated. The cocoa butter melts and runs off in the form of chocolate liquor which cools into a solid brown block. This is the basic ingredient of plain chocolate. Equal quantities of chocolate liquor and sugar, strengthened with pure cocoa butter, make ordinary chocolate. The extra cocoa butter is obtained by squeezing chocolate liquor under hydraulic presses.

Milk chocolate has from 12/20 per cent. of whole milk solids in it, but contains less chocolate liquor. Cocoa for drinking has a lower content of cocoa butter with special ingredients added to make it dissolve more easily in water. Some of the surplus cocoa butter is used in the manufacture of medical products and cosmetics.

SHADES OF MONTEZUMA

It goes without saying that there is much more to the making of chocolate in all its forms and flavours than we have been able to describe. The best way of understanding the complexity and importance of modern chocolate manufacture is to see chocolate being made. Visitors are welcomed to most chocolate factories, and are encouraged to sample the products!

THE LAST FRONTIER

Doesn't it seem extraordinary, in these exciting days of space travel, that man has yet to explore the greater part of the earth's surface! We have seen more of the surface of the moon than we have seen of the surface of the earth. For more than two-thirds of our earth is covered by the waters of the sea, and we are only just beginning our investigation of the wonderful world that forms the ocean floor.

In places, the ocean is so deep that we could sink Mount Everest with Ben Nevis on top of it, and the pair would still be covered by the waters of the sea. The cold black depths, often stretching over seven miles down, form the unknown territory that man has named " Inner Space ". It is well named, for its secrets are as hidden from us as are the secrets of space, and it is almost as difficult to explore as is the surface of the moon. Yet this fantastic underwater world could bring immense rewards to the explorer. It is vast enough to take the entire land surface of the earth twice over. And it could be a treasure house of riches far greater than anything we have found before on earth.

THE UNDERWATER EXPLORER

With the help of echo-sounding equipment, man has measured and mapped the mountain ranges, the gigantic troughs, canyons, pot-holes and shelves on the bottom of the sea. He can follow the great underwater rivers or " currents ", some of which have a flow greater than the Mississippi. Our real exploration of Inner Space began when Professor Auguste Piccard built a vessel with a metal cabin strong enough to withstand immense pressures of up to eight tons per square inch, and capable of descending to the bottom of the sea and then coming to the surface again.

Professor Piccard's underwater vessel is called a bathyscaphe, which comes from the words *bathos*, meaning deep, and *scaphos*, a ship. The cabin of the bathyscaphe has to be much stronger than a capsule used for exploring Outer Space, as it must withstand the immense pressure of water when it is beneath the surface. Space vehicles, on the other hand, are in a pressureless world in space, and must be strong enough to withstand only the pressure of air inside the vehicle.

The bathyscaphe invented by Professor Piccard operates like an underwater balloon. It has a special cabin with steel walls several inches thick. Inside the cabin, which is capable of withstanding immense pressure, are the crew with all the sensitive instruments and equipment that they need.

On its own, this heavy steel " gondola " would sink through the water like a stone. But Professor Piccard gave it buoyancy by attaching it to a huge float filled with lighter-than-water petrol. This float corresponds to the gas-bag of the balloon.

Attached to the float are containers filled with ballast in the form of iron shot which is held in place by electro-magnets. When the bathyscaphe is preparing for a dive, its buoyancy is adjusted so that it is just floating. Then, when all is ready, seawater is allowed to enter special buoyancy chambers similar to those in a submarine. The bathyscaphe begins to sink.

NAVIGATING THE BATHYSCAPHE

The bathyscaphe needs to be just a little heavier than water to make it sink. It gathers speed as it descends, owing to compression of the petrol, and the navigator has to control it by switching off his electric power to release some of the iron shot. The deeper he goes, the colder the water becomes, causing further compression of the petrol; the navigator releases more ballast to slow the rate of descent.

Beneath the bathyscaphe there is a chain to act as a brake as the vessel is nearing the ocean floor. The moment this chain touches the bottom, some of the weight of the bathyscaphe is being supported, and the ship slows down; by the time the bathyscaphe reaches the bottom the entire weight of the chain has been taken away, and the vessel comes quietly to rest. Let us imagine that we are in a bathyscaphe setting out on a dive to the bottom of the Mediterranean.

The thing which will surprise you immediately, is the delicate balance of the buoyancy of our ship. As soon as we are ready, we let in a little sea water, and we begin to sink. As we leave the choppy surface, we experience a feeling of great calm. Gradually, the green of the water disappears and at about 200 fathoms we enter a world of perpetual darkness. The water above is absorbing the daylight.

We switch on our electric lights and find ourselves in the midst of a blue aquarium. The life of the sea is all round us; jellyfishes float like dancing balloons and millions of " snowflakes " sweep past the tiny porthole as if blown by fierce winds. These shining points of light are some of the small creatures of the plankton, the rich harvest of living organisms which provides food for the fish of the sea.

We watch the rising needles of our pressure gauges, and note an increase in our speed of descent. The only sound in the cabin is the whistle of the oxygen coming from the

Trieste—the self-contained, self-propelled bathyscaphe, which reached a record depth of 37,800 feet in the Pacific.

During the Project Diogenes, two men lived under the sea for several days, exploring the sea bed with the aid of aqua-lungs and returning to their underwater home through an air lock.

cylinder; without this supply of air we would die. But all is well. Air is coming in and the water is keeping out. We release a little of our iron shot ballast so that we will not drop too fast.

The tachometer registers three feet per second when we are at 800 fathoms; it is time to pull the electric current switch and let more of our iron ballast fall away. The moment the craft is lightened we feel as if a brake had been applied. We slow down even more as our chain touches the ocean bed and the craft sinks on the sediment with only the slightest of bumps.

1,000 FATHOMS DOWN

Our depth is over 1,000 fathoms. Imagine it; 1,000 fathoms beneath the Mediterranean! We switch on our propellers, and the ship moves gently over the sea-floor. We find that we are not the only form of life down here. Little fish the size of sardines dodge to and fro. All too soon it is time to go up again. We push a lever, releasing the main weight of ballast to make our Inner Space vehicle lighter than water, and off we go towards the surface.

Our speed increases as we rise; we can feel it, as well as check it on the instruments. Gradually, the darkness of the sea turns to the green of a swimming bath, and we know we must be close to the surface. Suddenly, with a bounce, we are there. We open the hatch and climb out into the world of sunlight and air.

Why should man use all this skill and ingenuity to build a craft which will take us down to the very bottom of the sea? Why indeed? Why should man climb Everest, reach for the moon and the planets?

One answer lies in the sheer joy of exploration for its own sake. But there are plenty of practical reasons too. The sea is a vast storehouse of mineral wealth. There is gold and uranium, copper and magnesium, chlorine and bromine—vast quantities of every element we find on earth are available to us in sea-water and in the rocks that form the bed of the sea. Some day, we shall learn how to mine the sea for the minerals it contains.

There is also an interesting scientific problem that has been

posed by our researches in the sea: the theory that the moon was formed when a mass of matter whirled away from the molten earth, leaving a gap which is now filled by the waters of the Pacific Ocean. This theory, however, now seems to have been disproved as a result of the first tests carried out on samples taken from the moon.

Scientists are now studying methods of living under water; one of the latest inventions is a " diving saucer ", a mobile runabout which can be driven like a car down to 1,000 feet. This machine is being developed by the famous French underwater explorer Jacques Yves Cousteau, who plans to " motor " under the sea for periods limited only by supplies of air and fuel.

UNDERWATER TOWNS

More ambitious than the underwater car is an air-filled house known as Project Diogenes, in which men lived on the seabed for a definite time period to find out how the human mind and body react to a long stay under water. They left the house and explored the sea bed with the help of aqualungs, returning home via an air-lock in the bottom of the house.

This was no stunt, but a serious attempt to assess the possibility of man's living beneath the sea. It is probable that underwater towns will eventually be built. Men will harvest the seaweed with the help of underwater tractors. They will run fish-farms, and mine coal and minerals.

Sea-farms and sea-ranches are no mere pipe-dream. Down in the depths of the sea, it will be possible to fence in the fish by electricity. The water could be enriched with fertiliser to increase the sea vegetation and plankton, so that fish would fatten more quickly. Man could breed fish to his requirements and they would have no means of escape. By warming the water the fish could be made to grow faster; experiments with plaice have already been successful.

In warm water, plaice grow to their full size in eighteen months, whereas growing naturally in the sea they take five years to mature. By rearing fish under proper control, it is possible to increase the returns. Fishing is no longer a form of hunting, but becomes a farming operation.

Underwater farmers of the future may be divers wearing aqualungs and driving tractors in shallow, inshore waters warmed by electricity. Bigger schemes of fish-farming, such as might be attempted in the Dogger Bank, would be profitable if it were not for the fact that this region is not owned by any one nation. The ocean floor belongs to nobody at the present time, but the rights of ownership will no doubt be laid down as the exploration of the sea floor becomes a practical proposition.

It may be that our fish-farms of the future will be organised under United Nations control. Anyone wishing to develop an area of the sea would do so under licence from the United Nations.

WATER-AGE MAN?

In his desire to learn to live beneath the sea, man has experimented with animals, pumping water into their lungs and fitting them with artificial gills like fish. Surgeons now consider it feasible to do the same for man, enabling him to live in the water as effectively as he does in air.

These experiments are a continuation of experiments that have been going on for centuries as man has tried to find ways of living beneath the sea.

From the earliest times the pearl divers of Japan have used heavy stones to take them quickly to the sea floor. Four hundred years ago Leonardo da Vinci described many forms of diving apparatus, and fastened webbing to his feet to provide himself with the forerunners of modern flippers.

WORKING UNDERWATER

The discovery of the diving bell enabled man to stay underwater for longer periods. You can see how a diving bell works by taking a tumbler, turning it upside down and pushing it into a basin of water. Better still, float a piece of lighted candle on a cork, then push the tumbler over it. The candle will continue to burn even though it is below the water, and it will burn until all the air inside the tumbler is used up. Diving bells have been used for many underwater engineering operations, for example in laying the foundations of the Forth Bridge. Workmen in the bell are provided with a constant supply of air which is pumped down from above.

Salvaging jars from a Greek ship sunk in the Mediterranean over 2,000 years ago.

Without this air, they would die as quickly as the candle flame.

The idea of using a helmet into which a supply of air is pumped was considered for centuries before the first practical diving suit came into use. Nowadays, the diving suit is in widespread use throughout the world, enabling divers to work safely at depths of up to 600 feet. The normal diving dress is a comparatively cumbersome apparatus, and requires an organisation operating between the surface and the sea floor. About 20 years ago, a new form of underwater equipment was invented by the brilliant French engineer, Emile Gagnon; this was what we now know as the aqualung.

The aqualung enables you to swim freely underwater, carrying your own breathing mixture with you. You can stay down as long as your air supply lasts. The mixture you breathe is commonly oxygen and helium, enough for 15 minutes or so at depths of around 200 feet. By using special techniques, the young Swiss mathematician Hannes Keller hopes to be able to dive to 1,000 feet. Great care must be taken to ensure that the correct mixture of gases is used in the aqualung, or the diver's judgment is quickly affected.

At present, oxygen and helium form the most effective breathing mixture. Even with this mixture, the skin diver, wearing face mask and rubber flippers, must be careful not to stay down too long, or he will have to undergo decompression at various levels on the way to the surface.

Because of the high pressures underwater, divers have to go through the routine of decompression to rid their bloodstreams of dissolved nitrogen. If the diver comes up too quickly this nitrogen will be released as bubbles, causing the disease known as the "bends". The "bends" is painful and may be dangerous or even fatal. A diver called Christianini, one of the most experienced of Mediterranean skin divers, suffered so badly from the disease that he was in hospital for six months and had to have his toes amputated.

"FROGMEN"

Aqualung divers are commonly known as "frogmen", a name which aptly describes their wonderful ability in the water. Most famous of all the frogmen is Captain Cousteau, who has carried out many feats of underwater salvage and exploration. One of Captain Cousteau's best-known adventures was his salvage of treasure from a Greek ship sunk in the Mediterranean over 2,000 years ago. The ship had been carrying a cargo of wines and Cousteau was able to sample some of the unpalatable vintage from a jar whose seal was still intact after all that time. He said he had now tasted all the mustiness and age there is in this world.

Cousteau and his fishmen have opened up a new field of archaeology. With the aid of underwater television cameras, they can send pictures to the surface, where experts may study the treasures of bygone ages that are lying on the sea floor.

Cousteau used this technique in exploring the wreck of the Greek vessel. The archaeologists on the surface were in touch with Cousteau by radio, so that the cameras could be directed and controlled to the best effect.

To-day, the science of oceanography is moving forward hand in hand with exploration of Outer Space. The problems and difficulties of the two fields of technology have much in common, and progress in one will often mean progress in the other. The underwater explorer, like the explorer in space, must be equipped with everything he needs to maintain life, and he must be protected from the strange environment in which he finds himself.

HOUSES AND FLATS

Our houses and flats reflect the evolution and development of human society down the ages. From the caves and rock dwellings that sheltered man in prehistoric times, the house has evolved by a process as slow and gradual as the growth of civilisation itself.

FROM CAVES TO SKYSCRAPERS

Primitive man built his shelters from any material that came easily to hand. The trunks and branches of trees, straw and animals' skins all helped in the building of huts and cabins. Rough stones set one on top of the other gave added strength and protection, but the manoeuvring into position of these massive blocks was a laborious task. What was needed was a lighter building " block " and in due course bricks—made originally of mud and straw and later of hard baked clays—were devised. These began to take the place of stone, and the early builders learned how to hold them together by means of a mortar made by mixing lime and mud.

These developments brought a complete change in man's concept of the house. Primitive peoples had regarded it as a safe and convenient retreat which could protect them from their enemies and shelter them from the weather. Now it became a well-planned dwelling where everything had its proper place and function. The husband provided for its maintenance while the wife saw to the domestic chores and the daily needs of the family. A way of life was developed which finds its ultimate expression in the housing estates and skyscrapers designed by modern architects to give the greatest possible amount of air, light and heat to those who live in them.

MODERN BUILDING MATERIALS

If an architect were asked what has been the most important addition to building materials in recent times, he would undoubtedly reply—*reinforced concrete*. This material, sometimes known as *ferro-concrete*, has enabled us to construct buildings much lighter and stronger than any that could be built from stone, or bricks and mortar.

REINFORCED CONCRETE

This is really nothing more than cement and sand strengthened with wire mesh or steel bars. The cement mixture is poured into place, and people who have watched it being used, for example in building bridges or dams, are often astonished at the speed with which the work goes forward. In the last twenty years or so, reinforced concrete has been used more and more for tall buildings and for those parts of smaller ones which must support great weight. Yet it is doubtful if this material, which combines so well with glass when handled by a skilful architect, will ever completely replace the traditional stone and brick.

STONE

Pride of place must be given to stone, which has found favour with architects throughout the ages. Among the favoured building stones we must include granite, the famous Portland stone with which much of the City of London was built, sandstone, and marble in all its beautiful and varied range of colours. To-day, stone is used mainly for facing walls, for steps and stairways, and for decorative features both inside and outside. In many parts of the Continent it is still used for paving roads that must withstand constant wear and tear.

BRICKS

These have long been used and in a great variety of shapes sizes, each country having its own characteristic type of brick for house building. The English brick of soft and rosy hue, as used for example in Queen Anne-style houses, was made by hand. Since the middle of last century, bricks have been manufactured by mechanical processes and production in Britain now runs at the rate of over 7,000 million units per annum. Bricks are made from selected clays and may be solid, hollow, wedge-shaped or moulded to any pattern. In parts of Europe a large, light brick of tile-like quality is used, together with concrete, for making the under-structure of the floor. These, too, are produced in kilns, as also are roof tiles and the glazed and enamelled tiles such as we normally see in bathrooms and kitchens.

CONCRETE AND MORTAR

These are the materials used for holding together the bricks or stone used in constructing a building. Concrete is made with cement, sand and gravel, and its hardness depends on the quality and quantity of the cement used. Mortar requires less cement, a little slaked lime and a large amount of fine sand. Brick or stone dust may be added. Good concrete and mortar will set quite solid and weather well without shrinking or expanding. No substitute has been found for these materials, and the strength of many buildings will always depend on the proper proportioning and mixing of the ingredients in the cement or mortar that was used.

TIMBER

Timber is another material still very widely used for building purposes. In Switzerland and other mountainous countries it is used for the main structure; but timber is also widely used elsewhere as beams and laths to support the roof and ceilings, as floorings, doors, window frames and so on. The scaffolding on which the builders work may also be of wood. So, too, are the moulds which shape the reinforced concrete used for walls and pillars. There are two main classes of timber: softwoods such as pine, spruce and fir, and hardwoods such as oak, afzelia and beech. Demand for the latter is mainly for the construction of fittings and furniture and for special carpentry work.

METALS

In the case of large buildings the structural frame-work may be entirely of *steel*. Reinforced concrete buildings make use of considerable quantities of steel, for instance, as girders. These are often set in fours and surrounded by cement to carry the main weight of the building. In certain

1. *Foundations prepared; 2. scaffolding erected, outside walls going up; 3. roof timbers in position, ready for fitting of tiles, windows, etc.; 4. exterior and interior work finished, site levelled and lawn laid.*

types of floor, slender steel bars are used to hold together a layer of hollow bricks, the whole surface being cemented over and flattened into a solid mass in which the steel provides great tensile strength.

OTHER MATERIALS

These include mixtures of different types of *concrete* in which the proportions of cement, slaked lime, sand and gravel are varied to meet specific needs. Columns and slabs of artificial stone, blocks for sea walls and sewer ducts, garage and storehouse floors are made in this way. *Asphalt and bitumen compounds* have their uses too. Outside terraces, underground basements and, in fact, any structural work which is exposed to the rain and weather may be treated with watertight and damp-proof materials of this type. Nor should we forget other compounds, those of *asbestos, cork, pumice stone, wood shavings* and *vegetable fibre*, even *seaweed*, all strange materials to go into the making of modern buildings—almost as strange as the mud and wattle used in times gone by. But in compressed form they make excellent partitions and wall sheathings which are fire-resistant; they also absorb the noises that would otherwise irritate neighbours living in flats and semi-detached houses.

ORDERING A NEW HOUSE

Before an architect can estimate the cost of a house he must know exactly what type of building is required, and in what surroundings it is to be erected. It may be a large or a small house; it may be in a suburban setting or in open country, with hills around it; or it may be beside the sea. The client may wish to use part of it for himself and let the rest as flats—a very sound investment. Without such information, no decision can be made as to style, materials and building techniques.

Once he has the facts before him, the architect can go ahead with his plans. This involves him in producing a number of designs, the most impressive of which are those which show what the house will look like both from front and back. Separate designs are drawn to show every interior detail: the rooms, passages, stairs and attics—all must be worked out with exact measurements. The garage, terraces and outhouses must be designed in a similar way.

When the design has been approved the architect passes his plans to a firm of building contractors whose staff includes an expert capable of estimating the quantity of materials necessary. This is the quantity surveyor. The materials are then ordered, the site is marked out and the foundations are dug. Bricklayers and their labourers appear, followed by carpenters, joiners, cement-layers, plasterers, plumbers, electricians, glaziers and decorators. Gradually the house takes shape until, finally, all the internal fittings are installed, and the woodwork painted. A final inspection is made by the architect and the client's opinion is sought. If he is satisfied, he takes possession and writes out two cheques: a larger one

183

for the builder and a smaller one—though quite substantial—for the architect.

BUILDING BEGINS

To most people, the building of a new house is an important step in their lives, and it is natural that they should show a close interest in its construction. So let us follow the work of the builders through its various stages.

First the site is excavated to a depth where the soil is sufficiently firm to bear the weight of the structure. Working to the architect's designs, a series of trenches are dug to correspond with the outside and the main inside walls of the building. Into these go the foundation materials: broken stone mixed with cement and lime to form a solid base to the structure. If the house is to be a really large one, it may be necessary to erect supporting pillars; in this case rough wooden moulds must be constructed to contain the metal frames and liquid concrete. The boards are removed when the concrete has set.

THE MAIN WALLS AND FLOORS

If specified by the architect, cellars and basements will by now have been excavated and the foundation walls raised to a point slightly above ground level. These must support the main walls, which may not be as thick as those beneath the surface. The actual thickness depends on the number of stories, as the walls of a three-story house naturally require greater strength than those of a bungalow. The base may be of stone, but the main area is usually of brick. A double wall is normally used, providing insulation against passage of water, heat and sound.

As work on the walls proceeds, we notice that the masons leave many gaps and untidy ends. These are for the doors, windows and balconies. We may also notice that building halts at a height of ten or eleven feet. The bricklayers move to a different section of the building while another group of men put in the first floor and with it a ceiling for the rooms below. One method is to make a network of beams and laths and cover them over with boards. To-day it is usual in many continental countries to use light girders for this purpose, and to fill in the spaces with hollow bricks or tiles. These are then cemented over and the top flooring is laid.

A ROOF WITH A TERRACE

The bricklayers now return to their work on the main walls of the upper stories. As these increase in height it will be seen that they are not necessarily as thick as the ones below. A lighter type of brick may be used. Spaces are left here and there for chimneys, ventilating flues, and for plumbing and electrical fittings. Similarly, the men who laid the floors have not forgotten to leave an appropriate space for the stairs. And, in the unlikely event that our house is to have a lift, a shaft will have been prepared for its installation. By this time, work on the inside walls and partitions should be well advanced. Here the aim is to build something light and strong, and for this reason many European architects favour hollow bricks. But the choice of these, as of other materials, will always depend to a large extent on climate, tradition, taste and cost.

When the walls have reached their maximum height the roof must be added, and perhaps a terrace as well. This means building a supporting structure to carry the weight of slates or tiles. Normally, laths are placed lengthwise across a broad framework of wooden beams and the tiles are laid on these. But many modern builders prefer to use reinforced-concrete beams rather than wooden ones for the main struts of the roof. It is then possible to lay a stronger lining of cement and plaster in which to set the tiles. This technique is widely adopted for flat roofs. If the roof is to be used as a terrace, strength is essential; it must be constructed as solidly as a floor, with the addition of a top layer of asphalt or other water-tight material to prevent the rain from getting through. Heat is another problem here, and in countries where the summer is hot and long, a double roof is built with a space between for better insulation.

PLASTER AND STUCCO WORK

Now that we have a roof over our heads we must not imagine that the house is ready for occupation. Much work awaits the plasterers, the carpenters, the plumbers and the electricians. While watching the completion of the upper walls and the roof we may not have noticed that a first layer of plaster was being applied to the inside walls. About half-an-inch thick, it adheres to the rough surfaces of the bricks and their interstices. This is only a rough layer and, as it hardens, it must be scratched, criss-cross, to take a second one, called the " floating coat ". Good plastering requires three coats, but before the final application the whole surface must be roughened with a wire brush. The walls are then ready for the top layer, which is of fine texture and needs to be spread with skill to obtain a uniform surface suitable to take the wallpaper. Plaster is made of lime, fine washed sand and water, to which ox hair or, better still, hemp fibre is added for its binding qualities.

The external walls require different treatment and, if the brickwork is not to be left bare, the plasterers will probably have been watching the weather for fine days when they can work outside on the stucco facing. Stucco is applied in two coats, the main layer being Portland cement mixed with white sand. This is extremely resistant to rain and frost and provides a surface which resembles stone. While the plastering goes ahead other smaller jobs are completed: window sills, doorsteps and paving are laid; the stairs, which have already been set in position, are given their banisters; enamelled tiles are fitted in the kitchen and bathroom; the windows are installed, either in prefabricated sections or pane by pane by the glaziers.

MORE FINISHING TOUCHES:

At this stage we might be getting impatient. But, as everyone knows, you cannot hurry plumbers and electricians. Their work requires special skills and techniques, and we must wait while they install the bathroom, lavatory and kitchen fittings. As it is always preferable to know something about the lighting arrangements, we might watch the electricians as they wire the house, installing the necessary circuits which are linked to the fuse boxes and meters.

So far, we have said nothing about fireplaces and gas mains. This is because our architect has kept a little surprise in store for us. Down in the basement the heating engineer has been supervising the erection of a modern central-heating plant, and now that the interior is nearly finished, the oil heater is turned on and the radiators warm up in all the rooms. So the decorators are able to finish their jobs in comfort, and when at last the architect comes to inspect the building we shall want to congratulate him on his excellent work. In fact, we decide to invite him to our house-warming party.

RICE

In Britain and most other countries of the Western world, we think of rice as something from which we make "milk puddings" once or twice a week. But to people living in eastern countries, rice is the most important food of all; it is the mainstay of the daily diet.

"Eat your rice in peace and Heaven will see to the rest." For thousands of years, the Chinese people have followed the advice of their proverb and have acquired a reputation as a serene and placid race.

"Have you eaten your rice?" a Chinese will politely inquire of a friend in the street, where we might say "Good morning" or "How are you?" And if the answer is "Yes", it is like replying "Fine" or "Very well, thank you". The eating of rice, in other words, is a custom so deep-rooted in China that it has long been associated with the habits and conventions of everyday life.

A THOUSAND MILLION POUNDS PER DAY

In the West, we regard rice as a pleasant, nourishing food which can be cooked in many appetising ways. In Italy, rice is the basis of risotto; it is fried with onions and butter, then boiled with broth and flavoured with saffron to make a really tasty dish. The rice grown in northern Italy is commonly eaten in this way; Milanese risotto has been praised as "a gastronomic pearl of inestimable worth".

In Britain, we tend to eat rice as a pudding or a sweet, and seldom think of it as a savoury dish.

The human race as a whole is so fond of rice that it eats more than one thousand million pounds of rice a day! This seems an incredible quantity until we remember that there are about 700 million Chinese, most of whom regard rice as their main item of food. It is reasonable to estimate that half of the world's population—one thousand five hundred million people—eat a substantial dish of rice apiece at least once a day.

Rice has been eaten with this enthusiasm for at least five thousand years, yet the earth has never tired of producing its mammoth crop of countless millions of grains of rice from year to year. Nature has indeed been bountiful in providing us with the rice we need.

HOW RICE GROWS

Rice grows best in a warm, damp climate. Plenty of water is needed to flood the fields, and rice is cultivated usually in plains, river valleys and low-lying deltas where there is abundant fresh water. Almost all the great Asian countries produce rice, and 95 per cent. of the world output comes from this continent. The rest is grown in scattered districts of the United States, Brazil and southern Europe.

Rice is an annual grass with edible seeds. It belongs to the *Gramineae* family which includes all the 5,000 species of grass that grow in the world. These grasses are classified in thirteen main groups, one of them being called *Oryzeae* which includes *Oryza sativa*, Linnaeus's botanical name for rice. Like reeds and bamboos, it flourishes best on marshy soil to which it attaches itself by a bushy cluster of fine fibrous roots. Its smooth, slender, lance-like leaves grow to

a height of about three feet. These surround the spikelets which contain flowers, stamens and ovaries that ripen into grain after fertilisation. About 150 rice grains are borne on each plant.

Except in some parts of America, where seed is sown from the air, rice cultivation is a more laborious process than the growing of other cereal crops. The best results are obtained by making a first sowing in nursery beds, and then transplanting the seedlings into the paddy fields when they are about six weeks old. This is possible only where unlimited labour is available. Most rice fields are therefore sown direct, and flooded gradually as the plant grows to maturity.

AMONG THE WEEDS AND WATER

Let us look at a typical scene in one of the rice-growing districts of southern Europe.

It is early May, and the sun of springtime is already as hot as on a summer's afternoon in England. An immense field, flooded to a depth of about six inches, with its ploughed ridges showing dark above the water, stretches before us. Here, the rice is germinating in a warm, muddy soil which has been well tilled and fertilised.

Six weeks later, the wide expanse of water has turned to silvery green. The seedlings, now rising a foot above the water level, make the field look like a vast swamp of weeds. And there are indeed many weeds among the rice plants. That is why groups of girls are wading through the water, their backs bent as they pull out the young weeds which, to an inexpert eye, look exactly like the growing crop. With their legs bare and their heads covered with floppy straw hats, the girls make an attractive picture in the flat, uninteresting countryside. In Italy alone, 200,000 women and

Left: *The rice plant.* Top right: *Spikes or ears, each ear containing a flower of six stamens and an ovary, from which the grain develops.* Bottom right: *Sectional view of flower.*

185

girls perform this task throughout the month of June. It is an arduous one, but essential to the production of a worthwhile crop.

During weeding, the crop is thinned. If the seedlings are growing in nursery beds, the best plants are selected for transplanting; this is the usual practice when high-quality rice is being cultivated. Normally, when the worst of the weeds have been removed, the fields are drained to air the soil and to allow more fertiliser to be applied if necessary. The fields are then flooded again, and for the rest of July and August the rice matures in a wide expanse of darkening green that shimmers and rustles in the warm summer breezes. It ripens just as any other cereal does. The scorching sun catches it, and heads and stalks turn a golden brown. Then the farmer drains his fields again and, when the land is dry, brings out his harvesters.

RICE IN ITS MANY GUISES

More than fifty different varieties of *common rice* are grown in the manner described. They range from small round grains to the much larger and more elongated types, which are used for making risotto. Before it is ready for human consumption, the rough rice must be dried, stripped of its outer and inner husks, polished, perhaps coated with glucose, and finally graded. These processes are carried out in special mills where the grain undergoes as many as twenty different operations before it is ready for the cooking pot. During processing, small grains and rice dust are sifted out and used for making rice flour and starch.

In addition to common rice, the best qualities of which come from Burma, Thailand, Indonesia, North Italy and parts of the United States, there are several other main varieties. One of these is *mountain rice*, which is grown in terraces on hillsides in eastern countries where a heavy rainfall coincides with the period of cultivation. In hot, wet climates, rice is also grown on low-lying ground as a fodder crop for animals. *Glutinous rice*, which dissolves when boiled, is reserved principally for the manufacture of starchy products. More exotic than these is the rare *perfumed rice* that comes in small quantities from the Orient, and the *wild rice* of North America. Wild rice may cost as much as twenty

In some countries, the weeding and transplanting of rice is done by women.

shillings per pound; its dark purple grains, over half an inch in length, are eaten by gourmets with pheasant, grouse and other game dishes.

Although rice is inferior to wheat in food value, it is the " staff of life " to more than half the world's population. The demand for rice is so great in India, China and Japan that these countries consume almost all their home-grown crop. For hundreds of miles along the great Yangtze River, junks ply from bank to bank carrying rice for distribution over huge areas of China. Whether he is a simple fisherman or a high State official, whether he eats with wooden or ivory chopsticks, the Chinaman loves his rice. He may prefer it with pungent or aromatic flavourings, or with spices and rich sauces; he may cook it with worms and strange insects, or boil it in the simplest possible way. But in one way or another, the Chinaman will make a meal of rice at least once or twice a day. It is his staple food.

Nobody knows where rice was first cultivated as a human food. We *do* know that the growing of rice was an important feature of the earliest Asian civilisations. In 2800 B.C., the Chinese Emperor established a special form of ceremonial to be observed at each year's first official sowing. The word for rice occurs in ancient Sanskrit, in a form that is still recognisable in the Indian words *ruzz* and *aruzz*. When the Aryans invaded India from southern Russia, they would bring their knowledge of rice-cultivation with them. Rice is also associated with Orissa, a province of India from whose ports on the Bay of Bengal rice was shipped to the West. Hence the Latin name *oryza sativa*.

The Greeks under Alexander the Great brought rice to the western world from the Indus valley in the fourth century B.C. Climatic conditions, however, were not suitable for rice cultivation, and it is probably for this reason that we find no mention of rice in the Bible, nor any evidence of rice fields in the Roman Empire. The Arabs introduced rice cultivation into southern Europe via Spain. It was then taken to Italy by the Aragonese. Here rice thrived in the well-irrigated plains of the Pisa province and the Po valley. It is cultivated in these regions to-day in sufficient quantity to supply all the rice needed for Italian risotto and British rice pudding.

In Ancient China the cultivation of rice was considered an important ceremony and the emperor presided over the ceremonial planting.

INDEX

191